Sixty-five case histories form the heart of this unique study.

CASE 3. The 23-year-old B-24 bombardier whose enthusiasm for combat ended with an epileptiform seizure on his eighth mission.

CASE 5. A death-phobia that ended the combat career of a B-26 radio operator.

CASE 10. The engineer-gunner who went to pieces after his pilot saved him from drowning.

CASE 13. A B-17 top gunner, exploded out of his plane just before it crashed inside enemy territory, returned only to find himself unable to fly again.

CASE 23. Though his terror grew even worse after he was hospitalized, this 25-year-old B-17 tail gunner managed to complete 49 combat missions.

CASE 40. The pursuit squadron flight leader who fought successfully until a friend, flying on his wing, went down in flames.

ROY R. GRINKER, Sr., M.D., is Director of the Institute for Psychosomatic and Psychiatric Research and Training of Michael Reese Hospital Medical Center, Chicago.

JOHN P. SPIEGEL, M.D., is Associate Clinical Professor of Psychiatry, Harvard Medical School, and Lecturer on Social Relations, Harvard University.

Men Under Stress
Roy R. Grinker, M.D.
John P. Spiegel, M.D.

McGraw-Hill Book Co., Inc.

NEW YORK
TORONTO
LONDON

MEN UNDER STRESS

Library of Congress Catalog Card Number 63-12127.

First publication as a McGraw-Hill Paperback in 1963.

24883

Dedicated

to the

COMBAT CREWS

of the

ARMY AIR FORCES

Preface for Paperback Edition

It is now more than fifteen years since this book was first published. When it was being written in 1945, though we were close to the end of World War II, the fighting was still going on. Our outlook was strongly colored by the war and by our sense of identity with the combat personnel of the Air Forces who were our patients, our research subjects, and our friends. The cases of war neuroses reported in the book, accordingly, demonstrate the freshness of our very recent experience with them and the urgency which we then felt about communicating our findings to the professional and lay public.

In considering the prospect of re-issuing the book in paperback form, we were tempted to introduce changes in the material, bringing it into line with the findings of contemporary behavioral science research. But we finally decided to preserve the material in its original form. This means that the new publication will stand as a record of our original thinking on the topic of the interaction between external, environmental, and internal, psychological factors in the production of psychopathology. It does not represent the way we would deal with these issues were we to approach them from the standpoint of the research both of us have conducted in the area of social psychiatry since World War II. This decision needs some further comment.

During the time that these studies were being conducted we were only vaguely aware of the existence of the social sciences. Our materials were gathered through clinical interviews and through what we later learned could be called participant-observation. The conceptualization of our data was grounded in psychoanalytic theory, supported by some restricted neurophysiological notions. What we had to say about the influence of the combat group upon the personality of the soldier had no theoretical grounding whatsoever, beyond the thoughts generated by a reading of Freud's *Group Psychology and the Analysis of the Ego*. The social psychological insights which we were able to develop grew from mutual discussion of our own experiences in combat groups and of those reported by our patients.

It is probably difficult for a contemporary reader—especially if he is a graduate student in the social sciences or a medical student—to comprehend the degree to which the psychiatrist of the 1940s was isolated by his training and professional circumstances from the social psychological, anthropological, and sociological research of his day. For example, we knew nothing of the work of Stouffer and his colleagues on the social determinants of the attitudes of servicemen—a study that was later reported in the several volumes of *The American Soldier*. A knowledge of the methods and findings of this research would have been of immense value to our own work. Nor were we aware of the writings of Sapir, Mead, Linton and others who contributed to the Culture-and-Personality literature in the 1930s and early 1940s, though this approach was directly relevant to what we were doing.

Since then the behavioral sciences have come into their own. Ego psychology has brought psychoanalytic theory and method into a somewhat uneasy commerce with experimental and social psychology, on one side, and with ethnology and physiology, on the other. Sociology and cultural anthropology have made many contributions to our understanding of the environmental variables correlated with mental illness. Group dynamics has developed rigorous methods for determining the structure and function of group processes in a variety of circumstances. Studies of family behavior and its impact upon the individual, in sickness and in health, have thrown light upon the development of the ego and its characteristic modes of defense. Interdisciplinary methods of collaboration have vastly enlarged the techniques available for determining the sources of psychopathology in the community and in various national groups. Throughout all this bubbling research activity and melting away of traditional scientific boundaries there runs the theme of a constantly broadening therapy. Personality disturbance—whether mild or severe—is currently approached through biological, psychological, and social strategies, either separately or in combination with each other, in the effort to relieve the stress upon the conflict-resolving mechanisms of the ego.

Of all these matters we were innocent in 1945. True, it can be said that much of these subsequent developments was foreshadowed in our approach to our subjects. Still, in view of the sophistication which characterizes contemporary studies, one may well ask what purpose is served in republishing, unchanged, this unsophisticated investigation of a phenomenon which may never be seen again. The material is manifestly out of date. Even the use of intravenous sodium pentothal in the abreactive procedure which we called "narcosynthesis"—a therapy upon which we placed great hopes at the time—has proved to have little utility in the treatment of the emotional disturbances of a peaceful society. So far as war itself is concerned, the frightful possibility of thermonuclear destruction and the instrumentation of the space age has changed the organization of the military establishment so that it no longer conforms to the groupings which we described. Considering the scope of the changes which have taken place in the sciences and in the social order, would it not be best to let this book quietly gather dust in the libraries of universities and hospitals?

The answer is that this has not, apparently, been the book's fate. As a matter of fact, it has been disappearing from library shelves, but not from disuse or decay. Over the years it has enjoyed a lively readership. It is much used for educational purposes, both at the undergraduate and graduate level. Its case histories and its theoretical formulations have been widely quoted in introductory college texts as well as in specialized monographs. Since this has been its history, there is reason to expect that interest in it will be maintained for some time to come.

But perhaps this is not so surprising. The cases reported in it are examples of human beings responding unsuccessfully in extreme situations. From this point of view, the title of the book is an understatement. The intense physiological, psychological, and social pressures to which its subjects were exposed made it easy to observe psychological processes which are ordinarily concealed. As we pointed out at the time, war is a natural experiment—a laboratory which manufactures psychological dysfunction at an appalling rate. There is no other situation which guarantees such easily observed failures of adaptive function in such large numbers under such standardized conditions. For this reason the case histories represent excellent teaching materials, illustrative of a variety of clear-cut, rather uncomplicated clinical states, developing in response to precipitating factors in the environment. The relation between the endopsychic, predispositional factors and the external, social factors is usually easy to assess. The vagueness of the ordinary human predicament which makes the environmental variables so difficult to estimate in most circumstances is replaced by the dramatic contingencies of the combat situation.

Yet, quite apart from these didactic considerations, the failures of adaptation precipitated by the strains of combat are instructive with respect to a variety of contemporary contexts. Limited warfare has been going on somewhere in the world almost continuously since 1945 and can be expected to occur in various countries for an indefinite period. Equally chronic—and equally pertinent—are the strains arising from the constant migrations of peoples throughout the world. Although the stress associated with migration is not as great as that of combat, many of the social psychological factors responsible for combat stress are comparable with those which the refugee or migrant faces. Similarly, revolution, domestic disruption, and rapid social change can be expected to appear in one country or another over the next several decades. These represent extreme situations characterized by strains similar to those in combat. Finally, there is the average expectable number of local disasters and catastrophes—the earthquakes, fires, floods and hurricanes, the explosions, crashes and collapses—which generate strains ramifying throughout the social groups involved in them.

All these current events qualify as extreme situations likely to produce the emotional traumas whose effects are examined in this book. Because the resulting clinical states need to be widely understood and rapidly treated, we are happy that the book is again being made available to the public.

                                                      The Authors

December 1962

Introduction

THE STRESS OF WAR tries men as no other test that they have
encountered in civilized life. Like a crucial experiment it exposes the underlying physiological and psychological mechanisms
of the human being. Cruel, destructive and wasteful though
such an experiment may be, exceedingly valuable lessons can
be learned from it regarding the methods by which men adapt
themselves to all forms of stress, either in war or in peace. In
truth, it is a moot question whether, in the peace which will
follow the present conflict, the degree of stress on the average
individual will be much less than that imposed by the war. Because of the current and future necessity of such large populations
throughout the world to face a difficult reality, never in the
history of the study of human behavior has it been so important
to understand the psychological mechanisms of "normal" individuals in situations of stress.

Under sufficient stress any individual may show failure of
adaptation, evidenced by neurotic symptoms. Such symptoms
then are pathological only in a comparative sense, when contrasted with the symptoms of those still making successful adaptations. From this point of view, the psychological mechanisms
under discussion in this book are those that apply to Everyman
in his struggle to master his own environment. In this realm, a
hair divides the normal from the neurotic, the adaptive from
the nonadaptive. The failures of adaptation of the soldier
described herein mirror Everyman's everyday failures or neurotic
compromises with reality. The problem thus resolves itself not
into the detection of normality or its lack, but into a study of the

psychological methods of dealing with a harsh reality. The manner in which this reality is handled in battle constitutes the
observable clinical state in combat soldiers. The manner in which
this reality is handled by the returned soldier in the United
States is portrayed by his individual symptoms and his degree of
resocialization.

Our first military monograph, "War Neuroses in North
Africa," related our observations of psychologically wounded
Ground Force soldiers. Subsequently we have restricted our
work entirely to Air Forces personnel, who show quantitative
rather than qualitative differences in reactions from the foot
soldier. Because the case material of this book concerns flying
personnel almost exclusively, Flight Surgeons will find it useful
as a basis of preparation for their psychiatric work. Our material
is roughly divided into a discussion of war neuroses appearing
overseas and those in combat veterans returned home for relief
from flying or for rehabilitation. Military regulations prevent
us from citing statistics of incidence of war neuroses, and security
precautions are responsible for the omission of a few details, but
little is lost from the over-all picture because of these restrictions.

Our experience in military psychiatry has been limited to
working with combat soldiers overseas in an active theater of
operations and returnees suffering from war neuroses hospitalized
for rehabilitation. We have seen literally several thousand cases.
But space permits us to document our observations with only a
selected group of case histories. From these, others may form
conclusions that have escaped our attention. We have written
this material as free from scientific jargon as possible, hoping to
make this book useful to everyone in military and civilian life
who is interested in human beings under stress.

Roy R. Grinker
John P. Spiegel

AAF Convalescent Hospital (Don Cesar),
St. Petersburg, Florida.
May 1, 1945.

Acknowledgements

FIRSTLY WE TAKE THE greatest pleasure in expressing our indebtedness to Colonel Richard E. Elvins, our Commanding Officer overseas and later in this country when he joined us at the Don Cesar Convalescent Hospital. Colonel Elvins always showed a deep understanding of the emotional problems of the men entrusted to his administration. He permitted us complete professional and intellectual freedom; and enabled us to organize, institute changes and carry on overseas and in this country the work that made this book possible.

To Lt. Colonel John M. Murray and Colonel William P. Holbrook we are grateful for our assignment to the rehabilitation program in this country and ultimately to work together again. Both officers encouraged and supported our work to the fullest extent that their administrative positions permitted. Psychiatry in the Air Forces and particularly the rehabilitation work for combat veterans suffering from "operational fatigue" owe much to the dynamic vision and persistent constructive efforts of Lt. Colonel John M. Murray.

Among the psychiatrists who cooperated fully while on the staff of our hospital, participated in seminars and contributed case material were: William Y. Baker, Carroll C. Carlson, Floyd Fortuin, David Leach, Milton L. Miller, Frederick Rosenheim, Carel Van der Heide and Jack Weinberg. We are happy to have been associated with all of them.

Russell J. Spivey and Asher S. Chapman cooperated with us from the medical point of view, Morgan Sargent from the surgical and Winfred L. Post from that of the eye, ear, nose and throat, in attacking psychosomatic problems. Raymond G. Vinal and Ottis E. Hanes, Chiefs of the Convalescent Services Division, were extremely enthusiastic and cooperative in furnishing adjunctive therapy for our patients, showing a real understanding of their needs. Benjamin Willerman, Robert P. Barrell and Herbert J. Zucker, psychologists, ably performed our psychometrics and psychological testing and cooperated in our research program.

The following general medical officers, who were trained by us in our first teaching conference, remained on our staff, valiantly doing excellent work as assistant psychiatrists, and proved to us the value of such a teaching program: T. Louis Bacchiani, R. Stanley Bank, Werner Blade, Hayden H. Donahue, Ernest W. Furgurson, Daniel Goldstein, Paul H. Harwood, John E. Helm, Kenneth H. Johnson, Pasquale A. Ruggieri. They demonstrated an incredible devotion to the welfare of their patients. Others, too numerous to mention, who followed this group, profited by their experience and also did excellent psychiatric work.

Dr. Frank Fremont-Smith, Medical Director of the Josiah Macy, Jr., Foundation, was earnestly interested in our work and we are deeply indebted to him for arranging for the Macy Foundation to publish our first book on military psychiatry, for visiting us, making suggestions and giving encouragement, and for stimulating us to publish this work. Molly Harrower-Erickson, psychologist from the Macy Foundation, initiated a new test while working at our hospital, and gave us many helpful suggestions. We are grateful to our secretaries, Jean K. Orr and Beth T. Guild, for their excellent, speedy and accurate work in transcribing our notes and typing the manuscript.

Contents

V. CIVILIAN APPLICATIONS

CHAPTER 1

The Men: Their Background and Selection

WHAT KIND OF MEN want to be fliers? Two decades ago the average American parent would have reacted with indignation and alarm to a son's intention of taking up flying as a career. It was too dangerous, an uncertain risk. Today all this is changed and thousands of our young men are cluttering up the skies, as if it were their natural right, and the firmament the only place where a man could draw a deep breath. Flying is as safe as riding a bicycle but infinitely more fun, and it is exciting. There's nothing to worry about, nobody gets hurt anymore. Nothing at all to worry about.

Or is there?

In thinking it over, the parent may still not be so certain about it as the cocksure son, and may wonder what possesses him. In thinking the same matter over more than two thousand years ago, the Greeks lifted a similar doubtful eyebrow, and with wonderful clarity—one is tempted to say clairvoyance— expressed their concern in the myth of Daedalus and Icarus. This story points so obvious a moral to the would-be flier that it is worth while repeating it, if only to admire the Grecian foresight. Daedalus was said to have been a native of Athens, eminent for his skill in architecture and statuary. A hot-tempered man, consumed with professional jealousy, he became envious of his nephew and coworker, Perdix, and attempted to murder him by throwing him down from the summit of the Acropolis. Perdix, however, was saved by supernatural intervention. He became transformed into a low-flying partridge and escaped by hedge-hopping over the temples and market places of Athens, a tech-

3

nique which is still good today. This appears to have given
Daedalus an idea. Somewhat later he was banished to Crete,
where he displayed his undoubted engineering talents by con-
structing the famous Labyrinth for King Minos. Unfortunately,
he eventually quarreled with the King, who forgot his gratitude
and imprisoned Daedalus along with his son Icarus in a lofty
tower. There they brooded until Daedalus, remembering Perdix'
happy tactic, resolved to try the same thing without benefit of
supernatural help. He fashioned wings for Icarus and himself
out of feathers and wax. Then, after cautioning Icarus not to
fly too near the sun, they took off and flew high into the air and
over the sea. But Icarus disregarded his father's instructions
and approached so near the sun that the heat melted the wax
which held the feathers together. He could no longer sustain
himself, fell and was drowned in the sea now called Icarian
from his name.

Icarus, the prototype of the "hot" pilot, defied his father's
will and all the forces of nature. As a result he met an untimely
end, since shared by a long line of similarly minded, if not so
illustrious, airmen. The point is only a special elaboration of
the moral, made so often in Greek drama and mythology, that
it is dangerous for man to give expression to his envy of the gods
and godlike creatures. Swift is the wrath and terrible the punishment. Since the Wright brothers improved on Daedalus' idea,
the airplane has effectively illustrated this point though with
decreasing emphasis, as aircraft casualties resulting from
structural failure, bad weather and pilot error have diminished.
Although today the danger of injury or death in flying is sta-
tistically small, nevertheless it is still a real and powerfully
moving fear. Since it is not true that no one gets hurt, anyone
who intends to accept this risk as a career must, like Icarus,
have good reasons for the choice. Behind such a choice lie both
psychological and economic motives. Flying must be fun, an
emotionally fulfilling experience, and it must pay. If this is
true, an analysis of the specific emotional and practical attrac-
tions in aviation should give much information regarding the
kind of men who want to be fliers.

Everyone would like to feel that he can control his physical
environment. On earth such control is at best two-dimensional,
flat and definitely limited. Flying is the apotheosis of this desire
for control and mastery. The child's dreams of omnipotence in

the face of his toddling weakness are usually abandoned with fairy tales and toys. They become true again, however, by virtue of the airplane. This supertoy, this powerful, snorting, impatient but submissive machine, enables the man to escape the usual limitations of time and space. Truly godlike, the flier soars above the earth and the little men confined to its surface. He feels his mastery of space and time by means of the intense speed of modern aircraft and their ability to maneuver without obstacle into any desired position.

Nothing is so powerful and yet so responsive to delicate touch as modern aircraft. Flying a plane requires skill, strength and fine control, which is demonstrable at every turn and each landing. The mastery of the power in the machine is a challenge which gives a justified sense of accomplishment when it has been successfully met. Furthermore, the flier increases his sense of power by identifying himself with his plane, which he feels as an extension of his own body. He thereby achieves a feeling of aggressive potency bordering on the unchallenged strength of a superman. This is well illustrated in Colonel Robert Scott's book, "God Is My Co-Pilot," where, in an account of his flight over Mount Everest in a little P-43, the author describes how he felt that he had humbled this highest mountain and then patronizingly saluted his fallen opponent (55).

The flier's opportunity to master his environment and to dominate a powerful machine represents an attraction which is emotionally satisfying to the average young man in our civilization. Its appeal is universal and many respond to it out of a perfectly healthy interest. On the other hand, it is also a very satisfying compensation for feelings of inferiority. It is a purposeful and socially acceptable escape from and compensation for personal defeats among ground-bound humans. It is the perfect prescription for those that are weak, hesitant or frustrated on earth. Give them wings, 2000 horses compressed into a radial engine, and what can stop them? Furthermore, this denial of weakness and dependence is highly exhibitionistic. The flier is universally recognized as someone daring and courageous with dash and glamour. To the extent that this exhibitionistic satisfaction covers a real, underlying sense of inferiority, the attraction to flying represents an unhealthy motivation. This point will be further elaborated later on. For the present it is sufficient to point out that, among the men who become interested in flying, there are many whose motives are psychologically healthy and a smaller number whose interest arises from a basically unstable or possibly neurotic drive.

In most fliers the urge to fly is felt as an impulse and is not subjected to introspection or analysis. The emotional factors outlined above are, therefore, largely unconscious. In addition to the emotional reasons, the men who choose the Air Forces in which to fight their share of the war have a number of good conscious and rational reasons for their choice. Chief among these are the occupational and economic advantages of commercial and military aviation. Many young men think of flying as an attractive and well paying occupation and seek flying instruction as a preparation for a future career. Relatively few opportunities for training have been available at reasonable cost in civilian life. Suddenly, with the tremendous expansion of the Army Air Forces, unlimited opportunities have beckoned to almost anyone who can meet the physical, educational and intellectual requirements for flying training. Although some may question the ability of the postwar commercial airlines to absorb such a tremendous number of fliers, and their interest in employing men accustomed to exhilarating lives of danger in which they must deliberately take chances with death, many exhibit an easy optimism concerning the future. The common opinion that the Air Forces in peacetime will be greatly expanded and will need flying personnel of all types in great numbers has induced men to plan on remaining in the regular army, where they can continue to fly the fastest and most modern ships.

Regardless of their status in the future, candidates for flying training are attracted to the Air Forces by several practical advantages they seem to afford over other branches of the service. Members of air crews, that is, the pilot, copilot, bombardier and navigator, are automatically given commissions or warrants as officers on completion of their training. This satisfies a desire both for the prestige of rank and for the increase in security provided by the higher income that goes along with it. In addition, the Air Forces have increased the economic incentive by providing a 50 per cent increase in basic pay allowance for those on flying status. Another practical inducement has been the prevailing impression that the air combat crews fight a cleaner war than the men of the ground forces. An opportunity to get into the fight without having to endure the mud, marching and foxholes of the infantry is appealing. Unfortunately, this aspect has been overemphasized in the past, with the result that combat fliers have been unprepared for the actually unpleasant living conditions which they frequently find awaiting them in a theater of operations, or for the terrifying experiences frequently arising out of aerial combat. In the face of the actual experience in combat, the practical advantages which seemed to loom so large at the time of application for flying training may not stand up well.

It can be seen, accordingly, that neither the emotional nor the practical or intellectual motivations which induce men to apply for flying training are in themselves any guarantee of future success in the field. The more healthy and realistic the motivation, the greater the chance of success. In general, however, although the personal reasons for interest in flying tell us something about the kind of men who want to be fliers, and from whom the candidates for flying training must be chosen, the actual selection of the candidates must be based on certain requirements which experience has shown to be necessary for the greatest chances of success. Among these the most obvious and the most rigid are intelligence and age.

In the original plan for the selection of the expanded flying personnel in the Air Forces, intelligence was equated with schooling and the educational requirements were set rather high, two years of college being demanded. As the need for men increased, high school graduates were accepted. Still later, manpower shortages forced the acceptance of men regardless of educational achievements, provided they were able to attain a certain grading in intelligence tests. As a result the educational classification of flying officers ranges from college graduates to those with two years of high school. Many men even have advanced degrees. The average enlisted man has less education, some having only finished grade school. The educational pattern of the men who are selected for flying training, then, represents a cross section of what the American educational system has to offer.

Experience has shown that the best fliers, allowing for the usual exceptions, are young men. Older persons cannot easily or thoroughly acquire the coordination and skill necessary to handle a fast-moving ship successfully. Beyond the age of 27 years, failures are more frequent than successes. For this reason an arbitrary age limit has been set at that point. At first the average age of the men accepted for training was 22 years, because of the initial educational requirements. As these were relinquished younger boys have been accepted, many being only 18 years old. The average age is now, therefore, somewhat lower.

The rigid limitations of age and intelligence contribute a definite cultural cast to the group of men who are selected for flying training. It is worth while to examine the social and psychological factors involved for the purpose of understanding the type of human material which is later subjected to the supreme test of combat. There is a popular impression that Air Forces personnel represent an elite of American youth, the cream of the crop. Because of the large numbers of men who have had to be accepted, this is not strictly true. Rather they represent a cross section of all that is good and bad in American men within the specific limitations of age, intelligence and physical endowment previously mentioned. For the most part, in their adolescent or postadolescent years, the men show a wide gradation of educational and occupational achievement prior to their acceptance for training. Many have come directly from school into military service. Others have made no effort to find permanent work, knowing that they would soon have to enter the army. Some men have struggled through the lean years before the war, attempting to gain a foothold in industry, business or farming. Although quite a number were able to achieve some success in this and held good positions before being accepted for training, the work record of many men shows considerable shifting about from one job to another. The general economic situation compelled a large number of these to enter the CCC camps, which were a sort of extracurricular preparation for army service but yet represented no test of the individual's ability for independent effort and achievement.

An examination of the work record and past history of a large number of fliers shows that, at the time they were accepted for training, they were still in the adolescent phase of testing themselves against the world and of developing confidence in themselves. From the standpoint of both practical achievement and psychological maturity they show a wide range of success. Many have retained considerable emotional and economic dependence on their families. Immediately prior to induction a great number were still living at home, where they were inclined to be spoiled by their mothers and dominated by their fathers. A large percentage of these youths have an emotional attachment to their mothers far more intense than their chronological ages should permit. In this regard they conform to the average contemporary product of our past decades, which is the result of an excessive gratification of children combined with an insincerity in instilling mature standards of conduct (cf. chapter 20).

Among enlisted men and, to a smaller degree, among officers, a large number of broken homes have been responsible for a disturbed family life. Parents separated or divorced, stepfathers and stepmothers, familial discord, a drunken, sadistic father and other disturbing family settings give an unexpected view of a cross section of family life. The relationship of such specific factors to psychological disturbances arising out of combat will be considered later (cf. chapter 10). The general background considered here can be delineated in this way: the men selected for flying training are in the normal transition stage between the emotional and economic dependence of their adolescent years and the self sufficiency of adult life. In this process some of the men have had more than the usual amount of economic difficulty because of either chronically poor family circumstances or personal limitations, or both. Others have had more than the usual amount of emotional dependence on their families. In either case the circumstance is apt to lead to an interest in flying which represents an overcompensation for and an escape from previous difficulties. This is entirely a quantitative matter, a question of how much of an individual's motivation represents an overcompensation, how much of his past history indicates excessive economic or emotional dependence. The point he occupies on this spectrum, which shades subtly from the normal to the seriously maladjusted, has a great significance for the future career of the would-be flier.

In order to select from this mass of men interested in flying those who have the greatest chance of success, a much finer combing of the material must be made. It is necessary to choose those who will be able to learn how to fly with the least difficulty, and this is the task of *psychological selection*. It is further necessary to choose those who will be the most suited to withstand the emotional stresses of flying and of combat. This requires adequate *psychiatric selection*. Although they are closely associated, these two selective functions are independent of each other and require different techniques.

Although it is probably true that anyone can learn how to fly, just as most people can learn how to drive a car, there is a tremendous variation in the speed and ease with which such skills are acquired. The goal in selection for training in military aviation is to choose the men who can learn easily and rapidly, requiring the minimum of time from available teachers and representing the minimum of risk to themselves and others. The role of psychologists, who have always been professionally interested in the problem of occupational selection, was recognized and authorized relatively early in the planning for the expansion of the Air Forces. The psychologists have perfected a battery of tests designed to select those men who can be easily and safely trained to fly. Utilizing paper and pencil tests, questionnaires and special testing machines (41), all of which give objective criteria, they have been able to function with great speed and with minimal personnel. The psychologists are thus able to function even under the pressure of thousands of applicants, who must be selected quickly. The various tests need not be discussed here except to indicate that they are numerous and have not yet been given scientific validity as to specificity or efficiency. On the basis of the response to the psychological tests, a candidate is given a numerical score indicating his flying aptitude. Trial classification of the successful applicant for flying training as a pilot, bombardier or navigator is then based on a combination of personal preference, previous experience, psychological aptitude and the immediate or anticipated needs of the Air Forces for men in one of these categories.

The goal of successful psychiatric selection is the weeding out of candidates who, although capable of learning to fly, will readily succumb emotionally to the stresses of danger, especially the dangers of combat. At present far too many fliers are permanently grounded in transitional training, staging areas, overseas training commands and after their first few combat missions. It is this group that the psychiatrist attempts to recognize and screen. Among them are individuals with overt or latent neuroses, men with unhealthy neurotic motivation or with low thresholds of anxiety endurance, and those with behavior problems and personalities that make group activity and teamwork difficult or impossible.

Psychiatrists in the Air Forces have carefully analyzed the men who develop nervous reactions in training, in Continental commands and in combat, in the hope of determining what kind of person is unable to endure the stresses of flying and combat after having learned to fly, so that psychiatric selection and screening could be improved (26, 27). It has been found that the earliest and most flagrant breakdowns are among men whose personalities were previously unstable and who had not effected a satisfactory life adjustment. A selection that does not weed out these persons, permitting unfit men to be accepted into cadet training and graduated, is obviously inefficient. Selection, however, is complicated by the evidence that, no matter how "normal" or "strong" an individual is, he may develop a neurosis if crucial stress impinging on him is sufficiently severe, while on the other hand many combat soldiers with lifelong anxiety neuroses are able to withstand considerable stress. Furthermore, it has been learned that the important psychological predispositions to "operational fatigue" are usually latent and therefore difficult to detect until they are uncovered by catastrophic events. It must be concluded that for the vast majority the *only valid test for endurance of combat is combat itself*. This does not prevent us from analyzing our material to determine which characteristics of the personality are invariably associated with breakdowns, which are sometimes associated with them and which are only rarely found to be present. Concerning these correlations our experience has now been extensive.

In everyone who applies for flying training we have described a combination of emotional and rational motivations. For this reason selection cannot be based solely on "zest for flying" but must detect a *healthy or unhealthy motivation*. From a study of the correlations between precombat personality structures and failures under combat stress, it is possible to delineate certain "personality profiles," combinations of unhealthy motivations with unsuitable emotional trends, who can be expected to have difficulties in combat.

A large heterogeneous group of adult behavior problems cause difficulties, not in learning to fly or in combat, but because they lead to personality clashes. Schizoid individuals, who are motivated for flying largely on account of a desire to get away from interpersonal contacts, create problems because they are unable to achieve close teamwork. They clash with other personalities and show peculiar quixotic judgment in flying, often refusing to follow operational routines. Such personalities are frequently aggressive in combat and are difficult to control and maintain in formation. They resent retreat and cautious maneuvers. Psychopathic personalities are openly critical and disrespectful of leadership, and resent lack of personal recognition. They may refuse to fly because of these personal difficulties, or become paranoid, with little insight into their own problems (cf. chapter 4). They are not amenable to military authority and openly disobey regulations, frequently flying low in hazardous exhibitions. Their very aggressiveness frequently leads them into courageous exploits but creates serious problems when they return as heroes and are unable to resume a normal existence (15). Many of them have had to be separated from the service under administrative and disciplinary procedures. Since the only check on their asocial behavior is external, for they lack a well developed ego-ideal of their own, it is difficult to impose new social restrictions on them, once combat has permitted them to be openly aggressive and hostile (cf. chapter 14).

At the opposite extreme one of the most important tasks is to evaluate the quantity and dynamic importance of dependent trends in applicants. Our adolescent candidates usually have no background of experience from which we may draw conclusions as to what they will do under future stress. It is much more important for psychiatric judgment to have several examples of previous behavior under external difficulties than to talk with the patient briefly and get his carefully prepared and controlled responses. This is particularly true when we attempt to evaluate the amount of immaturity that a boy has maintained in his adult existence, to which are directly related the type and quantity of stress he will be able to endure in combat. It is for this type of problem that psychiatric observation in a training command would be most valuable.

Men with obsessive-compulsive characters often make good bomber pilots, since their rigid patterns of behavior cause them to be steady and reliable. They learn slowly and retain tenaciously what they have learned, but are slow to adapt to new or emergency situations. Interferences with their rituals by dirt, bad food, poor living conditions and excessive pressure, and new and unexpected combat experiences often break down their compulsive defenses and throw them into reactive depressions (cf. cases 4 and 5). Persons with latent depressions react badly to the death and maiming of people around them and to the lack of dependent gratification. It is these men who succumb to an irrational sense of guilt when they are even indirectly involved in mishaps to other soldiers. Men who have tendencies to develop hysterical symptoms often use somatic conversion mechanisms after moderate stress of combat, taking on symptoms in relation to minor injuries or related to Air Forces stress. A minor bump on the head may cause intractable headaches, or anxiety stimulated by night flying may produce visual disturbances (cf. case 14).

Psychosomatic disturbances (cf. chapter 11) are serious predispositions to devastating reactions to the stress of battle. It may be said that these visceral-functional manifestations are definite contraindications against assignment to a combat unit. The most frequent psychosomatic disturbances are related to the upper gastrointestinal tract and are manifested by nausea, abdominal pain, vomiting or severe loss of appetite. When such symptoms have existed prior to acceptance for training or if they develop during training, they are adequate causes for dismissal from further flying. When they develop in anticipation of combat in commissioned officers who are already flying, they constitute adequate contraindications against overseas duty. The natural development in people with previous psychosomatic disturbances is that they are unable to continue combat for more than a few missions and must be grounded overseas at great expense of time, money and personnel. Other less frequent psychosomatic symptoms consist of diarrhea, cardiac irregularities and chest pains, as well as disturbances of the blood vessels in the upper respiratory tract and the skin. Persistent air sickness including vomiting and vertigo, occurring even in quiet weather, belongs in the same category (cf. chapters 5 and 11).

Dunbar (13) has been able to delineate a "psychological profile" of people who are prone to accidents. These are "good fellows" of impulsive temperament, whose essential values in life are short term or immediate. They are restless and seek out dangerous occupations. But, when under too great pressure from authority, they become involved in accidents. Unfortunately, we have been unable to apply Dunbar's excellent studies on civilians to selection of fliers, because airplane accidents in a theater of operations are the results of failure on the part of groups of men rather than individuals. The most that can be derived from our studies are the several psychological profiles which we have indicated as predisposing to breakdowns *after* accidents or less than average combat stress.

Difficult problems are the anxiety states that appear in various stages of training, particularly the later phases when the flier begins to use a dangerous combat plane, or in the first few combat missions. These occur in individuals predisposed because of emotional instability or pre-existing neurotic trends (cf. chapter 4). These men have been accepted as aviation cadets by mistake. The appearance of symptoms of anxiety is only the final evidence of the flier's low anxiety threshold and hence unsuitability, when it is not the result of severe or even average stress. Anxiety is then related to the total flying situation, involving all phases of flying and all types of planes (cf. case 2). When a careful history is elicited, it is usually found that anxiety has been present since earliest flying training. Because of pressure by instructors or fear of drastic administrative action or because of intense personal pride, many cadets endure the early anxiety, attempting at all costs to finish their training. Their tremendous efforts are often successful, yet, if symptoms become obvious to the Flight Surgeon, who grounds them, they accept grounding with relief because they have good insight into their condition.

Other men have less insight and, although suffering from symptoms, fight against grounding, rationalizing their difficulties on such factors as poor instruction, malassignment as to type of plane or incompatibilities in crews or squadrons. They experience conflict between their incapacitating anxieties and a strong ego-ideal, which insists on continued effort, so that they cannot accept grounding, reacting with depression when it is threatened. The basic conflict is, however, between a passive-dependent desire for safety, security and protection, and a desire for the overcompensated role of a heroic aviator. That such individuals may be surprisingly successful in combat is demonstrated by the following case.

CASE 1: *Copilot, with lifelong anxiety, nevertheless able to endure a full tour of combat duty.*

This patient was a 25 year old B-25 copilot, who endured fifty-three combat missions. He flew copilot for his entire tour, an unusual occurrence, and probably an essential condition to the degree of success he was able to achieve. After twenty-five missions he began to develop anxiety. On his thirty-fifth mission the hydraulic system of his plane was shot out, forcing him to make a belly landing. After this he showed considerable anxiety and physical incoordination, even during noncombat flying. He complained of irritability, restlessness, sleeplessness and headaches. An overseas medical board returned him to the United States for rehabilitation, crediting him for extensive effort.

At our hospital the patient stated he had suffered all his life from chronic anxiety and restlessness. In combat he was not upset by any one event but was always afraid and "sweated everything out." He persisted in spite of fear until his performance suffered. The patient improved considerably under psychotherapy alone, to the state where his nervousness was "just like before flying."

. . . . . .

If this officer had not dissimilated when passing through the examination for aircrew training and had confessed his previous anxiety state, he would have been rejected. Yet with all his anxiety he did very well. In our previous experience with ground forces, we saw similar examples of men with fairly severe anxiety states of long standing going through several battles undisturbed. As this patient stated, "It was nothing new for me to be anxious." Sometimes experience in dealing with anxiety protects the soldier against severe neurosis, whereas, by way of contrast, a boy who had never experienced conscious anxiety developed a psychotic-like condition when sufficient stress overwhelmed his defenses (cf. case 59).

Low thresholds of anxiety or tendencies toward flight as a response to anxiety are common among those who succumb early to anxiety neuroses in combat. Neither tendency can be determined prior to the actual experience of stress. The types just described are those who may do well or badly, depending on unpredictable external events. When they are recognized in their manifest states prior to combat either they should be rejected from training or their training should be interrupted; certainly they should not be sent overseas. If their latent forms are suspected, they should be watched for early signs of disturbances, so that therapy can be quickly instituted or appropriate disposition made before they become involved in loss of life or damage to themselves and others.

When classical psychoses or psychoneuroses of the types found in civilian life become overt in combat personnel, they are usually precipitated, not by anxiety related to flying, but by the minimal stimuli of the hostile environment of war. They are exaggerations of undetected neuroses and represent failures in selection primarily because the candidate has hidden the difficulty which would have caused his rejection. Other individuals without insight into the nature of their neuroses, who have been erroneously passed through the screening processes of selection, attribute their breakdowns to combat experiences. On the other hand, men whose previous neuroses have given them experience with the subjective sensation of anxiety may be able to endure new anxieties created by war, but also their internal anxieties may become less disturbing. For the first time the anxious and conflictual neurotic may be able to feel as well as his neighbor, because he can project his anxieties to the stress of battle and feel that he is no more afraid than the person with normal fears of combat.

The greatest difficulty in selection is to determine the quantity of stress and the type of stress that will cause specific personality types to react adversely. Even if this were possible, it is asking too much from a military organization to assign an individual in combat to an environment or a function that is least likely to disturb his particular stability. Furthermore, it is extremely difficult to know what criterion of success should be used. If he is able to complete at least three fourths of the average tour of combat duty, then effort and expense expended on him may be called successful. But it is not always the man himself and the stress he endures that combine to result in success or failure. The quality of leadership, the morale of the group and the prophylactic measures prescribed by the Flight Surgeon are significant factors in determining the end result.

All these difficulties confront the psychiatrist in selection. He is unable to deal with large quantities of men objectively and is unable to control the goal of his selection or the subsequent disposition of the men. He has no laboratory means of duplicating the stress to which an individual will be exposed in combat, hence the tolerance of the ego for the quantity of anxiety stimulated by combat cannot be measured. Since anxiety is a psychologically adaptive mechanism, economically necessary for survival in the presence of danger, its presence is not necessarily a handicap. In fact, individuals who are not stimulated to anxiety are predisposed to severe psychotic-like breakdowns when stress reaches their personal threshold. The subjective emotion of anxiety and its physiological concomitants force some men to fight, others to retreat. In some the anxiety reaches a stage of uneconomical and destructive influence on the ego, paralyzing or freezing the individual. In still other fliers, anxiety is stimulated in economic quantities and it evokes an adequate aggressiveness, but it persists pathologically without decrement. Thus it gradually accumulates on successive missions, resulting eventually in a breakdown.

The rapidly changing adolescent boy may maintain or improve his skills during training but, because of the demands made on him for an unnaturally speedy maturation, he may show the first signs of emotional disturbance after he has gone through part of the training program. Hence, a boy whom the psychiatrist diagnoses as emotionally normal at the moment of selection may, on account of accidents or interpersonal difficulties, become disturbed and must subsequently be disqualified. It is apparent that, although far better psychiatric selection is necessary, superior results can only be achieved if it is accompanied by a psychiatric program for maintenance of emotional stability during the first year of extreme stress in training. Selection and maintenance are inseparable problems (17, 44).

PART II

The Environment of Combat

CHAPTER 2

The Combat Units

COMBAT UNITS of the Air Forces are unique associations of men with affection for aircraft, fused into tightly integrated organizations. The men are the same individuals whose civilian backgrounds we have already described, only somewhat toughened by their experience in training units at home and confident in their abilities. But their presence overseas in a theater of operations brings about a transformation in their personalities; something new is added as a product of the environment of the combat unit. It is upon this new personality that the stresses and strains of combat react. Therefore, it is important to examine the social, emotional and physical atmosphere of the combat units.

The basic characteristics of every combat unit are derived from the banding together of teams under leaders to fight a dangerous enemy. While the unit is in training at home, the enemy is theoretical, too far away to have any real emotional significance. In the theater of operations, however, the presence of the enemy, and his capacity to injure and kill, give the dominant emotional tone to the combat outfit. All other emotional attitudes become secondary to the need to be strong and protected, and united against the enemy. The threat of enemy action and the isolation from home and family in a strange land of foreign people produce a definite change in the relations and feelings of the fliers toward each other. This new emotional environment is the basic and specific feature of all combat units, and is not limited to the Air Forces.

The impersonal threat of injury from the enemy, affecting all alike, produces a high degree of cohesion so that personal attachments throughout the unit become intensified. Friendships are easily made by those who might never have been compatible at home, and are cemented under fire. Out of the mutually shared hardships and dangers are born an altruism and generosity that transcend ordinary individual selfish interests. So sweeping is this trend that the usual prejudices and divergences of background and outlook, which produce social distinction and dissension in civil life, have little meaning to the group in combat. Religious, racial, class, schooling or sectional differences lose their power to divide the men. What effect they have is rather to lend spice to a relationship which is now based principally on the need for mutual aid in the presence of enemy action. Such powerful forces as antisemitism, anticatholicism or differences between Northerners and Southerners are not likely to disturb interpersonal relationships in a combat crew.

Although the usual social, religious or sectional ties that bind men into groups in civil life are sloughed off in the combat unit, the over-all social atmosphere more than offsets the loss. The camaraderie is so effective that even the arbitrary distinctions imposed by the military caste system, probably one of the most rigid social devices in the world, are noticeably weakened. Friendships between officers and enlisted men satisfy urges, based on mutual interest and gain, that are much more powerful than any distinctions of rank or grade. Not only do the officers and men become very close to each other, but they become friendly with each other's wives, families and sweethearts, through correspondence. Their association is not limited to working hours but includes their social activities. In the combat theaters, opportunities for entertainment during free time are frequently limited to what the entire squadron may create by its own ingenuity, a product of cooperation regardless of rank.

The most vital relationship is not the purely social. It is the feeling that the men have for each other as members of combat teams and toward the leaders of those teams, that constitutes the essence of their relationship. It is an interesting fact that, although the members of combat crews are thrown together only by chance, they rapidly become united to each other by the strongest bonds while in combat. The character of these bonds is of the greatest significance in determining their ability to withstand the stresses of the combat situation.

Air Forces combat teams are of two sorts, depending upon the type of aircraft employed. In bombers and all multiplaced aircraft, the basic element of the team is the aircrew itself: the six, eight or ten men who fly in one plane. This small group is composed of the pilot, copilot, navigator and bombardier, who are usually officers, and four to six enlisted men, including the gunners, radioman and flight engineer. Each has his own specialized duties for which he has been highly trained, and yet no one man's function, except the pilot's, has any special significance except as related to the function of the crew as a whole, which is to bomb enemy targets. The crew of a single, medium or heavy bomber is a compact although miniature army, and contains all the elements necessary to accomplish a military mission. It can find its way to the target, drop its bombs accurately and protect itself against enemy attack. The leader of this self-contained combat unit is the pilot, since it is upon his shoulders that ultimate responsibility for all decisions rests. From the point of view of the situations met in combat, the responsibilities of the pilot as a leader are great. It is he who decides when the crew or the plane is in trouble and what to do about it. If the motors are failing, or the ship is on fire, it is he who must decide whether to press on to the target and risk the lives of his crew, or to turn back. When it is clear that the plane is fatally damaged, he must determine whether to abandon the ship and bail out, or to attempt to bring the plane in for a crash landing. His character, skill and capacity to assume responsibility are of the utmost importance to the other crew members, both because of his responsibility for their safety and because responsibility for effectively carrying out the tactical mission is chiefly in his hands.

Nevertheless, neither the tactical efficiency with which the job is carried out, nor the safety and protection of other members of the crew are completely in the hands of the pilot. As with any team, the center of activity shifts from one crewmate to another in accordance with the combat situation. At one time it may be the waist gunner, at another, the tail gunner, upon whose skill and courage depend the lives of all the others. The combined efforts of all the crew may be wasted if the bombardier is incompetent or anxious and fails to line-up correctly on the target. All members of the crew are dependent upon each other to an unusual degree. Day after day, on mission after mission, this mutual dependence is made to pay dividends in safety and effectiveness of the combat crew. It is no wonder then that the emotional relationships between these fliers assume a special character. The men and their plane become identified with each other with an intensity that in civil life is found only within the family circle. Crew members habitually refer to each other as "my pilot," "my bombardier," "my gunner," and so on, and their feeling for their plane is equally strong, since its strength and reliability are as important as those of any human members of the crew.

In combat the dramatic events through which the crew and their plane fight produce the most immediate and telling psychological impact, so that in the mind of each flier combat is usually represented in terms of his crew. Yet, on actual tactical missions, hundreds of such crews fly together to form the striking force. Thus, the basic team comprising the individual combat crew becomes a part of a larger team, organized by flights, squadrons, groups and wings. In relation to the mission the pilot of the combat crew is under the leader of the flight, group or wing. The actual responsibility of leadership is thus staggered through several echelons of team organization. The fate of the individual crewman therefore is controlled not only by his pilot but also by the group and flight leaders. For this reason, the fliers form strong emotional attitudes toward their tactical leaders. In fighter and fighter-bomber units flying single-seated aircraft, the basic team is the flight of six planes under the flight leader. Men, flying together day after day under the same leader, form the same kind of relationship toward each other as the crew of a bomber plane. The mutual dependence for protection is no less vital even though fighter pilots have a great deal more freedom of activity and independence in combat. The safety of one pilot in the flight depends upon the alertness of all the others in spotting enemy aircraft coming in for attack. The success of the mission is dependent upon the courage, persistence and wisdom of the flight leader.

In this atmosphere of mutual dependence, the task of carrying out complex, highly coordinated maneuvers in the face of great danger imposes upon the men and their leaders a special relationship. The emotional attitudes the fliers take toward each other have less to do with the accident of their individual personalities than with the circumstances of their association. We have already described the intensity of their feeling for each other as resembling the closeness of relationship between members of the same family. In truth, they are brothers-in-arms in more than a figurative sense. They actually feel toward each other as if they were brothers. It is a very common thing to hear a flier say of his buddy, "He reminds me of my brother" or "I felt closer to him than to my own brother." The men in the combat teams are brothers by virtue of their constant enforced association, their dependence upon each other, their common ideals and goals, and their relation to their leaders. In the family circle of the combat group, the leader is in the position of the father. Again it is extremely common to hear a combat flier describe his commanding officer as reminding him of his father. As with the fraternal feelings of the men toward each other, this seems to have less to do with the physical appearance of the leader or his actual personality than with his relation toward the men in combat. From a psychological point of view, the combat leader is a father and the men are his children.

The men are in the position of children by virtue of the ordinary army administrative setup. As in the case of children, they must do what he says, whether they want to or not. He may give them what they want, or deny it, as he wills, rewarding them when they are good and punishing them if they are bad. But in combat the vital relationship derives less from the channels and routines of army administration than from the actual helplessness of the combat team without the aid and protection of the leader. He can lead them into certain death and destruction, or skillfully extricate them from a desperate situation. Their fate is in his hands; their future, their chance of survival, depend upon him. It is small wonder, then, that they feel, for better or for worse, that he is their father. Whether he is a good or bad father is reflected in the morale of the unit in a manner which will be described later. However, it is clear that in such a situation the type of combat personalities developed by the men greatly depends upon the character of the commanding officers and subordinate leaders.

The banding together of teams under leaders in the face of danger should be expected to have the effect of molding all combat groups into the same form. In actual fact, however, subtle variations are found. After a group has been in combat for some time, it begins to take on a definite form and color, making it distinct from other, similar units. A group character or personality is developed which is as definite and detectable as an individual's. Such differences among groups are related not only to their degree of efficiency in combat, which is subject to wide variation, but to many other factors. There are "hot" outfits with an impressive record of tactical efficiency and outstanding accomplishments in combat, rewarded by citations, news and radio publicity, and other forms of public recognition. On the other hand, one finds "snafud" units, badly organized, bogged down with bad morale and discontent, and exhibiting chronically poor combat efforts. "Hard luck" groups are particularly disconcerting to the men in them. Troubles and difficulties of all sorts seem naturally to gravitate to these units. They get the worst locations in the theater of operations, the most difficult combat assignments, the poorest weather on missions; the greatest force of the enemy attack is always concentrated on them and they have the highest losses in combat. Any combat outfit may have a streak of bad luck, but the "hard luck" units have it all the time. Then there are gay, carefree units noted for their reckless exuberance and dash, in contrast with sober outfits characterized by a quiet dependability. Many factors lie behind such variations in color and character, but in general they depend upon differences in leadership, in tactical missions, in types of aircraft employed, and in the geographical and climatic setting of combat.

Differences in leadership will be discussed in detail in a later chapter devoted to morale. It may be said here that, owing to his psychological position as the father of the men, the character of the leader has the most profound effect upon the combat group. In Air Forces combat units the leaders are, for the most part, young men whose primary interest is in flying; the commanding officers are always flying officers. They have had little training in administration of large organizations, and quite frequently have poorly developed executive capacity. The detailed type of responsibilities referred to disparagingly as "desk work" is often enthusiastically neglected or else delegated to some ground officer, a favoritism which may negate the commanding officer's otherwise good leadership. In the Air Forces, since executive ability is a matter of accident rather than of careful training, the units naturally show greater variation in efficiency of organization than in other branches of the services.

The type of aircraft flown by an organization has a pronounced effect upon the personality characteristics of the group. This is due to the close identification of the men with their aircraft. The plane itself has definite characteristics, which have their effect on the flier. The flying characteristics of a high altitude, multiengine heavy bomber are so different from those of a single engine dive bomber that it requires a different sort of person to fly each type successfully. Or rather, the pilot tends to develop a different flying and combat personality when he is exposed to one type of plane or to another. In general, the flying characteristics of heavy, four engine or two engine bomber type aircraft are those of steadiness, lack of maneuverability, reliability and great power over a long distance. Combat missions consume many hours and require considerable persistence and endurance. The fliers in such groups, especially the pilots, tend to fit in with these characteristics. They are usually older, more mature, steadier and less willing to take risks and indulge in flashy maneuvers than fighter pilots.

Single engine fighter planes, on the other hand, have a short range and a high maneuverability. Speed, especially in climbing and diving, and tremendous fire power are among their outstanding attributes. As a result, the men who fly them tend to be youthful, eager for excitement, enthusiastic, almost exhibitionistic and somewhat reckless. These qualities are accordingly imparted to the group as a whole, and to that extent account for part of the group personality. The reaction to the aircraft is so intense, moreover, that even the make of the plane is a factor in the personality of the group. The Airacobra and the Mustang are both fighter aircraft, yet there is a definite difference in the characters of the groups flying these planes. Pilots of the latter, for instance, know they are flying the top-flight, unbeatable Allied fighter plane and have accordingly an immense pride in their aircraft and a feeling of superiority. Airacobras, on the other hand, have proved to have only a limited value in combat and, in addition, are somewhat tricky to fly. The fliers of these planes therefore feel rather depreciated and disappointed. The same types of differences in reactions to aircraft are found between B-17 and B-24 heavy bomber groups and between B-25 and B-26 medium bomber groups.

Last but not least of the environmental factors which lend color to the group is its geographical location. There is a sharp contrast between the combat groups located in England and those situated in the deserts of Africa or the jungles of the Southwest Pacific. Differences in landscape and climate have a well known effect upon health and well-being, but in a combat theater the most striking factor is the relative helplessness against the most unpleasant features of the terrain, dictated by tactical considerations. This is especially true for those groups which most closely follow the movements of the ground forces in the front lines. There is no getting away from the ubiquitous heat, sand, thirst and flies of the desert; no escape to a pleasant oasis. What the weather brings, the men in their tents and foxholes must endure. The tactical situation in the European Theater, on the other hand, places combat groups in the beautiful English countryside and makes available the civilized pleasures of London and other cities. In Burma, India and China, the almost complete isolation of American combat units among peoples so foreign and unfamiliar makes for even greater cohesiveness and closeness among the fliers independently of their combat experiences. In addition, the monotony of their lives exclusive of combat and the almost complete deprivation of the ordinary comforts and pleasures of civilized existence produce a special type of strain which is reflected in the group personality.

The personalities of the fliers are shaped not only by the specific character of the combat units, but also by the singular flavor of combat itself. The environment of combat produces an almost indescribable combination of physical and emotional stress on the soldier. It possesses an insane, nightmare quality, like a bad dream which keeps recurring. This is due not only to the senseless destruction and incredible waste of battle, but also to its interminable nature; it cannot be stopped or brought under control. In civilian life, every effort is made to resolve conflicts and abolish misery, to reduce stress, strain and pain, and to make life as comfortable as possible. Every technical resource of a brilliantly scientific age is concentrated on these aims. Even great natural catastrophes, such as fires, floods and earthquakes, which may be difficult or impossible to control, nevertheless come to a rapid spontaneous termination. In battle the stress is never concluded, nor can it be controlled. Rather, the intent is to increase the stress continually in the furious pursuit of victory. It is man-made, it is intended that way, and therefore it cannot be escaped, avoided or controlled, but only endured.

The physical stress of aerial combat is severe but is not as prolonged or as debilitating as the physical strain to which ground combat troops, especially the infantry, are subjected. Foot soldiers frequently have to withstand incredible demands on their physical resources. They are required to make long marches with little sleep in order to go into a battle lasting many days. Often they have inadequate food, and even water may be scarce. Bathing and shaving are forgotten luxuries. Mud, rain and insect pests are constant companions, and what little sleep they can snatch during a lull in the battle is due more to their profound fatigue than to any physical arrangements favorable to slumber. The noise of battle seldom lets up, and even in sleep it is difficult to escape the constant auditory irritation of exploding bombs, artillery shells and small arms fire. Even though ground force men are usually in top physical shape, each has his own limit of endurance, and after prolonged exposure many succumb purely to physical exhaustion (27).

Air Forces combat crews endure physical stress of a different order. It is intermittent rather than continual, and in general much less exhausting. When not on a combat mission, they are usually in safe and comparatively comfortable quarters, although the conditions vary considerably from theater to theater and depend on the location of the unit with reference to the front lines. As a general rule, they sleep away from the sounds of gunfire, and have a fair opportunity for rest and relaxation in their bivouac areas. Boredom is usually more of a problem than acute discomfort. On the other hand, there is a special type of physical strain connected with flying which is felt most keenly by the pilots although also to some extent by other members of the crew. This is due to the immobility on long flights. They are required to sit in uncomfortable postures for many hours with little opportunity to move about. During much of this time they are under severe emotional strain, which becomes registered as muscular tension. Yet there is no way in which they can adequately relieve this muscular tension as long as they are in the plane. Gunners who can move around in the plane have only a few moments of actual activity suitable for release of tension and during the remainder of the time build up large quantities of tension anticipatory to the battle.

Much mental and physical energy is required to maintain the state of alertness and psychological preparation for hair-trigger reactions imperative in combat flying. Unfortunately there are not always sufficient opportunities to relieve the tension accumulated in combat. In their free time, physical activities are encouraged in order to dissipate accumulated tensions. Enforced idleness and rest are bad therapy for these states.

Prolonged drains on the body's resources of energy prove very fatiguing. The ability to recuperate and restore this energy depends upon the frequency of combat flights. In this there is tremendous variation in accordance with the prevalent tactical situation. During an active campaign, for instance, fighter-bomber pilots may be required to make two or three missions a day of several hours' duration, over a period of weeks, with only one or two days of rest each week. In good weather, crews of heavy bombers and their fighter escorts may go out on daily missions lasting nine to twelve hours. Such variations in frequency are influenced by many factors, including the weather, the number of replacement crews available, the number of planes fit to fly, and the physical and mental states of the men themselves. If the missions are very frequent, there is little opportunity for real recuperation in the intervals and moderate states of physical fatigue develop. The constant emotional stress, which interferes with adequate relaxation, is then superimposed upon the physical fatigue, so that the effect is increasingly cumulative.

In this chain of events a refreshing sleep becomes of the greatest importance. Unfortunately, sleep is often seriously disturbed by several factors. The men are likely to be awakened in the middle of the night for briefings on early morning missions. Going to sleep itself may be difficult because of the emotional tension of the previous day's mission, not yet worn off. Varying amounts of insomnia are almost routine among combat crews. It is possible to walk into any barracks or tent containing fliers supposedly asleep and find several pacing the floor or smoking cigarettes. Some give up entirely the idea of obtaining any sleep on the night before a mission and prefer gambling, drinking or talking to tossing in their bunks until it is time to get up. Others would like to sleep but are continually disturbed by slight noises or by their crewmates talking in their sleep. A restless sleep broken by dreams of combat occurs frequently among fliers who have been in combat for more than a few missions and it is not unusual for such dreams to be accompanied by vocal or physical activity. Frequently his tentmates awaken the dreamer from a nightmare in order to quiet him so that others can go to sleep. In this atmosphere of tension a long, refreshing sleep is a rarity and its absence increases the mounting fatigue. Only quick and short-acting sedatives are practical for fliers who need to be extremely alert on the next day's missions.

Prolonged muscular tension and lack of sleep are not the only sources of physical stress. Combat crews of heavy bombers have to withstand extremely low temperatures at high altitudes. For this they are protected by heavy winter flying clothing or by electrically heated suits. With either type of clothing, severe frostbite of the extremities is not unusual. At high altitudes, a less frequent but more fatal physical menace than the extreme cold is oxygen-lack. The men constantly have to wear oxygen masks connected with the source of stored oxygen in the plane. Although this equipment has now been perfected to a high degree, it is still somewhat uncomfortable, and there is an ever present possibility of failure either in the connecting tubing or in the mask itself. If failure occurs, serious or even fatal states of oxygen-lack may supervene.

Fighter pilots likewise have to be prepared to withstand the cold and lack of oxygen at high altitudes. Because of the relatively small size of the fighter aircraft, these pilots are considerably cramped for space in the cockpit and have little room for movement. As a result, they are apt to feel the effects of continued muscular tension and sluggish circulation of the blood in the extremities most keenly. In addition, they are subject to the well known effects of extremely rapid changes of altitude during power dives. The increase in atmospheric pressure during such dives tends to produce pain in the ears or sinuses and, if there is even slight inflammation of the nose or throat, it leads to the development of aero-otitis media or aerosinusitis. The sudden pull-up at the end of the dive produces marked physical discomfort occasioned by the powerful change in centrifugal force. Viscera are sucked into the lower portions of the body and blood is drawn away from the brain, resulting in a disconcerting greying or blacking-out of vision, or even in momentary unconsciousness. Not only is this reaction wearying, but in combat, when all the mental faculties must be kept constantly alert, the loss of vision, even though brief, can prove very dangerous.

Another drain on physical energy lies in the dietary regime of combat crews. The diets are generally adequate, with high caloric value, but are not particularly palatable. Their chief defect is the lack of variety. This of course varies in different theaters of war with the degree of organization of the base services. At times the menus may consist wholly of C rations, a canned product, whose appeal when they are used over a period of time becomes rapidly limited. Gas-forming foods are difficult to avoid because of the problem of supply and because of the individual idiosyncrasy. Many Americans accustomed to a wide diet, with emphasis on meat and fresh vegetables and large quantities of milk, find it very difficult to eat the same monotonous canned foods day after day. Their caloric intake falls far below their ordinary levels, although their physical expenditure of energy is probably as high as or higher than usual. A loss of 5 to 10 pounds in weight is therefore not uncommon in combat theaters, and, if the food intolerance is marked, the physical depletion becomes a serious threat to fitness for combat. The timing of combat missions, moreover, frequently interferes with food habits, especially among bomber crews. Many men are reluctant to eat a heavy meal before taking off on a mission. Before early morning missions they snatch a cup of coffee, and then are in their plane for eight to twelve hours. Recently food warmers have been installed in bombers, enabling the crews to have hot lunches and palatable snacks. On their return they may be too tired or excited to eat. When they have subsequently rested or calmed down, either they may have missed their meal or they may find it particularly unappetizing. Several days may thus pass with very little food intake. Furthermore, as fatigue and large quantities of anxiety accumulate, there is a natural reduction in appetite, with the formation of a vicious circle of physical depletion.

The various factors involved in the physical stress of combat cannot be regarded as independent entities since they mutually reinforce each other. Long flights would not be so wearying had there been adequate sleep the night before. Tolerance for monotonous food would not be so low if the man were not so fatigued. On the other hand, sleep would be less elusive after a full and satisfying meal. The effects of the physical stress are cumulative and gather a momentum that can only be interrupted by removal from combat activity. But the most serious reinforcement of the effects of physical stress is supplied by the emotional stress of combat.

The emotional stress is a complex network of unusual strains inherent in the combat situation. The stress is derived from different sources, which again mutually reinforce each other. Although complex, they can be reduced to four principal categories: the all-pervading threat of personal injury or death, the injury or death of friends with its powerful effect on the interpersonal relations previously described, the necessity to engage in continually hostile and destructive activity, and finally the effect of all these strains, both physical and emotional, on individual motivation to remain in combat.

The universally hostile atmosphere of the combat scene gives rise to an equally universal fear in combat men. Among so many dangers no one is safe. Ground force troops face dangers coming from many widely different sources and as a result their fears are apt to be generalized to the entire battle. Because of the more highly specialized nature of aerial combat, the possible dangers are more limited in that sphere, and the fear reactions are therefore more specific. But fear itself is the most potent source of emotional stress in combat. Fear is cumulative, because the longer the individual stays in the battle, the more remote appears his chance of coming out alive or uninjured. At one time in one overseas Air Force it was a mathematical certainty that only a few men out of each squadron would finish a tour of duty. The threat is inescapable and ubiquitous, although it varies greatly in degree. Under such circumstances the somatic and psychological effects of fear are a source of strain on everyone.

Of what is the airman afraid? In later chapters we shall discuss the subjective anxiety and fear resulting from long-standing intrapsychic tensions and their relation to the combat situation. While he is in combat, the flier has a sufficiently objective source of fear, which receives constant stimulation from daily events. Flying itself is not a safe pursuit and the combat aircraft is continually subject to mechanical or structural failure. The life of the flier is therefore threatened not only by enemy activity, but by the very thing he loves and depends upon for safety—his airplane. His insecurity can be referred far back: to the designers of the plane (have they devised an aerodynamically safe, rugged ship?); to the manufacturers who may have left structural defects; to the ground crews responsible for maintaining the motors and the fantastically complicated electrical and hydraulic mechanisms of the plane in shape to withstand the rough handling during combat missions. The flier's security depends as much on the efficiency of his friends as on the activity of his enemy.

There are always a sufficient number of routine accidents to leave a veneer of anxiety attached to any type of aircraft. The element of human failure figures as largely in such accidents as structural or mechanical failure. The safety of the pilot, crew members or passengers depends on the judgment and alertness of the pilot. Thus one finds the pilot worrying about his reactions when he becomes fatigued, and fear then attaches to his own person: he is afraid of himself. This fear may be no greater than that of his own crew who have noticed his reactions and are "sweating him out." To a lesser but still definite extent, the reactions of other members of the combat crew may be sources of fear. The bombardier who freezes over the target and forgets to drop his bombs, the navigator who becomes preoccupied and loses his way, the gunner who stares fascinated at yellow-nosed Messerschmitts, unable to shoot, arouse severe anxiety in the rest of the crew.

Although fear of the aircraft and of human inefficiency are a constant source of stress, the greatest fear is attached to enemy activity. The enemy has only two forms of defense against our combat aircraft: fighter planes and flak. The enemy's fighter aircraft are efficient and highly respected by our combat crew members. But they are not as great a source of anxiety as flak. Enemy planes are objects that can be fought against. They can be shot down or outmaneuvered. Flak is impersonal, inexorable and, as used by the Germans, deadly accurate. It is nothing that can be dealt with—a greasy black smudge in the sky until the burst is close. Then it is appreciated as the gaping holes in the fuselage, the fire in the engine, the blood flowing from a wound, or the lurch of the ship as it slips out of control. Fear of enemy activity is seldom concrete until the flier has seen a convincing demonstration of what damage can be inflicted, and how little can be done to avoid it. After a series of such demonstrations, the men are fully aware of what can happen, and the expectation of a repetition produces a drag of fear which is difficult to shake off. This load of apprehension constitutes the chief emotional stress in combat. Almost everyone has to make some conscious effort to deal with it. The extent to which a man is able to control it determines his success as a combat crew member.

The loss of friends in combat is the second most important source of emotional stress. We have already described the extremely close attachments which are formed between the men. The death of a buddy is felt as keenly as the loss of a brother. The men suffer not only from the sense of bereavement, but from having seen the anguish of a bloody and painful death. They cannot look away when the ship flying on their wing receives a direct flak hit and bursts into flame. The sight of their tentmates bailing out with burning parachutes, or exploded out of a disintegrating ship, becomes stamped on their memory. The empty beds in the tent at night reflect this memory, which does not disappear with the sending home of their buddy's clothes and personal effects. The grief persists and, though it is dulled by time, new losses may be added to it. In addition, the loss of friends stimulates increased anxiety. What happened to his buddy may well happen to himself, since they are so much alike. This double load of grief and anxiety is part of the heritage of emotional stress incidental to combat.

Some of the men suffer a great deal of emotional tension on the score of having to be involved in an activity associated with so much death, injury and destruction. In this they are not so much upset by the possibility of their own death, or even of that of their friends, as they are by the thought that what they are doing is responsible for someone else's death. They cannot tolerate well the guilt of killing, even though in aerial warfare the victims are remote, almost abstract. It is interesting that those chiefly affected by this are the heavy bomber crews, who are farthest removed from their targets. Fighter-bomber pilots who go in low to strafe troops, because these are soldiers who intend to kill their compatriots, are seldom affected, but many a bombardier tosses in his bunk at night to think what his bombs may have done to the civilians miles below his plane, especially if he is not quite certain that he was on his target. An exaggeration of this feeling occurs in the rare instances of the bombing of our own troops near the front lines, or the shooting down of our planes through mistakes in identification. This is the least common source of emotional tension, yet it plays a definite role.

The tensions stimulated by fear, grief or horror at his own destructive capacity, are dynamic and constantly press the flier to seek relief in escape from the combat scene. Similarly, the mounting physical exhaustion cries for surcease. But the flier cannot well give in. Though he would welcome an escape, his loyalty is bound to his job and will not permit it. The internal conflict cannot be resolved except by the honorable conclusion of combat which for fliers comes with the completion of a stated number of missions or combat flying hours. The only other honorable escape is through injury, illness or death. For this reason, the announced goal of the number of missions which is considered to constitute a tour of duty comes to have the greatest importance for the men. It is not only the point at which they can go back to their homes and families, but it is the legitimate relief from the complex tensions under which they have been struggling. Up to that point, they have had to withstand the tremendous tension of fear and the countertension put up by their pride and sense of obligation, and thus have had to endure the fight within themselves as well as the battle with the enemy. How intense this internal conflict can be is attested by the statements of many combat crew members that they suffer more when they are on the ground and their crew is flying without them on a combat mission than they do when they are flying. Since their motivation is based principally on their identification with their combat unit and their loyalty to their friends, such a conflict is inevitable.

The intensity of the conflicts resulting from emotional and physical stress in combat varies greatly in individual cases, in different theaters of war and in different stages of a campaign. Everyone reacts to stress somewhat differently. Some are able to handle it with the greatest efficiency and experience little difficulty. Others are crippled sooner or later and find themselves unable to carry on. At times during a campaign the motivation may become so intense, the morale so high, that even the weakest are stimulated to tremendous feats of endurance, completely disregarding their physical fatigue and their fears. At other times, the morale may sink so low that even the slightest stress becomes unendurable. In general, however, there is a fixed limit of tolerance to the physical and emotional stress of combat. What happens to the individual if this limit is exceeded will be discussed in the description of the clinical states.

CHAPTER 3

Motivation for Combat—Morale

MORALE IS A DIFFICULT TERM to define because it is so loosely used. We take.it to mean the psychological forces within a combat group which impel its men to get into the fight. "Good morale" is ordinarily used to describe a state in which the men feel confident, satisfied, united and eager for combat activity. "Poor morale" implies that the men are dispirited, dissatisfied, disorganized and shy of combat. Thus "morale" refers to the collective state of motivation for combat throughout the group and to the many factors which influence this motivation (4). Leighton, for example, expresses "morale" as the capacity of a group of people to pull together persistently and consistently for a common purpose. The factors most concerned in its production and maintenance are: (1) faith in the common purpose; (2) faith in the leadership; (3) faith in each other; (4) adequate health and a balance of work, rest and recreation (37). Since motivation is the nucleus of morale, it is of some importance to analyze it in relation to the individual flier before discussing it with reference to the group as a whole.

In the previous chapter, we described the alteration in the flier's personality produced by associations within the combat group. No facet of his new combat personality thus produced is more important than his motivation. What is the force that compels a man to risk his life day after day, to endure the constant tension, the fear of death, the teasing threat of flak ("if I don't get you today, I'll get you tomorrow"), the steady loss of friends, the empty beds in the barracks? What makes him willing to put up with the sight of the injured, the bleeding, the dying,

37

the burning plane on his wing exploding into a thousand anonymous fragments? What drives him to dump four thousand pounds of death on the little people in the factories miles below him? What can possess a rational man to make him act so irrationally? As in any aspect of human behavior, the forces are complex, multiple and not always discernible.

Some of the forces which compel him to fight are external, others internal. Some are conscious, some are unconscious. Some have always existed, while others are wholly the product of his combat associations and experiences. Between fanatical eagerness and utter lack of appetite for battle lie complex mechanisms arranged in such varying patterns that a complete understanding would require a detailed analysis of each case. In general, however, the salient factors can be arranged into those which the flier has brought with him from his civil life and training at home, and those which have been added as a result of his experience within the combat group.

Prior to his introduction to combat, the average flier possesses a series of intellectual and emotional attitudes regarding his relation to the war. The intellectual attitudes comprise his opinion concerning the necessity of the war and the merits of our cause. Here the American soldier is in a peculiarly disadvantageous position compared with his enemies and most of his Allies. Although attitudes vary from strong conviction to profound cynicism, the most usual reaction is one of passive acceptance of our part in the conflict. Behind this acceptance there is little real conviction. The political, economic or even military justifications for our involvement in the war are not apprehended except in a vague way. The men feel that, if our leaders, the "big-shots," could not keep us out, then there is no help for it; we have to fight. There is much danger for the future in this attitude, since the responsibility is not personally accepted but is displaced to the leaders. If these should lose face or the men find themselves in economic difficulties in the postwar world, the attitude can easily shift to one of blame of the leaders. Then the cry will rise: "We were betrayed—the politicians got us in for their own gain. The militarists made us suffer it."

There is much that is lacking in the political education of American troops, for which army policy cannot be criticized in view of the similar apathy on the home front. Late in the struggle the army became aware of this weakness among our soldiers. The Information and Education Division was then organized to repair this gap in the psychological preparation for combat. Some progress in the face of considerable resistance has been made by this service, but at the time of writing the men still have only a dim comprehension of the meaning of the fascist political state and its menace to our liberal democratic government. The war is generally regarded as a struggle between national states for economic empires. The men are not fully convinced that our country was actually threatened, or, if so, only remotely, or because of the machinations of large financial interests. In such passive attitudes lie the seeds of disillusion, which could prove very dangerous in the postwar period. Certainly they stand in startling contrast with the strong political and national convictions of our Axis enemies, which can inspire their troops, when the occasion demands, with a fanatical and religious fervor. Fortunately, strong intellectual motivation has not proved to be of the first importance to good morale in combat. The danger of this lack seems to be less to the prospect of military success than to success in the peace and to stability in the postwar period.

What then are the decisive factors responsible for good motivation? Those that are the most compelling are largely unconscious. They are concerned with the individual's past history and especially with his capacity to form identifications with other groups of people and to feel loyal to them. This process, as with any identification, is based on strong love and affection and begins very early in life. By identification is meant the feeling of belonging to, being a part of, or being the same as another person or group of people. The earliest identification made by an individual is with members of his family circle, and is at first confined to those that provide love and care, the parents, and especially the mother. Later the feeling of identity spreads to include both parents and then brothers and sisters and other members of the family. During childhood, the range of identification becomes constantly broader as the horizon of social contacts expands. Eventually, the school, then the community and finally the nation itself are included.

Two factors of the utmost importance are fused in the process of identification. One is that the person or group with whom the identification takes place is loved or needed to some extent. The other is that this person or group is in a position of authority and in this capacity makes demands upon the individual. The parent, the school, the community and the nation all are authoritative figures and all make constant demands for work, discipline and curtailment of personal interest and liberty in the interest of the group as a whole. In return for fulfillment of these demands, they give continued care, affection and support. At times such demands may be resented, but, because of the love and the need to be loved, they are ordinarily accepted by the individual and *included within his personality* as his superego. As he comes to feel himself a part of the group, such demands are later not felt to be external. They do not seem to be foreign to him or hateful— they seem to exist within himself. Thus a feeling of obligation, a social feeling, is born which, if the identification is strong, is powerful and can overrule all of his selfish, personal interests. The pressure to conform to the demands of the group is almost a compulsion, of which the individual is largely unaware and probably could not explain even to himself.

The formation of such feelings of obligation and loyalty to any group with which one is identified is of the highest significance to good morale. It is the essence of the powerful patriotic feelings which are stimulated in times of war, but which have their origin in earliest childhood. Although unconscious, they are of much greater importance than intellectual concepts. Their effect upon motivation in contrast with that of intellectual rationalizations is beautifully illustrated in the patriotic slogan: "My Country, right or wrong!" It would be much better if "my country" were in the right, but, when the chips are down, it isn't important. Thus, in the present war, it would be better if our troops were fully convinced of the merit and sense of the sacrifice they are making. If the justice of the agony they are inflicting on others and are going through themselves were clearly appreciated, they would have less conflict about it now and in the future, but its lack does not abolish their feelings of obligation to make the sacrifice. Loyalty is exclusive of ethical, political or moral considerations. It is intolerant of all considerations in opposition to the welfare of the person, group or idea for which the loyalty is felt.

Not all Americans have been able to develop a range of identification large enough to include the nation and thus to develop strong feelings of loyalty and obligation. To some extent this ability seems to be a measure of social maturity. There are individuals who feel loyal only to themselves and are not identified with any other individuals or groups. Others remain identified only with their families, and feel strong resentment at having to make a sacrifice for some larger group. Many such men have been taken into the army, but the pressure to make the sacrifice and give service has been largely external. They perform their duties and carry out responsibilities mostly out of fear of receiving punishment if they refuse. Resentment at having to make the sacrifice of personal interests involved in army service, and especially in combat, is reflected in the constant griping and complaining of the soldiers. But in those who are firmly identified with the national aims and the army group, this resentment seldom exceeds verbal levels. If it does lead on occasion to breaches of discipline or acts of hostility, the individual later reacts with some shame or guilt. Shame and guilt are only possible when the compulsion is internal, since they develop from failure to live up to the superego's demand. Resentment in men who feel no internal obligation nor loyalty may also not be overtly expressed because of an external fear of punishment. Occasionally such men become fliers. Usually they fail to develop adequate combat personalities, and their combat records are characterized by a type of reaction which will be described in detail in chapter 4. It can be anticipated, however, that their inability to identify with the group will lead to inferior motivation, and therefore have a harmful effect on their personal morale and the morale of the unit.

The ability to identify with a group and the past history of such identification are probably the most important but not the only emotional components of good motivation for combat. There are other, more personal identifications which operate in individual instances. A father or an uncle who was a soldier in the last war, and whose war experiences have been family property since that time, transmits powerful incentives to the son. Driven by the identification, he seeks to recapitulate the father's experience and perhaps outshine him. In families with a long military tradition, the effect upon the motivation of the masculine members needs no comment. But America has been a peaceable country where there are few families with a military tradition. As a kind of substitute, however, there are families with a strong aggressive tradition in sports and economic and social activity. The past attitude of the authoritative members of the family in regard to carrying out aggressive activities and obligations produces a strong urge in the children to respond to the military call. Quite frequently this urge is not only based on past and now unconscious identification, but is also the product of definite conscious pressure on the part of the families. Fathers and mothers, even wives, may urge the men to get into the fight, and make them feel ashamed to stay out. Similarly, the example of brothers or other members of the family, already injured in this war, makes the men eager to get into the battle and avenge their injury or death.

On the other hand, the expressed attitude of the family may have no effect on the motivation of the individual, or may even be harmful. Essentially the effect of the family's attitude depends on the type of soil it falls upon. Many families plead with their sons to stay out of combat—to let someone else take the risks. If a man has already become strongly attached to a combat-destined unit and is a stable, well balanced person, this may result in a quiet determination to conceal his combat activity from the family. But, again, it may produce considerable emotional conflict. In some cases such a conflict is merely an intensification of previous long-standing feelings of insecurity and inferiority, stimulated by an overprotective family who have always babied the boy. Now is his chance to escape, and combat is visualized as a certain, if somewhat radical, method of making a man of himself. If he accepts the challenge and defies his family, or even if he is thrust into battle by the routine of army assignments, the result on his personal motivation is usually good. He is likely to develop strong intentions of making an excellent combat record in the effort to compensate for past deficiencies (cf. case 27). Unfortunately, this type of motivation is somewhat fragile. There is a serious possibility that at the first taste of the stress of combat it will collapse, and the man, suffering the pangs of anxiety and fear, will regret that he did not listen to his family in the first place. Some men, however, maintain their motivation and then suffer even greater pangs of anxiety and depression because of this new failure and increased sense of inferiority in the face of their family's warning. A third possible reaction to an overprotective family, demanding avoidance of combat, is an easy compliance with the appeal. Such men make all sorts of conscious attempts to get out of combat duties, and, if forced to participate, are motivated only by fear of punishment. Their subsequent records in combat will be discussed in the next chapter.

There is another facet to motivation for battle, which has sometimes been overemphasized. That is the respectable, socially approved release of aggressive and destructive impulses provided by combat. Few Americans anticipate pleasure from destruction or killing, and, although some chronically hostile, aggressive individuals may be fascinated by the prospect of getting all the fighting they want, they frequently find it impossible to adapt their habitually irascible personalities to the controlled environment of teamwork and coordination necessary in battle. The most frequent reaction among American troops to the universal and excessive destruction, which is inseparable from war, is disgust. Not until he feels that he has been personally injured by the enemy, usually after the death of close friends, can the American soldier think of killing enemy personnel without inner revulsion. Ruthless killing and disregard for individual life and integrity have been too foreign to our training. The necessity to kill is usually something that is endured or accepted as necessary. It is erroneous to consider that hatred of the enemy is necessary for a good fighting morale, for hatred and sadistic gratification from killing are sources of guilt to the hater and are not the best motivation for objective and successful combat.

There is, however, an aspect of aggressive activity in combat that is more acceptable to the men because it is in line with their previous training in sports and all sorts of athletic activities. The idea of pressing on to a victory over a strong opponent by virtue of superior force, skill and training has considerable appeal to any American. Aerial combat provides repeated opportunities for employing the kind of talent needed in the planning of strategy and the execution of tactics in football—with maneuvers comparable to through-the-line plunges and end-runs carried out by the bombers, and others resembling blocking and tackling by the fighters. The satisfaction that comes from victory by superior maneuver, deception or strategy is one of the important props to good motivation, rather than a central part of it. The men soon learn that the enemy plays for keeps, and that a life and death struggle is not the same as a game of football. Yet our fliers maintain the illusion of good sportsmanship in battle, refusing to shoot parachuting enemy pilots and sometimes ostracizing those who do (cf. chapter 13).

These are the essential components of the individual motivation for combat which exist within the men before their exposure to battle conditions. Before going overseas the men are usually assigned to combat replacement crews, or to whole new groups alerted for shipment to a theater of operations. Here a crystallization of their previous attitudes takes place, which is the beginning of group morale. Whatever intellectual motivation they possess is about to be fulfilled, as is the case with their personal identifications, and they are at last a part of a combat group, to which they rapidly develop a strong attachment and feeling of loyalty. The anticipation of going overseas and getting into the fight stimulates a powerful excitement, which the men habitually refer to as "eagerness." They become very restless for combat and impatient of delay. If for any reason one of them has to be removed from the combat team, it is a great blow to all. We have seen men break down into uncontrolled tears because of having to be taken from the combat crew at the last minute on account of illness. Nevertheless, there is a certain aspect of the "eager beaver" reaction which is unrealistic and theatrical. The men seldom have any real, concrete notions of what combat is like. Their minds are full of romanticized, Hollywood versions of their future activity in combat, colored with vague ideas of being a hero and winning ribbons and decorations for startling exploits and with all sorts of exhibitionistic fantasies to which few would publicly admit. They anticipate the same kind of thrill and excitement from combat as they derive from flying itself— only intensified. They are not at all prepared for the nightmare experiences in store for them, partly because they have not been told about them, partly because they would not have believed them or taken them in if they had been told. Combat is always a surprise and a shock, because there is no way of preparing for the emotional impact short of the actual experience.

When the men join their group in the combat theater, their "eagerness" rapidly becomes tempered by the realities of the battle situation. After a few exposures to the stress of fighting, on combat missions, they become increasingly realistic. At that point a great strain is placed on their individual motivation. As they begin to realize what they have let themselves in for, it is only natural that they should search their souls as to why they ever allowed it to happen to them. Blind faith and unquestioning submission to fate are not part of the American character. Thoughts of friends at home, peaceably going about their jobs as instructors and transport pilots in the AAF, arise and depreciate the strongest motivation. The personal necessity to fight the war appears dim in view of the millions at home who are not fighting or suffering in any way. Any desire to be a hero evaporates in the heat of combat and most of the men are content to have a hero's role thrust upon them only if the situation cannot be avoided. They are not looking for it. Personal identifications tend to weaken in the face of the combat stress. The father who lived through the last war to tell about his combat experiences may not be so important now to the son who sees little chance of living through this one.

If the weakening of personal motivation were not counterbalanced by some other force, the desire to fight would rapidly diminish. The additional force necessary to keep the men's determination to continue in combat at a high level stems from the effects of the combat group, and is recognized as group morale. It is therefore more than the simple sum of the individual motivations found in the men before they came into combat. It is the result of the interpersonal relationships described in the previous chapter, and, specifically, of the intense loyalty stimulated by the close identification with the group. The men are now fighting for each other and develop guilty feelings if they let each other down. As Herbert Spiegel (58) puts it, the men seem to be fighting more *for* someone than *against* somebody. Individuality, the personal fate of one man, becomes of secondary importance. If his own future seems dim and its span brief, the flier is not unduly disturbed, since so large a portion of his self interest has been transferred to the interests of the group. He thinks less about himself and more about others than at any previous period in his life. This spirit of self sacrifice, so characteristic of the combat personality, is at the heart of good morale and is not easily achieved in a cultural group so traditionally individualistic and self-assertive as the Americans. Once achieved, it must be carefully and continually nurtured. If it is lost, the battle is as good as lost. Military men have long recognized this, and have considered the spirit of the fighting troops the most important single factor in success in battle—more important, for example, than equipment, training, freshness or advantages of terrain.

The principal factor governing the maintenance of this type of spirit is the quality of the leadership. The necessity for good leadership is, of course, obvious, if considered only from the standpoint of the leader's technical ability. Certainly as important as his technical ability is his personality, upon which, in the final analysis, depends his capacity to influence morale. The spirit of self sacrifice among the men is not achieved without cost. For what the men give up they expect to be paid in the form of continual and effective attention to their needs. They have given up most of their selfish interests for the sake of the group. But they do this for their buddies and for their leaders, on a personal basis, out of affection and loyalty. They can only be paid back on a personal basis. The leaders must return the loyalty and affection in kind. In his role as the father, the leader exerts the most profound effect upon his men, and the way this relationship works out in the combat unit is of the utmost significance to good morale and success in battle. It is useful, therefore, to examine the requisites for a successful combat leader.

First of all, the leader must be technically competent in his military duties. The personal safety of his men depends upon his skill, knowledge and good judgment in battle. If he demonstrates his tactical abilities to the men, they feel thereby protected, but, if he should prove himself to be inefficient, they lose confidence, feel insecure and become naturally unwilling to follow him and resentful of his orders. They are not unwilling to die, if they must, but they have no inclination to court death because of an incompetent leader's stupidity.

The leader must be not only technically sound, but strong in character and decisive. There must be no question of his courage, since the men become so strongly identified with him and from this identification absorb strength. The identification makes all his personal attributes infectious. His strength and courage are communicated to the men, who are thereby enabled to show a similar courage and strength to a degree they might never have suspected was possible. The ability to make the men surpass themselves, to stimulate the men to rise above their usual level of efficiency and courage, must be wisely used. The good leader is demanding of the men, and gets more out of them not only because he communicates his own strength, but because he asks for or insists upon superior performance. Naturally, he is more likely to get such a performance in combat if he makes the same demands on himself, thus perpetuating the identification. The leader who demands a sacrifice from his men which he is not willing to make himself is not likely to get a good result. Nothing is worse for morale than a leader who leads from the rear, where it is safe. This completely destroys the personal basis upon which American soldiers, at any rate, are motivated and stimulates a resentment which is apt to color the whole future military career of a man.

At the same time, the leader must have good judgment concerning the limit of tolerance the men have for combat conditions. He must demand results in order to get them, but, if he demands too much and drives the men past their tolerance, their spirit may break. Then, if they do not become psychological casualties, they are usually left with so much resentment that the morale of the entire group deteriorates. On the other hand, he must avoid the opposite fault of not demanding enough. Some leaders, overconscientious in their responsibility for the men's welfare, hesitate to ask them to go through the repeated hardships and sacrifices. Such a leader becomes too strongly identified with his men and is incessantly worried about them. He becomes upset at combat losses and finally reaches a point of inefficiency as a leader. The seasoned leader knows how to avoid the twin evils of lack of consideration and overconsideration. This entails walking an exceedingly narrow rope, especially if the tactical situation turns bad or if the replacements or relief fails to appear. Yet it has again and again been demonstrated to what incredible lengths of sacrifice and effort the men willingly go for a leader who has their confidence and affection.

To keep his men's affection, the leader must be a just and impartial father. Those who have exceeded the ordinary call of duty in acts of outstanding merit or self sacrifice are rewarded fairly with public citations, promotions and decorations. If there is even a suggestion that such rewards are given out unfairly, on the basis of personal friendship or for political considerations, the leader destroys his good relations with the men. They feel depreciated and resentful and may refuse to go through further sacrifices for a man who does not appreciate what they are doing. On the other hand, those who fail in their duty through lack of loyalty and unwillingness to make the effort must be firmly dealt with. Failure to do so, because of softheartedness or overconsideration, again depreciates the efforts of those who are giving their best and sets a premium on weakness. The men are not in combat because they enjoy it. Most of them permit themselves a well controlled desire to escape it but it does not help their self control to see other men escape too easily. Promptness in punishing any activity inimical to the welfare of the whole group is always appreciated by the men, and is important to the maintenance of good morale.

The good leader gives every consideration to the creature comforts of his men on a concrete level in so far as the military situation allows. It is amazing what degrees of physical discomfort can be withstood cheerfully, jokingly or philosophically, if the men feel that everything possible is being done for them. Mud, rain, days in wet and cold clothing, or intolerable heat, poor food, even lack of water, can be tolerated without too much difficulty. But, if it becomes known or suspected that the poor living conditions are due to someone's stupidity, inefficiency or lack of interest, the men develop intense resentment. Their whole attitude may change, tolerance for the situation is lost and morale disintegrates.

Morale, the willingness to endure any sacrifice necessary to achieve success in battle, is contingent upon definite psychological rewards for that sacrifice in the form of continued affection, interest, support and appreciation. Though their immediate leaders and commanding officers are the most important to the men in maintaining this spirit, the attitude of more remote elements both in the army and on the home front are also significant. The men's ability to identify themselves not only with their immediate combat group but with the whole army, and with the nation and the people at home, depends upon the degree of backing they feel they are getting from them. For this reason, they become noticeably disturbed by adverse news from home of strikes, black markets, hoarding, profiteering and political chicanery. Anything which indicates indifference to the war is interpreted as indifference to their sacrifice and thus disturbs their morale. Their motivation continues because their suffering and possible death has the greatest meaning to their friends in their combat unit and parenthetically to all the other men in the combat units involved in the war. But how much better would their motivation be if they could feel that it had the same meaning to their people at home! Either the entire nation is in the thing and willing to make a little sacrifice, or there is no sense in what the men are going through except for the sake of other combat troops.

In this respect again, both our Allies and our enemies have had the advantage over us because of a thorough identity of feeling throughout their nations. Their military and civilian populations feel close to each other to an extent undreamed of in our country, which has not been directly hurt by the enemy. With us, the psychological gulf between combat troops and civilians, or even military personnel at home, has remained wide. The attitude at home toward our fighting troops has been one of overemphasis of glamour, the winning team, the success story. There is no realistic appreciation of the meaning of combat, no actual identification with the experiences and feelings of combat troops. The home front has supplied the men with good training and good equipment, but has not been able to provide adequate emotional support on the same lavish scale. That morale at the front has remained sufficiently high to supply the successes so avidly devoured by the public, has been due to the excellent relations between the fighting men and their immediate leaders. Their intense loyalty to each other has seen them through every sort of difficult situation and has been a tribute to the capacity for self sacrifice and devotion among the men from the farms and villages, the cities and factories of America.

PART III

The Reactions to Combat

CHAPTER 4

Reactions to Combat Based on Previous Emotional Disorders

F<small>LIERS</small> <small>REACT</small> with varying amounts of physical and psychological disability to the physical and emotional stress of combat. In this book we are concerned chiefly with the psychological disabilities, since states of pure physical exhaustion are rare among flying personnel. The psychological deficiency resulting from combat stress is of the greatest practical concern because no one is immune. If the stress is severe enough, if it strikes an exposed "Achilles' heel" and if the exposure to it is sufficiently prolonged, adverse psychological symptoms may develop in anyone. Once symptoms have appeared, it then becomes a question of good medical and military judgment how much longer the sufferer should be exposed to the combat situation, and what can be done to help him. The immediate tactical needs for personnel may require their maintenance in combat despite their symptoms. On the other hand, such needs must be balanced against the effect of the symptoms on the fighting efficiency of the men, the dangerous effect on the lives of crew members, other crews and expensive machines and the possible effect on the future health of the individual. For the purpose of making valid decisions, there must be a clear conception of the nature of the psychological reactions.

The psychological symptoms can be thought of as neurotic manifestations in the sense that they are maladaptations or inefficient reactions to specific stress situations of reality. Initially most men react well to the combat situation. They are eager, enthusiastic, cool and competent. Under the most harrowing circumstances, they are able to control fear or anxiety, to think

53

clearly and to make appropriate decisions with rapidity, no matter what their previous personality types may have been (29). With their previous training and the experience gained in combat, they develop a striking efficiency, both as individuals and as teams. It is this efficiency, which our enemies had not anticipated, that lies behind the notable string of victories achieved by all combat arms in the present war. It is also this aspect of the soldier's combat personality which has been given the widest publicity. What happens to the men upon continued exposure to combat has been more or less overlooked.

The unending strain eventually produces distress signals affecting any part of the mind or body. Enthusiasm and eagerness easily give way to a great weariness of battle, which is then endured because there is no way out. Transient fears turn into permanent feelings of apprehension. Anxiety may be related for a time only to a reaction limited to the most dangerous moments over the target, but it has a tendency to spread until it is continuous or is stimulated by only trivial sounds. Good muscular coordination is replaced by uncontrollable tremors, jerky manipulations and tension. Constant tension leads further to a restlessness which is never satisfied by activity and is intolerant of repose. Sleep dwindles and may give way altogether to insomnia punctuated by fitful nightmares. Appetite is noticeably reduced, and gastric difficulties may appear. Although air sickness is rare, nausea and vomiting after meals, especially breakfast, are fairly common, as is a functional diarrhea. Frequency of urination, headache and backache are also common signs of the body's reaction to the emotional stress. With the growing lack of control over the mental and physical reactions come a grouchiness and irritability that interfere with good relations among men. Some give way easily, and are always in a quarrel or argument. Others become depressed and seclusive, and stay away from their friends to avoid dissension, or because they feel ashamed. Thinking and behavior may become seriously altered. Forgetfulness, preoccupation, or constant brooding over loss of friends and combat experiences destroys purposeful activity. The behavior of the men may become not only asocial, but completely inappropriate and bizarre.

The danger signals may appear in anyone in various degrees. The extent to which they can be labeled pathological depends upon two factors: their severity, or the degree of inefficiency they produce; and the amount and type of stress which were required to produce the symptoms.

A great many men experience some degree of anxiety or some psychosomatic response to combat stress, which nevertheless at no time becomes severe enough to incapacitate them for full duty. The common wheeze, "Are you nervous in the service?," owes its universal appeal to its grain of truth. But whatever their difficulties, most fliers are able to control them during the time that control is desperately needed, and thus never become psychiatric casualties while they are overseas. What happens to many of these apparently successful soldiers upon their return home will be dealt with in later sections of this book. Here, we are concerned with those individuals whose symptoms become so marked that they are unable to continue in combat, and thus must be considered psychiatric casualties.

Repeated observation has demonstrated that the men who become psychiatric casualties can be divided into two arbitrary groups on the basis of the intensity of external stress to which they have been subjected. In the first group the stress has been minimal, and yet has led to severe symptoms. In the second and by far the larger group, the stress has been severe, and has only produced marked symptoms after a prolonged exposure. It is apparent therefore that some other factor besides the intensity of stress is responsible for the production of symptoms. This factor of course consists in the initial psychological preparedness of the individual to react to specific stimuli. In the presence of a previous emotional disorder, small amounts of stress to which an individual is sensitized may lead to severe symptoms. Conversely, men who have considerable psychological stability can withstand large amounts of stress before giving way to crippling symptoms.

Some combat fliers have slipped through the Air Forces' psychiatric screening in spite of overt emotional disorders suffered in the past, which they carefully conceal in their determination to obtain flying training. In others, the psychological difficulties are masked, and adaptability has at least been good enough to deal with the ordinary vicissitudes of life. The underlying weakness is only revealed clearly under the stress of combat when overt psychological difficulties appear. After the appearance of symptoms, a careful case history will usually reveal evidence of personality traits which prepared the patient for the neurotic reaction. Such hindsight, based on data easily obtained when the patient is preoccupied with his symptoms, should not unduly prejudice the observer against the original medical and psychiatric examination. All men showing symptoms *early* after *minimal stress* are instances of misclassification for combat duties, and many of them are misclassified for any type of flying duties. However, only a certain proportion of these could have been detected before the crucial test of combat (cf. chapter 1).

The types of early reactions to combat, based on obvious or concealed previous emotional disorders, fall into three groups which shade into each other. The individuals in the first group show neurotic symptoms of every type, obviously related to an intrapsychic conflict between their underlying insecurity and their sense of duty and obligation to continue in combat. They are characterized by a rather weak ego and a strong sense of duty, and as a consequence are usually distinguished by large quantities of anxiety, invariably accompanied by depression. It is into this group that by far the largest proportion of the early failures fall. The second group consists of men whose underlying insecurity and weak ego likewise lead to the early appearance of anxiety, but who lack a conscience reaction to their failure. They have little or no sense of duty or loyalty, and therefore a minimal or no internal conflict. Their conflict is only between their egos and reality. Although their anxiety is easily stimulated, it is short-lived, since they make an immediate effort to remove themselves from the combat situation which arouses it. Because of the absence of internal conflict, they show few clinical symptoms when they are distant from the battle scene. The psychological disability lies principally in their behavior toward escape from combat duties, and in the effect this activity has on the morale of their units. In the last group, the disability consists in difficulties in behavior which are not related to anxiety but in which the stress of combat has intensified a long-standing inability to adjust to groups, to work in teams and especially to yield to authority. Such men are in continual trouble with their commanding officers and, because of either excess alcoholism or constant bickering and feuding with other men, are a threat to the morale of their organizations.

The men in the first category, showing primarily neurotic symptoms and rapid loss of efficiency under combat stress, are among the most interesting and most unfortunate examples of what war does to individuals. The degree of insight into their difficulties varies tremendously—from good to none at all— yet they all suffer greatly. During the early phases of their reaction, while the symptoms are still mild, the untrained observer is apt to be more aware of the secondary gain of the symptoms than of the true nature of the disturbance. These men are therefore likely to be accused by commanding officers and even by some medical officers of malingering, or made to feel that they are cowards. Sometimes because of the pressure of these attitudes, sometimes simply because of the pressure of their own ideals, such men are kept in combat until their mild symptoms have become severe, at which time there can no longer be any question of the diagnosis or the proper disposal of the case. The longer they are maintained in the stress of combat, the more severe the symptoms become. This immeasurably complicates future treatment and rehabilitation.

The following series of cases gives examples of such reactions, arranged to show the differences in severity of stress rather than the particular symptoms evoked.

CASE 2: *Early breakdown in a highly predisposed pilot under minimal stress.*

A 25 year old P-40 pilot was sent overseas with a group of replacement officers in March 1943. There he remained in a replacement pool and waited for three months to be assigned to a tactical organization. In June, just as he thought he was about to be assigned, he was transferred to another theater, and again found himself in a replacement pool awaiting assignment. After being shifted to a fighter training center, he was finally assigned at the end of July to a fighter group, flying Spitfires. During all this time he was very much upset by the frustration and uncertainty of waiting so long for active combat duty. However, he was even more upset by his conversations with pilots going through the replacement centers on their way home after completing a tour of duty. These men related hair-raising and gruesome stories of their combat experiences, concentrating on the horrible details with which they love to intimidate the neophyte. By the time he was finally assigned for duty, he was already in a tense and anxious state, and had difficulty in sleeping as a result of being so attentive to these ultrarealistic accounts of combat stress.

Although his apprehension was immediately apparent, he was accepted by the Spitfire organization, and after three weeks' training was allowed to go on a routine combat mission. However, he had difficulty in maintaining proper formation, and kept talking volubly over his radio about the possibility of enemy attack. When he returned from the mission, he was so agitated that he required sedation to sleep that night, although there had been no contact with the enemy and nothing of consequence had happened during the flight. Because of this reaction, it was proposed that he be transferred to some other organization for noncombat flying, but he expressed such anguish and disappointment over this proposal, and begged so desperately to be given another chance, that he was assigned several days later to another mission. On this occasion his flying was extremely erratic. He became confused about orders received from the flight leader during a minor skirmish with enemy planes, and broke up the formation so badly that he was a source of more anxiety to his colleagues than was the enemy. He was accordingly told that he was through with combat and in a few days was referred for psychiatric consultation.

At the time of his psychiatric interview, a week after his second mission, this officer was severely agitated and depressed. He had a gross tremor of the hands, his eyes frequently filled with tears, and his speech was rambling and occasionally blocked. The chief superficial content of his depression was his failure, and he alternated between severe self condemnation and wordy attempts to explain and apologize for his poor showing. He showed some insight into the fact that he was emotionally unsuited for combat duties, but this fact depressed him and caused so much additional anxiety that he would become convulsed with sobs and unable to talk. After several interviews he became able to tell about his severe anxiety regarding the combat situation, and he then admitted that he had always been somewhat afraid of airplanes, and that during his second mission his mind had become so confused that he had no idea what he was doing.

Treatment of this pilot was confined to reducing the intense pressure from his sense of duty (superego reaction) and helping him to accept future duties more realistically adjusted to his capacities. When he became calmer and less depressed, he described previous episodes of anxiety that had occurred during his high school and college days. It was evident that he was a dependent individual who had always reacted to uncertainty and strain with anxiety. After his graduation from college, he married a maternal woman, and his episodes of anxiety, which had never been incapacitating, decreased in severity and frequency. He entered the public relations field, and was fairly successful in the promotion of ideas and campaigns that stimulated his strong ethical and moral feelings. When the war came, his imagination was fired by the idea of serving his country as a combat flier. He visualized this role with the unrealistic but moral enthusiasm that had made him competent as a promoter of ideas, but which was no guarantee of success in combat flying. The idea was further attractive because it would give him the chance to deny his previous anxiety and insecurity. Accordingly he concealed these from the medical examiners, and unfortunately he possessed sufficient motor skill to complete his flying training. Occasional fears of flying and brief moments of doubt about combat he thrust firmly from his consciousness because they did not correspond with the goal he had set for himself. However, the mere approach to combat overseas upset his precarious balance and left him without any defenses.

.   .   .   .   .   .

This case illustrates nicely the small amount of stress required to evoke pronounced symptoms in a predisposed individual. It also illustrates the difference between the degrees of psychological deficiency which can be tolerated in Air Forces and in Ground Force combat troops, respectively. Since this individual was excessively conscientious and intent upon fulfilling his combat duties, he would never under his own volition have attempted to avoid the stress. He was removed because even slight inefficiency in a combat pilot is too much of a hazard to the other fliers. Had he been in a less responsible role in a ground force combat area, it is probable that he would have been exposed to much greater stress, resulting in much more regression to immature attitudes and behavior. The severe cases of ego regression to infantile patterns of conduct resembling psychoses, which we have described previously in Ground Force personnel who have undergone prolonged, severe fighting, are rare among fliers. This pilot would have been an ideal candidate for such a reaction in a situation where he could be pinned down by enemy fire for days with little protection and constant loss of life about him. Since he had experienced only minimal stress, his treatment was not difficult. He made a good recovery from his depression. Although still showing some mild anxiety, he was able to be reclassified for ground duties in special service activities in noncombat areas.

CASE 3: *Epileptiform seizure with little conscious anxiety, developed under minimal combat stress in an insecure, unstable flier with a strong superego.*

A 23 year old, slow-spoken, slow-moving B-24 bombardier had come into combat full of enthusiasm but was able to complete only seven operational missions. He was referred for psychiatric consultation after an epileptiform seizure which had forced an early return on his eighth mission. He ordinarily gave the impression of being calm and well controlled, though somewhat immature. On his first mission his flight had met an intense flak barrage. Many aircraft went down in flames or exploded, and his own ship was riddled with holes though no one was hurt. He remained calm and efficient throughout this trip. His second mission was a routine and safe expedition. On the third, heavy and accurate flak was again encountered, and he was very tense over the target, but performed his job efficiently. The fourth, fifth and sixth missions were attended by only slight opposition, but the officer was very tense over the target. On his seventh mission he developed acute anxiety while approaching the target through intense flak, and twice deviated sharply to the left when he saw close flak bursts ahead of him. During the run on the target the bombardier controls the ship and should maintain a straight and level course. These corrections took the plane off its course, so that the bombs widely missed their target. It was a foolish and impulsive act, dictated by anxiety.

His crew were angry and disgusted with him because of this evidence of unreliability, and he felt very depressed that night. He was much attached to the men on his crew. They had all been together a long time, and he felt that there were no finer men to be found anywhere, nor a better combat crew, and he wanted to be worthy of them. He begged them to hold off judging him too severely, pleading inexperience and promising that it would not happen again, whereupon they relented. The next day they heard that they would make a very long, very important mission. There was much excitement in the air. They went to bed but did not rest well because of the excitement. During the early morning hours there was a long briefing, during which the tension continued to mount. After the briefing the pilot took his crew aside and emphasized how eager he was to make a good showing on this mission, since they were new in the organization and still had to prove themselves. The target was top priority and very dangerous, and everyone had to be on his toes. On the way out to the plane in preparation for the take-off, our bombardier felt suddenly sick and panicky, and wanted to run away. With an effort of will, he controlled the feeling, said nothing about it and got into the bomber. Once inside he felt better, but after the plane was airborne he again became tense and uneasy. While they were over the sea only two hundred miles from their home base, the navigator unexpectedly fired several rounds from his machine gun to clear the gun. The bombardier was startled, suddenly lost consciousness and slipped to the floor. His arms and legs trembled convulsively and his facial muscles twitched, while he uttered low guttural sounds. After a minute of this, he began to beat savagely with his hands on the floor and sides of the fuselage, moaning, "Oh, God, don't let them do this to us." In about four minutes he relaxed and recovered consciousness. The pilot in the meantime had left the formation to return to his base with the sick officer. When he was told that the mission was aborted because of his seizure, the bombardier wept and begged the pilot to continue on the mission. The crew were enraged at the turn of events but returned to the field.

In a few days he was referred for psychiatric consultation, the opinion of the Flight Surgeon being that he was not psychologically qualified for flying duties. At the first interview he showed slight anxiety and restlessness, and was moderately depressed. He displayed very little insight, and pleaded earnestly for "medicine or something" to control his nerves on combat missions so that he could go back to his crew. He was desperately anxious to go back. He interpreted his reaction as a nervous strain, and could not appreciate its origin in fear or any emotion connected with combat, although in the light of his behavior during his seventh mission the connection was perfectly obvious.

The dissociation of emotions which allowed him to conceal his intense fears from himself in order to preserve the character of an enthusiastic and competent combat airman was highlighted during an interview under intravenous sodium pentothal. He was told, after the establishment of narcosis, that he was in his plane on the way to the target which had been the objective of his aborted eighth mission. He immediately reacted with uncontrollable anxiety. Calling out flak bursts in a voice of terror and panic, he jumped about with such frenzied movements that it was difficult to keep him on the narrow army cot used for the treatment. He kept pulling the pillow around his head as if it were a helmet he could use for protection against flak. He was inarticulate, with the exception of calling out each new flak burst. He had of course not actually run into any flak on his eighth mission, but this performance was a good demonstration of what he expected and of what his inner reaction was. Nothing was said to him during this time, and he gradually became calmer and finally relaxed. Then he suddenly began to talk to himself in a much altered voice. He spoke slowly, calmly and reassuringly. He was telling himself that there was nothing to get excited about. Sure it was dangerous, but why get excited about that; you either lived or died. Fellows died every day. *C'est la guerre*. It didn't pay to blow your top about it. There was no sense in worrying. He had a wonderful crew, a swell bunch of fighters. He had to be worthy of them. He couldn't let them down. What they were doing was too important to screw up now. Chances were he'd get killed sooner or later, but what was his life? What his crew stood for, what they had all wanted to do, was much more important. He couldn't let his country down either. The Jerries had to have their ears beaten back. It was up to everybody to do the job.

It was obvious that this bombardier was trying to subdue his anxiety through reassurance and autosuggestion. He was talking to himself like a combination of a kindly parent, a chaplain and a sympathetic superior officer. Unfortunately he was talking to a dependent and insecure child, who was beyond the help of such simple reassurance. There, moreover, something overly dramatic and unrealistic about the character of the reassurance, something closer to a motion picture script than to the actual reactions of combat troops. It fitted the immature and hysterical personality of this bombardier, however. As the effects of the drug wore off, he opened his eyes, recognized the therapist with a smile and asked what he had been talking about. He had no memory of his anxiety during the narcosis and was again in his usual slow-spoken, quietly harassed state. He wanted to know what had been found out about his "nerves."

This officer was the only child of rather elderly parents. His dependence and insecurity were the result of too much guarding and protection. While in college he had attempted to establish some independence from his family. He paid his own way by working at night and carried a full schedule of classes. The effort ended when he developed nervous spells, characterized by tension and frequent fainting. He thought he had heart trouble, but a doctor whom he consulted told him he was "just nervous" from overstrain. After he stopped working at night, the nervous spells disappeared. He had naturally withheld this information at the time of his examination for cadet training. He had a warm, friendly, rather naive and very conscientious personality, and it had been easy to mistake the superficially calm, slow-spoken manner for stability and miss the latent neurosis.

After a short period of treatment, he was able to acquire a very limited insight into the relation between his insecurity and fear and his symptoms. He was permanently removed from flying status and reassigned to ground duties at an air base, still complaining over the misfortune of not being able to go back to his crew. He was seen, by coincidence, four months later at the airdrome where he was working. He rushed up to greet the therapist and immediately stated that he was slowly "going crazy" from having to work on the ground and see so many of his friends on combat crews pass through the airdrome. He begged to be allowed to return for a re-examination to see whether he could not be restored to flying status. The request was denied. He did not appear to have any undue anxiety or depression beyond his usual inability to accept his own limitations.

. . . . . .

This case exemplified a very weak defense against long-standing anxiety and hostility, which broke down after a short exposure to combat stress. Only while unconscious could he explode his deeply repressed hostility in the form of an epileptiform seizure. Little of the anxiety was ever allowed to remain conscious. The conflict between his superego, into which most of his repressed aggressiveness had flowed, and his need for protection is strikingly illustrated both by his symptoms and by his inability to accept real insight into them. Because of his characteristic defense and his strong ego-ideal, he appeared to be good combat crew material until the actual exposure to stress. This is the type of case in which it is so difficult to evaluate the actual state of affairs and to predict how much stress can be tolerated. In the following case, the difficulty is even more dramatically revealed.

CASE 4: *Anxiety and depression developing under difficult living conditions but only minimal combat stress in a compulsive pilot.*

A' 29 year old B-17 pilot had been a commercial airlines and test pilot for ten years prior to his joining the AAF. He had over four thousand flying hours to his credit and had always been considered a quiet, steady, efficient flier. He had been given a direct commission and was immediately checked out in the B-17 and B-24 planes. He was theoretically passed through the three phases of operational training but actually was used in various capacities as a test pilot and instructor and never received training in formation flying. Apparently it was felt that he was such a good pilot that he could pick up what he needed for operational flying when he went overseas.

In combat this veteran of ten years' flying was able to participate in only eight operational missions. He had severe anxiety with the first mission. He had always disliked the idea of combat. When he joined the Air Forces, he had anticipated that he would be used as a ferry pilot or a test pilot because of his past experience. When he received the combat assignment, he had been too conscientious and too shy to state his true feelings. He had always been unaggressive and rather submissive, but hardworking and eager to do a good job. He resigned himself to the overseas assignment and determined to do his best. The idea of dropping bombs and killing people was very disturbing to him, but he kept his feelings to himself. However, he could not control his anxiety when on missions, and as a result his flying efficiency was very poor. He was obsessed with a fear of collision in the air and could not maintain his plane in close formation. Over the target he became so disconcerted by flak that his flying became erratic and dangerous to the other planes nearby. On the ground he felt tense, tired and depressed. By the time of his eighth mission he was so obviously disturbed and inefficient that he was transferred by a Flying Evaluation Board to a noncombat flying assignment, ferrying mails within the theater of operations.

During the next four months this pilot continued to go downhill. He developed headaches and chronic fatigue. Insomnia, with anxiety dreams whose content he could not remember, further increased his fatigue. He brooded constantly over his separation from his wife and two children. A depression, in which he felt that everything was turning against him, gradually deepened in him. He lost his appetite and decreased nearly 30 pounds in weight. When he did attempt to eat, he frequently became nauseated. He complained very little about his symptoms but was eventually referred for consultation because of the progressive evidence of physical and psychological depletion.

When seen in consultation he appeared thin, ill and emotionally dulled. He spoke of his physical symptoms and depression with a flickering smile on his face. His past history was that of a rigid, obsessive-compulsive character, who had found security and happiness in his marriage and in his work as a commercial pilot. He was very attached to his wife but had no close friends and no outside interests. It was apparent that his psychological defenses had been broken as much by the conditions of life in a theater of operations and the separation from his wife as by the specific stress of combat. The cautiousness and compulsive meticulousness which had made him a good commercial pilot were useless or actually a disadvantage to him in combat, and he could not give up these qualities without developing anxiety. Nor could he live the casual, disorganized life of the overseas soldier, surrounded by dirt, consuming unappetizing food, in close proximity to the filthy and demoralized native population, without becoming depressed. Because of the seriousness of his symptoms and his obvious unsuitability, he was returned to the United States for treatment and disposition.

. . . . . .

That this flier was not qualified either for overseas service or for combat duties was overlooked because of his long record as a pilot. It is probable that the unsuitability could have been determined by a psychiatric interview, in spite of the absence of a previous episode of overt neurotic symptoms. In the next case there was a similar breakdown of an old defense, with a more explosive outbreak of anxiety.

CASE 5: *Severe breakdown after moderate stress in a soldier with a stabilized anxiety neurosis, when his phobia of death became a reality in combat.*

A 22 year old soldier was the radio-operator gunner of a B-26 crew. His life at home with his parents, two brothers and a sister had always been congenial and happy. All members of the family were very close to each other and he could not remember any disagreements. As a child he had had an intense fear of the dark. On one occasion when coming down a dark staircase in his home he thought he saw a human form lying at the bottom of the stairs. He screamed and became hysterical and it took much persuasion to calm him down and convince him that there was actually no corpse there. This experience always remained in his memory. His family frequently teased him about his fear of a "bogeyman." He was always afraid of dead people or anything connected with death. His grandmother died when he was 9 years old but he would not go to her funeral. When he was 16 years old, a schoolmate died. He went to view the body, had a bad reaction and experienced anxious dreams about this body for weeks after. After his graduation from high school he held several nonskilled jobs and finally went to work at a state hospital for the insane. He was never enthusiastic about this work. He had a fear of contracting some disease, and always felt unclean during the six months that he held the position. He took numerous showers and washed his hands repeatedly. He always shied away from corpses, and if a patient died he would get someone else to prepare the body.

He enlisted in the army in 1941, shortly after he left the hospital. An enthusiasm for flying rapidly took possession of him and he obtained training in radio and gunnery. He was very eager to go overseas to combat, and, when he joined his combat group, he was elated. On his first combat mission there was a slight amount of accurate flak and the wings of his plane showed a few small holes. He felt tense and uneasy but was able to keep his mind well concentrated on his work. On the way back he felt relaxed and decided that he "got quite a kick out of it." He felt that it would be easy to breeze through fifty missions like that, and go home. During his next ten missions a various amount of opposition was met, but his reaction remained approximately the same, one of controlled tension. On his twelfth mission the bomb bay doors were open as they came over the target. A flak burst hit the right engine and it went out of action as the plane momentarily tipped. The pilot called back on the interphone saying that one engine was dead and they were falling out of formation. He was taken aback for a moment, and glanced up to see what Herman, the turret gunner, was doing and to make sure he heard the news. There he saw Herman lying on his right side, his head slumped on his right shoulder. His eyes were partly open and blood was running from his neck as if from a faucet. He called the pilot on the interphone and said, "Herman is hit!" He was told to do what he could for him, but replied that he was sure Herman was dead. Then he went to pieces. He began to tremble all over. He swung his loaded waist gun back into the plane and tried to bail out. The tail gunner saw what was happening and caught him just in time to save him from jumping out over the target. He sat down and began to smoke one cigarette after another. Thoughts tumbled through his mind without any order. He thought of his home and then began to pray with tears running down his face. When the intact engine began to belch black smoke, he again wanted to bail out and was restrained by the tail gunner. He felt he would never get back alive, and, when the plane at last made an emergency landing at a friendly airdrome, he swung his legs out of the gun hatch as soon as the wheels were down. The tail gunner again had to prevent him from jumping out before the ship came to a stop. He was afraid of an explosion and could not get away from the aircraft fast enough. After it rolled to a halt, he jumped out, ran a short distance, and then stopped, still trembling all over. Soon the pilot asked him to help get the dead gunner out of the turret, but he could not bring himself to do this.

During the days following his return to his base he continued to have intense anxiety. He seemed to be afraid of everything, especially of the dark. He could not shake off a feeling that some- one was following him. There was a severe insomnia, with terror dreams in which he saw the dead turret gunner with blood pouring from his neck. During one nightmare he dreamed that someone, an unknown figure, was standing stooped over the end of his bed. This frightened him more than the combat dreams. Because he continued to show such severe anxiety that it was necessary to give him sedation, he was sent to a rest camp for two weeks. Upon his return he was much calmer and also more depressed than before.

When, a few days later, he was referred for psychiatric consultation, he showed little anxiety but appeared considerably depressed. He stated that he was afraid he was losing his mind, and described his fear of the dark and of being followed. He was also depressed because of his inability to continue combat flying. Psychotherapy was kept on a simple level, designed to reduce his sense of failure and to reassure him in regard to his fears. After a short time he improved sufficiently to be reassigned as a radio-operator on noncombat operations. He made a fairly good recovery from his depression and was having only rare anxiety dreams.

. . . . . .

This gunner was clearly misassigned as a combat crew member, in which capacity he had no way of avoiding the specific stress against which he had no psychological defenses, that is, the sight of death. It is interesting that, in spite of his previous experiences in this regard, he ignored the possibility of trouble from this source in his enthusiasm for combat work. Thus once again there would have been little opportunity to pick up even such an obvious predisposition in a routine examination. He would probably have been able to stand up under a great number of missions had he not been confronted with a sudden, violent death, and it is not uncommon for whole combat crews to come through a tour of duty unscathed, with no one injured or killed. But war is the province of uncertainty, as von Clausewitz so aptly put it, and no such fortunate conclusion to a combat career can be foreseen or hoped for.

The distinguishing feature of all these cases is an ego sensitivity, which makes the individual particularly susceptible to one or all of the multiple stresses of combat and leads to the development of incapacitating anxiety, plus a strong superego, embodying a strict ideal of conduct, which causes the individual to struggle against his anxiety and to become depressed as he loses control. What is wrong with the ego will be discussed more fully in the chapter on Psychodynamics (chapter 6). The particular symptoms which develop are never of as much significance as an understanding of the basic problem of the ego in relation to the situation of stress, which is both external and internal. The internal stress set up by the pressure of the superego in the form of obligation to carry on because of loyalty and pride certainly increases the anxiety and intensifies the problems of the ego, which has to find some solution.

In the next series of cases to be discussed, the superego is weak or inactive in relation to a sense of military duty (cf. group 2, page 56). The ego therefore solves its problem simply by seeking an escape from the external stress. The problem is then complicated only by the external forces which are opposed to such an easy escape. It is to be expected that there is no sharp dividing line between a strong and a weak ego-ideal for appropriate behavior. Feelings of loyalty, pride and obligation shade through a spectrum from intense to nonexistent. When his sense of duty is particularly weak, the individual makes obvious or spectacular attempts to avoid combat stress. This extreme type of case has been called "lack of moral fiber," "fear of flying" and malingering. Military law names it "failure in the face of enemy action" and is prepared with suitable punishments. The individual's colleagues are more likely to be satisfied with the colloquial label "coward" or "yellow." In an army which has a good morale such cases are extremely rare, and are confined to men who have no capacity to identify themselves with any group and can think only of their own safety and welfare. When morale deteriorates, there is a general weakening of ties and loosening of obligations, with a universal tendency to shy away from combat. This reaches an extreme in times of defeat and disorganization, when the situation deteriorates to the level of "let's get out of here, fellows; it's everyone for himself." We read of our enemies countering this situation by increasing the external pressure and shooting all who attempt to escape. At the same time they try to reduce the general anxiety by ordering increased distribution of whiskey and wine.

Such extreme examples illustrate the problems of motivation for combat and their relation to emotional illness. The soldier who attempts to run away when everyone is running is not ill. The military situation is ill. The therapy needed to cure the tactical and morale situation lies in the hands of commanding officers and military leaders. The soldier who attempts to run away or avoid combat when morale is good is psychologically ill and should be dealt with through medical procedures. If psychiatric evaluation demonstrates that there is a weak sense of duty, that the individual is consciously attempting to evade combat stress and that no improvement in his attitude can be

effected, the disposition of the case is usually through administrative and disciplinary methods. Medical treatment in such
cases is of no avail, and the pronounced effect these individuals
produce on the morale of their units requires a military rather
than a medical solution. Since everyone is struggling with his
own anxiety and fear in combat, if one man is allowed to escape
because he does not wish to endure anxiety or the possibility of
death or injury, the others feel extremely resentful and are likely
to find their own motivation impaired. On the other hand, if
an individual is making an effort to control and master his
anxiety, but fails, his comrades take a sympathetic attitude
and his removal from combat stress does not have a harmful
effect upon morale.

The problem in this group of cases, then, is this: to what
extent is the force which compels the individual to control his
anxiety and remain in combat internal, proceeding from his
superego, or external, responding only to outside force if it will
respond at all? The medical officer's difficulties are increased
by the borderline cases in which the superego is weak but is
putting up some opposition to an anxiety for which there is
tremendous predisposition. The problem is further complicated
by units whose morale is weakened by poor leadership or overwhelming enemy opposition, or both. In such organizations men
who were weakly motivated to begin with rapidly lose interest
in coping with their anxiety. Where doubt arises as to the best
method of handling the case—whether it should be considered
a neurotic reaction and be disposed of through medical procedures, or whether it should be stigmatized as "fear of flying"
or "lack of moral fiber" and be dealt with by disciplinary
procedures—the guiding principle should be the effect of the
decision on the morale of the group. If this principle is followed,
it may work an occasional injustice on an individual who was
outrageously misclassified for combat duty, but, in combat
especially, the welfare of the group is more important than that
of the individual. In the overseas Air Force in which we had our
experience with combat troops, the morale was on the whole
very good and such situations were rare. In other Air Forces, in
which combat losses were higher and morale lower, difficulties
of this sort were more frequent.

The following two cases are examples of such borderline
situations, each of which was solved in a different way.

CASE 6: *Anxiety stimulated by minimal stress but evoking no superego reaction.*

An officer, a 24 year old B-24 bombardier, had experienced anxiety in flying throughout his training at home. He had originally applied for pilot training but had soon been washed out because of technical inaptitude characterized by poor flying. He was continually tense and apprehensive and believed this to be the cause of his poor flying. During his bombardier training he remained tense in the air but never to the point of reduced efficiency. Upon graduation he became an instructor and, in his own estimation, a good one. Eventually, however, he was assigned to a unit being trained for combat work. As the time to go overseas·approached, he became increasingly apprehensive. He had a dread of combat and debated the various alternatives by which he could escape it, but finally decided to accept his fate. It seemed harder to admit that he couldn't do it than to go over and try. The decision was difficult because he had always hated violence and conflict and had no interest in the war. He believed it to be a terrible mistake, in which nothing was to be gained except destruction and misery for everyone. He had been drawn into the unpleasant situation through the failure of his draft board to share his point of view and had been assigned to the infantry. There he had hated the discipline, the physical work and the general discomfort. He soon applied for cadet training in the Air Forces, not because he had any interest in planes or flying but because it seemed a cleaner life and more pleasant. This proved to be true and he had enjoyed his work as a bombardier instructor as much as he could enjoy any position in the army. When the threat of assignment to combat broke up this satisfactory compromise, it was difficult to take and yet he accepted it.

It was no easier for him to adapt when he joined his combat unit. He had no particular interest in the men on his crew, the idea of combat and of dropping bombs on people filled him with dread, and he hated the dust and dirt of the country and its flea-bitten populace. On his first combat mission he was tense and tremulous, although only very slight opposition was encountered. He was just barely able to hold himself together to do his job as a bombardier, and his anxiety was obvious to his crewmates. On his next three missions his anxiety was more severe and his motor coordination was so poor that he missed the target. He was very disgusted with the situation and was debating what to do, when he had to be hospitalized because of inflamed hemorrhoids. During his hospitalization, his crew were lost in action. He had felt rather calm in the hospital until he received this information. Then he became upset, not because of the loss of the men but because this was striking so close to home that he might have gotten it, if it had not been for his hemorrhoids. Once out of the hospital, he became so afraid of his next mission that he did not see how he could go, but still did not say anything. He was assigned to a mission, but at the last minute another bombardier was substituted in his place. This ship was the only one that failed to return from the mission. It was another narrow escape. The next day he was assigned to a mission. During the briefing he became very tense, and on the way out to the ship he suddenly decided he couldn't do it. He announced to the operations officer that he was too nervous and couldn't make it, and that he had decided to ground himself. He was ordered to have a talk with his Flight Surgeon and his commanding officer. He explained to them that he was entirely too nervous to fly any more and asked to be grounded. This was done and he was referred for psychiatric consultation and disposition.

On interview this bombardier was calm and did not complain of or show any anxiety. He had obviously solved his problem. He stated that he did not expect ever to fly again and would like to be sent home. The conditions of life in the theater affected him so much that he did not feel that he would be happy if he were kept overseas. He said he did not want to look at Arabs and dirt any more. He explained further that all his life he had liked to do a job well or not at all, and that he did not feel that there was any job he could do well overseas, since nothing interested him. When he was asked if he did not feel some obligation to give further service in the theater, inasmuch as he had been sent over to do a job which he had proved unable to perform, he looked hurt, and after a long silence he remarked scornfully that it was obvious the doctors didn't understand him or didn't want to understand him.

This individual was an only child of indulgent parents. His chief interest had always been in music. After graduation from college he had supported himself as a saxaphone player in an orchestra, and had been well adjusted in an artistic environment, with few close friends. He had always avoided strife and conflict and had repressed his aggressive drives. He was very well satisfied with his personality and his adjustment, and it was therefore impossible to establish any therapeutic rapport with him on the basis that he should make an attempt to adjust further to military life overseas. He had made his effort, it had been unsuccessful and now he was finished.

.   ,   .   .

It can be seen that this problem involved an individual whose ego structure was too weak to cope with the stress of combat, without being overwhelmed by anxiety, and whose superego reaction to the military situation was too weak to enforce more than a token struggle. He had no identification with the aims or purposes of the war and had many intellectual rationalizations to cover this attitude. There was no identification with his combat group. What he wanted was to get back to the kind of adjustment he had had in civil life. Accordingly, as soon as he had removed himself from combat, he had no more anxiety, nor had he any depression. The absence of clinical symptoms and of a superego reaction tended to classify this individual as a problem of "fear of flying" or "lack of moral fiber." On the other hand, he was clearly misclassified for flying or combat duty, in spite of which he had made some effort to conform to what was required of him. The decision whether or not to give him the stigmatizing diagnosis which would automatically lead to disciplinary action was left to his unit. His commanding officer and his Flight Surgeon reported that his group felt sorry for him because he was so obviously misplaced and incompetent, and that there would be no resentment or adverse effect on morale if he were grounded without disciplinary action. Therefore, he was permanently grounded, with a diagnosis of psychoneurosis, and retained within the theater of operations. He became a club officer with a headquarters organization, where in spite of his expressed reluctance to stay overseas he did an outstanding job and was commended for his efforts.

CASE 7: *Retreat from combat stress, resulting in no intrapsychic conflict.*

A 21 year old pilot received his operational training in the B-26. He was never checked out as a first pilot and went overseas with his crew as copilot. He had never experienced anxiety connected with flying or the aircraft and had no unpleasant experiences during his flying training. Upon arrival overseas his crew was transferred to B-17 planes because of an oversupply of B-26 crews. He was not worried by this shift, but the moderate enthusiasm he had felt about going into combat was shattered on his first mission, when he discovered that flak scared him. He witnessed one of the planes in his group go down in flames and for the first time realized that combat flying was not safe. The tension and tremulousness which he developed over the target area disappeared on the way back, but not the worry that perhaps he ought to have been assigned to some other type of flying. During his next twelve missions this idea became fixed. Every time he was over the target and realized that below him there was an enemy with devilishly accurate antiaircraft guns, and that the plane had to keep a straight and level course over the bomb run with the ack-ack following it, he felt certain that he was in a death trap. His fear was so great that he could pay no attention to flying. Luckily the pilot was steady and competent and did not need his help. On his fourteenth mission one engine was knocked out by flak over the target. He saw it smoking and was overwhelmed with the idea that the ship would catch fire and explode. Without waiting to assess the damage or to receive instructions from the pilot he attempted to bail out, but was restrained by the navigator. He had completely lost his head.

On the way back, as he became more calm, he decided that he had to get out of heavy bombardment aircraft before he lost his mind or was killed. It seemed useless to talk about it to the Flight Surgeon who would probably only slap him on the back and give him a sleeping pill. He remembered that there was a P-38 outfit on his field that needed pilots, being short of replacements. Fighter escort planes flew above the flak and could dodge about to evade the bursts. It seemed like a good idea and maybe they could use him. The next day, without consulting anyone in his outfit, he had a talk with the commanding officer of the fighter group, who was desperately short of replacements. This officer, seeing a young B-17 pilot who said he had always wanted to fly a P-38 and not knowing anything of his history, accepted him. Within a few days the transfer was completed. To the B-17 group the transfer was no loss, and, since they were not consulted about it, they did not feel obliged to send along a record of the pilot's performance. He received his preliminary training in P-38 combat tactics and was about to be scheduled for a combat mission, when the fighter group suddenly received an adequate number of well trained replacements. He was accordingly transferred to a photo reconnaissance outfit flying the same type of aircraft.

During the time when he was being retrained for this type of work he had ample opportunity to hear the photo fliers talk about their daring exploits. With a camera in the nose instead of guns, singly and unescorted, they penetrated deep into enemy territory in broad daylight, relying solely on speed and high altitude to escape flak and fighters. On the so-called "dicing" missions, where the fliers maintained minimum altitude to evade radar detection, hugging the ground or the water until they flashed over their photo target to obtain the picture and get away before the antiaircraft crews could be alerted, surprise was the only protection. Listening to these tales, he again began to have misgivings. It sounded very unsafe. There seemed to be little future in it, but he thought he might as well try it. Eventually he was assigned to a mission, an easy one since it was his first. On the way out to his target he encountered heavy cloud cover. As he penetrated deeper into enemy territory, he began to wonder what he would do if he met an enemy airplane. The idea of running through flak to get a picture began to fill him with terror. The more he thought about it, the sillier it seemed to keep on going as long as there was such thick cloud cover. His instructions were to penetrate to his target in spite of any cloud formation, unless the weather was extremely severe. But this seemed a waste of time, since he was almost sure to find clouds over the target. He turned around and returned to his base, reporting that he had found the target covered with clouds and had been unable to get a picture.

Unfortunately a weather mission from another outfit had penetrated to the area of his target at the same time and had found the objective clear of clouds. When this fact was learned, he was confronted with it and severely reprimanded by his commanding officer. He was told he would have to do better and was about to be briefed for another mission, when he calmly announced that he could not fly any more photo missions. He stated that he knew he would always break and run if there were a possibility of enemy action. It was useless to try again. The commanding officer was astonished at this information and gave the pilot a few days to think it over, hinting that if he persisted in this attitude he would be subject to disciplinary action. During the next few days, the pilot protested stoutly and volubly to anyone who would listen that he was a good pilot but could not fly combat because of his fears of being injured or killed. He felt he should be given a noncombat flying assignment. The other pilots, many of whom were struggling with similar fears but felt an intense devotion to their work, became increasingly disgusted and annoyed. When the situation reached explosive levels, the Flight Surgeon referred him for psychiatric evaluation.

He showed no anxiety and no clinical symptoms on examination. He reiterated his stand that he should not fly in combat because of his anxiety reaction when over enemy territory. The pilot felt that his position was perfectly logical and honest, and could not understand why anyone should object to it. He knew he could be of no further use in combat but thought he could be valuable as a ferry or transport pilot. He reported that he had always had a fear of injury. He remembered that for years he could never receive a cut or bruise without fearing that he would die of blood poisoning. A stomachache always brought about thoughts of cancer of the stomach. Both his parents were highly nervous and had similar hypochondriacal tendencies. The youngest of four children, he had always been considered the baby of the family and weaker than the others. He had come to expect protection in difficult situations and had usually received it. He had hoped that in combat he would outgrow his long-standing fears and insecurities. Since the opposite had occurred, he did not see any point in forcing himself further.

. . . . . .

This pilot presented no problem for therapy, since he had no complaints. He had solved his internal emotional problem and his difficulties now revolved about what external pressure would be brought to bear upon him. He felt strongly that the efforts he had made up to the present to remain in combat clearly discharged him from any further obligation. His insight into his inadequacy was crystal-clear and he had accepted it without conflict. What, then, should be the diagnosis?

Because this neurotic character was so obviously misclassified for combat duties and because he had made some efforts to adjust to the stress of combat, the question whether he should be given a stigmatizing diagnosis was referred back to his organization. There so much resentment was aroused by the possibility of his being given a medical disposition that it was felt this would have a harmful effect on the morale of the other fliers. He was accordingly returned to his organization, without a medical diagnosis, for administrative and disciplinary action.

It must be admitted that we possess no good descriptive term for this type of reaction. "Fear of flying" describes only one aspect of the total situation and not the most important part, since fear is such a common response to combat flying stress and is not necessarily indicative of psychological inaptitude. "Malingering" is inappropriate, inasmuch as it implies an attempt to deceive. Some individuals do try to magnify minor physical ailments in an effort to evade combat because of fear, but for the most part such men honestly admit that their behavior is motivated by fear. Such good insight is possible because they are not under pressure from a superego demanding mastery of their fear. Neither personal pride nor devotion to a group or an ideal requires them to make this effort, since ideals are lacking in them. The point is not whether fear or anxiety exists, but to what lengths an individual is prepared to go in order to overcome such an obstacle to the performance of his duty. From this point of view, fear is the same type of obstacle as a physical injury incurred in combat. Many men will completely disregard a severe physical injury in order to carry on their job or save the lives of their buddies. The extent to which a physical injury becomes disabling depends upon the nature of the injury but also upon the attitude of the individual. It is the same with fear. The difference is that the objective or mechanical disability of an injury is more easily measured than that of fear.

Since the most significant defect lies less in the strong tendency to develop anxiety under stress than in the attitude toward the anxiety, "lack of moral fiber" comes closest to describing the reaction. Yet "*moral* fiber" is not a good term, since it implies a philosophical or ethical value in an attitude which for most soldiers is based simply on identification with a group. Whether the group is right, whether its aims and purposes are ethical, whether giving one's devotion to it shows "moral fiber," must be left to history to decide. If it can ever be determined, it must at least be in the perspective of time. From a psychological point of view what is important is whether the particular individual has the capacity to give his devotion to anything outside of his own interests, whether he has the capacity to identify himself with any group. It may be that he would fight bravely for another cause; and we have seen soldiers who performed well in loosely organized guerilla bands but who became noneffective when back in a regular, tightly organized army. Other individuals, more narcissistically oriented, can never become loyal to a group or an idea. From a military point of view such psychological niceties are superfluous. The military interest requires only that an individual devote himself to the group, and does not ask why, after he has accepted induction and training, he should suddenly become unwilling to do so. The military society, like society in general, judges the man by his attitudes and behavior, and, if he is unwilling to conform, it disciplines him. In so far as he is unable or unwilling to identify himself with the military group and more specifically the combat group, such an individual displays a psychopathic personality rather than a true psychoneurosis.

The psychopath is represented in the combat unit by another type of individual, in whom the difficulty is also one of failure to identify with the unit but in whom anxiety is not a problem (cf. group 3, page 56). These are the men with mild paranoid trends, who are forever in difficulty with the authorities and are resistant to discipline. Because they are not troubled with anxiety as a result of combat stress, they may be brave soldiers, but they have a bad effect on morale owing to their critical, hostile personalities. They are a source of trouble wherever they go, and it is always difficult to decide how to handle them. They do not complain so much of subjective symptoms, but have a long list of complaints concerning the way they are mistreated, the inefficiency of the organization, the lack of interest or sympathy shown by commanding officers and the bad food or living conditions. Because of the selection of combat crews, one finds few confirmed or chronic psychopaths but rather individuals with tendencies in this direction, exaggerated by the stress of combat life. Poor morale in an organization, especially, brings to light such individuals, since it provides a realistic basis for many of their complaints. Complaints are universal in the armed forces, but, while the group is in combat they seldom reach a level where the individual becomes a threat because of his hostile attitudes, since the enemy absorbs most of the individual's hostilities.

CASE 8: *Failure of adaptation, not because of combat anxiety but because of a psychopathic personality.*

A 25 year old fighter pilot went overseas with his P-39 group and took part in the invasion of North Africa and the early phases of the Tunisian campaign. His initial attitude was one of enthusiasm for combat, but he was always known as an irritable and difficult character and had few friends. In the Tunisian campaign his organization provided close support for ground troops. Most of the missions were flown at very low levels against enemy tank and troop objectives. The losses from this type of work were exceedingly high. Though all the men were disturbed by the high losses, this pilot was loud and vociferous in his criticisms. He could not understand how the Generals and the commanding officers could allow them to continue in such suicidal tactics. Though he never refused a combat mission, showed no anxiety and always performed his job well, his persistent complaining finally began to wear on the men. His commanding officer ordered him to keep his opinions to himself. This resulted in his concluding that his commanding officer was weak and was afraid to bring the problem forcibly to the attention of higher commands.

Somewhat later the group was removed from ground support work and assigned to coastal patrol over the Mediterranean Sea. Most of the missions consisted in escorting large convoys and protecting them against enemy attack. As the German Air Force steadily weakened in the Mediterranean Theater of War, it seldom risked attack on convoys, confining itself to sneak raids at night. Contact with the enemy therefore became rare, and the missions were monotonous and boring. Furthermore, the flying characteristics of the P-39 were considered somewhat unpleasant. The aircraft had a tendency to "tumble" and needed constant attention during flights. The pilot's complaints now centered upon these two problems. He argued with anyone who would listen that the group should be transferred to a different type of tactical duties and given another type of aircraft. The morale of the outfit was not too good because these complaints were real. Most of the men, however, contented themselves with minor grumbling and were willing to accept their lot. This pilot steadily worried his bone of contention and eventually came to the conclusion that he was being discriminated against. He had not received a promotion in rank, nor was he ever made a flight leader, though he felt that his demonstrated capacity as a leader should have earned him both distinctions. Finally, after a stormy scene with his commanding officer, he requested a transfer to some other organization.

By this time the feeling against this pilot was running high. He was asked to meet a Group Flying Evaluation Board. This he felt to be degrading, since it implied that there was something wrong with his flying. The Board took a fairly punitive attitude. He had requested a transfer to an organization flying P-38 or P-51 type aircraft. These were the most popular fighter planes among pilots at that time. The Board recommended that he be transferred to a replacement center, that he be not assigned to P-38 or P-51 planes, and that he be not returned to the United States or placed in a position where early promotion could be expected, because its effect would be detrimental to the morale of the pilots remaining in the organization.

He was highly annoyed with this recommendation, but this was not the worst. He spent the next six months in the replacement center where he met the Theater Flying Evaluation Board. This Board recommended that he be transferred to P-38 planes for conversion training, but that he be demoted from First to Second Lieutenant, apparently on the theory that, if he was to be given the plane he wanted, he had to be punished in some other way. The Demotion Board met twice on his case, each time without definitive action being taken because the papers were lost or misplaced in transit between the various head-quarters. Finally, after the long period of frustration and delay, the pilot developed mild anxiety and insomnia and went to see a Flight Surgeon, who referred him for psychiatric consultation.

Psychiatric interviews revealed that his tension and insomnia were due to pent-up anger and disappointment resulting from the real frustration to which he had been exposed during the last six months. He had completely lost interest in returning to combat flying and requested to be sent home, expressing marked resentment against all the Air Forces authorities in the theater. His past history was consistent with a mild psychopathic trend, which had not led to any pronounced previous difficulties. It was felt that he still preserved enough ego strength to warrant returning him to combat, if he could be placed in a group with very high morale and good leadership and if his present equivocal status regarding demotion could be cleared up. Pursuant to this medical recommendation, the demotion proceedings were shelved and the pilot was sent to a P-38 outfit, where he satisfactorily finished his tour of duty, although he remained a difficult character.

. . . . . .

This case illustrates the general problems involved in dealing with the mild psychopathic personalities brought out by combat stress (15). These individuals resemble problem children and have a characteristic capacity for stimulating the desire to protect and help them in some of their associates, while they irritate and permanently antagonize others. They are childishly demanding and emotionally reactive and at the same time have a childlike clarity of vision. Unfortunately the truths they proclaim so loudly may be apparent to others, who are doing their best to ignore them or to get along in spite of them. To handle such individuals skillfully so that they can continue to give service without damaging morale requires superior leadership and knowledge of human relationships. In many cases it can be done successfully.

The cases described in this chapter do not picture the entire gamut of reactions seen in individuals whose previous personality disorders make them particularly unfitted for combat stress. Every case is necessarily a unique problem and classification is always arbitrary. However, these cases provide a background against which can be projected those in the following chapter, whose ego strength is overwhelmed only after withstanding tremendous quantities of stress.

CHAPTER 5

The Neurotic Reactions to Severe Combat Stress

IN THE LAST CHAPTER we described the reactions of men who were unsuited to combat flying because of previous emotional disorders or because of some personality defect rendering them peculiarly susceptible to combat stress. The defect, whether apparent or hidden, led to the appearance of marked inefficiency after exposure to what for the average combat crewman constituted minimal or slight stress. We now come to the much larger group of individuals in whom inefficiency appears only after very severe stress. Psychological difficulties in these men are due less to internal weakness than to the specific ways in which they were harassed by external events. Again, after the ego's strength has been weakened by constant pounding under stress, it is possible in some cases to detect details of the individual's past history which should have indicated the limit to the amount of psychological tension which he could stand. Yet no one has been able to achieve maturity without some psychological scarring, some crack in the psychosomatic equipment with which he faces the world. Everyone has a limit to the amount of stress which he can withstand. In this realm the airman's difficulties are merely seen in an enlarged focus as Everyman's struggles with a harsh reality, ending in some cases with continued strength and mastery of the circumstances, in others with a neurotic compromise and partial defeat.

The neurotic compromise, in these circumstances, consists in a breakdown of an otherwise normal individual's ability to deal with his mounting anxiety and hostility in an efficient manner. Fear and anger in small doses are stimulating and alert the ego, increasing its efficiency. But, when stimulated by re-peated psychological traumata, the intensity of the emotion heightens until a point is reached at which the ego loses its effectiveness and may become altogether crippled. In later chapters we shall discuss the dynamics underlying the control of these reactions. Here we wish to present the clinical picture which manifests itself as control is lost and the ego gives way under increasing pressure. The observable clinical symptoms, the anxieties, the phobic reactions, the host of physical and psychological responses to battle stress, should be considered as manifestations of this loss of control. The particular symptom which develops, although of great theoretical interest, is not so important as its intensity and its relation to the individual's ability to perform his job. Free anxiety may be tolerated for long periods of time without destroying efficiency, yet an equal intensity of anxiety which leads to vomiting or diarrhea may become immediately incapacitating.

The clinical description of the neurotic reactions to severe combat stress is thus a passing parade of every type of psychologi-cal and psychosomatic symptom, and of unadaptive behavior. For convenience and to avoid stigmatizing the flier unduly, these reactions are roughly grouped under the undiagnostic term of "operational fatigue." It is important, however, for all medical personnel to understand that this term signifies a reactive state in which the ego loses its power to control intense anxieties and hostilities in the given situation, and to maintain its functional efficiency. In many cases the ego readily regains its functional efficiency when the individual is removed from the precipitating situation. In others, a more serious psychologi-cal wound has been inflicted and recovery from the symptoms takes place only after a long time or after vigorous psychotherapy. Because the symptoms merely reflect the dynamic struggles of the ego in handling its overwhelming anxieties and hostilities in some manner, they do not fall into clear-cut diagnostic categories. Mixtures of anxiety, depression and psychosomatic reactions color almost every case. In addition, one of the most charac-teristic traits of neurotic reactions to battle is the manner in which the symptoms alter with the lapse of time, change of geographical setting, distance from the combat scene and progress or lack of treatment. What begins as a severe anxiety reaction in the combat area may end up as a severe depression in a rear area or at home. Nevertheless, we have attempted to present the following clinical cases in five categories, based upon the chief presenting symptom. These include *free anxiety states* of various intensities, *phobic states, conversion states, psychosomatic reactions* and *depressions.*

It is a rare thing not to see some degree of free anxiety intermixed with any of the other categories mentioned above. It is almost impossible to remain for any length of time in active combat without experiencing anxiety. The *free anxiety states,* however, are distinguished by the great intensity of this feeling, by the manner in which progressively greater portions of the combat environment become associated with it and by the accompanying weakening of the ego. As the ego becomes fatigued, it is unable either to suppress fear or to undertake capably the manipulative functions involved in flying. If the process becomes extensive, good judgment is lost and finally all power of intelligent action. Thus, one may speak of mild anxiety states in which the subjective and motor signs of anxiety are present but function is not yet interfered with. The flier may have a tremor and feel constantly jittery and apprehensive or display severe tension and fear over the target area, and still be able to carry on his tasks in flying. In moderate anxiety states, the same symptoms may have progressed to the point where the flier makes mistakes in flying and now has his own incapacity to fear as well as the other conscious and unconscious sources of anxiety. This is the most common neurotic reaction among flying personnel. Severe anxiety states, with much regression of the ego, confusion in regard to the environment, mutism and stupor, are not seen in fliers but only in ground combat personnel who are submitted to more prolonged, continuous and severe punishment (26).

In the free anxiety states, insight varies considerably. Some men are well aware of their own fear and its origin. In general, good insight is likely to be accompanied by larger amounts of depression. Those with poor insight tend to develop psychosomatic or conversion symptoms. In the latter case, the anxiety will disappear as the conversion symptoms develop. An occasional individual with poor insight will develop an unusually unrealistic, slap-happy attitude and will insist upon flying, when it is obvious to all that he is completely incapable of so doing because of anxiety. The degree of insight varies somewhat with the activities and attitudes of the unit medical officers, who have the first opportunity to deal with these reactions. Since they are the first line of medical defense, their efforts are of the greatest importance in increasing the fliers' insight as well as in aiding them in their control of objective and subjective symptoms (29).

These symptoms are the psychosomatic expressions of anxiety. The drawn and haggard facies give the young fliers the appearance of old men. The anxiety which can be seen in their faces in the daytime pursues them at night, interfering with sleep either through continued wakefulness and tension or by producing nightmares of combat. The constant tension numbs their appetites, and as a consequence they lose weight. Changes in personality are less common than the other signs of disturbance and are usually manifested by increased irritability. Little arguments rapidly lead to explosive rages far in excess of the demands of the disagreement. As sensitivity increases, many men withdraw from their former close contact with their buddies, and, although they do not brood and are not depressed, they feel better when they are alone. Others temper their reactions to suit the times, and, refusing to think about either the past or the future, live only for the moment. They throw themselves vigorously, sometimes too vigorously, into whatever amusement or distraction they can find. Athletic activity in the daytime gives way to drinking and card parties at night, often carried to such an excess that no one gets any sleep. Of all the symptoms, however, whether of personality or mood, whether physical or psychological, the most important are those that the fliers experience while actually exposed to the combat situation. These can best be illustrated by a case presentation.

CASE 9: *Stable individual with strong ego-ideals, who experienced gradually increasing free anxiety, eventuating in combat failure in spite of overcompensations.*

A 23 year old flier was a fighter bomber pilot, flying a Mustang modified for dive-bombing. He had been very eager to go overseas into combat and his eagerness reflected the spirit of his entire group, which went overseas as a unit. At that time, the techniques of dive-bombing pin-point tactical targets, such as railroad bridges, road junctions and troop concentrations, and low level strafing of convoys were still being developed, and enthusiasm for this type of work ran high among the fighter pilots. This pilot was one of the most enthusiastic. In addition, he was sincere, capable and very conscientious. He enjoyed the missions and showed a fine tenacity in attacking his targets. Although he had momentary periods of tension and anxiety when he returned with flak holes in his ship, he felt generally relaxed and carefree for the first half of his tour of duty. It was not until his thirty-eighth mission that his usual equanimity was shaken. At that time he was attacking an important airdrome target and he went into his dive, blind to everything except destroying it. Through being so preoccupied, he pulled out of his dive too low and his plane was caught in the explosion of his own bomb. The concussion wave tossed up his plane, which was also hit and partially disabled by bomb fragments, and he was momentarily stunned.

Luckily he recovered and was able to bring the limping ship back to his home base. But he was shaking with fear and was terrified by his own foolish carelessness, which had almost cost him his life. He could not understand it. Within a few hours he recovered from the acute fear reaction but his confidence in himself had been shaken. During his next missions he was tense and determined to keep a tighter grip on himself. He had no difficulty until his forty-second mission. While strafing an enemy troop concentration in a narrow valley, he became so intent on demolishing all the men and vehicles in the area that he did not notice the mountain looming up in his line of flight. Almost at the last moment he saw what was happening and, in the frenzy born of terror, pulled up his plane sharply and just managed to slip past the ridge of the mountain.

He brought his aircraft back from the mission without difficulty but now he was seriously upset. Twice he had narrowly missed death because of an unnecessary preoccupation with his job. He began to dread going on missions, afraid of what he might do or forget to do. He would lie awake at night, tense and anxious, and think about flying. He kept seeing the mountain suddenly flash in front of his field of vision. If he fell asleep, he dreamed that his plane had been disabled and was falling, and that, although he struggled in terror, he could not get out of it. During the day, when he was at leisure, it was impossible to relax. He stopped playing cards with his friends because he could not concentrate. Peculiarly enough, in spite of his dread of going on missions, he felt more relaxed in his plane than on the ground.

Mission after mission came and went with no change in his grinding anxiety. He decided to talk over the whole matter with his Flight Surgeon after his fifty-fourth mission, when his aircraft had caught some flak and he felt particularly disturbed. As he sat down and managed to light a cigarette, in spite of his trembling hands, he said in an anguished voice, "Doc, I can't eat and I can't sleep, and I feel jittery all the time. I don't know what's the matter with me. I'm afraid I'm going to screw up some time. All I know is, I can't quit flying. I can't stop now and leave the fellows when I'm so close to the end. I couldn't do it. But I'm afraid that something's going to happen to me. I don't know. I can't figure it out. I know I'm not the only guy who's got butterflies in his stomach, but I don't know what to do. What should I do?" The Flight Surgeon asked him to describe his traumatic missions, which he did in detail and with an increase in anxiety. He also told of a nightmare in which he dreamed he was emptying his guns at an enemy aircraft. He saw the tracers penetrate the enemy ship, but, instead of the disintegration which he expected, the German plane kept coming closer, shooting at him all the time until his own plane was disabled. He tried to bail out but could not escape from the plane.

The Flight Surgeon gave him an explanation of the nature of anxiety and its effect upon the mind and body, and reassured him concerning his fear of disaster. The pilot insisted that he was not unduly fearful of enemy action but was afraid of himself, and he begged to be allowed to continue in combat. Because of his attitude, the Flight Surgeon decided to let him fly a few more missions but to watch him closely, and meanwhile to try to control his sleep with medication. There had, up to this time, been no complaint from his associates concerning his flying in combat. During his next ten missions, however, it became evident that his flying efficiency was rapidly decreasing. On one occasion, he forgot to pull his bomb release switch over the target. On another, he forgot to strafe while diving. Finally, his flying in formation and his landings became so poor that his friends were worried about him. He was therefore removed from combat flying after his sixty-fifth mission and returned to the United States through a Medical Disposition Board. Most of the fliers in his group at that time were able to complete a tour of eighty missions before being returned home through normal channels of rotation.

.   .   .   .   .   .

This flier showed the common gradual increase of mild anxiety which is tolerated over a long period of time. As it becomes more intense, the individual suffers considerable emotional torture but cannot give up because of his strong ideals, his pride and his attachment to his unit. It is to be noted that in this case, as in others, the anxiety was also tolerated by the medical officer, whose aim was to maintain the individual on an active duty status, in spite of his symptoms, up to the point of diminishing efficiency and short of the point of serious disruption of the ego. That this goal was partially achieved in the present instance is witnessed by the fact that when he was seen by the Medical Board for disposition, his anxiety had greatly diminished, though he was somewhat depressed because of his failure to complete the tour of duty. It was felt at that time that he would continue to improve without further treatment. He had been previously a stable individual, with no discernible signs of emotional or behavioral difficulties in his past or family history. The only character trend worthy of note was a moderate degree of overconscientiousness. The ultimate degree of recovery in this case is not known, since it could not be followed up after the flier's return to the United States. We now know, on the basis of our most recent experience, that it is difficult to make any accurate prediction in the combat area concerning the extent of ultimate recovery, and this will be brought out in later chapters.

Certain interesting facts connected with the dynamics of anxiety in this case deserve comment. The emotion of anxiety was apparently free and was tolerated without secondary defenses. Yet, what was the source of anxiety? Clearly it cannot be stated wholly in terms of the common formula: fear of injury from enemy action versus desire to remain in combat. It was a realistic fear, however, based on his own experience. As is usual in the reactions of the more stable men, the anxiety had become projected, not to the enemy's hostility, but to the flier's own activity. There thus emerges a combat-precipitated carica- ture of the ordinary neurotic situation in which a capable, but overconscientious, individual suddenly loses confidence in his own ability and develops anxiety. However, it can be seen on careful analysis, and is nicely illustrated in the anxiety dream, that the real source of anxiety is not his own ego activity. The primary anxiety is, in general, an apprehension of insecurity and injury stimulated by fear of the enemy. This anxiety, however, is largely repressed at first and does not reach consciousness, because the ego undertakes strong defensive hostile and aggressive activity designed to destroy or paralyze the enemy or at least hold him at bay. As long as this activity is successful, the aggressiveness is protective against anxiety. But, since it is an overcompensation, the aggressiveness overcarries, as witness the pilot's unnecessary tenacity in attacking targets. As it overcarries, absorbing conscious energy that should be alert against danger and insecurity, it exposes the individual to even greater and unnecessary danger that may arise from any quarter.

Hostile, aggressive activity, therefore, becomes a boomerang that may result in self destruction, and, in this instance, on two occasions almost did. The threat is then from both internal and external sources and there is no way of escape as long as it is necessary to remain in combat. The anxiety can no longer be repressed, although it can be consciously attributed to the internal threat from mobilized aggressions. This results in a strong desire to give up any aggressive activities which even in a good cause may hurt or destroy people, and moreover ends in disaster for one's self. Unfortunately, the resulting scrupulousness can only be satisfied by the individual's becoming non-effective in the combat situation. This cannot be tolerated by the flier's personal ego-ideals and by the standards of the military group. The scrupulousness and conscientiousness concerning hostile destructive activity, which might be easily rationalized in different situations, here are incompatible with other obligations recognized by the military superego. This secondary conflict cannot be resolved and new anxiety piles on anxiety. The fact that this flier had always been a very conscientious individual suggests that he was sensitive to this specific conflict, and may be the reason that, although other individuals have similar experiences in combat, they do not all succumb at the same rate.

In the following case, the free anxiety, precipitated by a single catastrophic event, involved progressively more extensive aspects of the environment.

CASE 10: *Severe free anxiety precipitated by a single catastrophe.*

A 24 year old enlisted flier was the engineer gunner of a B-24, heavy bombardment crew. He was taciturn, phlegmatic, reliable and popular with his crew. All its members were very close to each other and had been happy and enthusiastic about going overseas into combat. He liked all the members of the crew but was especially friendly with and fond of the bombardier. After they had seen several ships shot down off their wing in flames, the whole crew's initial zest for combat rapidly became tempered into a quiet determination to get through the job. The gunner was momentarily upset by these occurrences, but managed to expel the thought of them from his mind. When his friend the bombardier talked from time to time about the possibility of getting a direct flak hit, he always said that the crew were lucky and had a good chance of getting through the combat tour without injury. The bombardier was a light-hearted fellow, who liked to relieve his apprehensions by joking about all the possible disasters that could occur. On the nine-teenth mission, a fragment of flak struck one of the motors while the plane was over the target and some other fragments pene-trated the fuselage, but no one was injured. The pilot brought the plane back safely on three engines.

After this occurrence, the bombardier did not joke quite so much and the gunner felt tense while over the target. However, he knew that he was performing his job in a competent manner and had no undue qualms. He did not allow himself to dwell upon the possibility of a serious mishap. If he didn't think about it and didn't expect it, the possibility seemed more remote. Yet, on his twenty-fourth mission, his calculations received a severe jolt. The target area was black with flak bursts. While on the bomb run, a nearby burst sent a shower of fragments through the plane. The bombardier was hit in the leg, one motor was knocked out and the wings were riddled, so that the ship gradu-ally lost gasoline greatly needed for the long trip back. The navigator dressed the bombardier's wound and everyone set himself to "sweat out" the long trip home on three engines with low fuel.

About two thirds of the way home, while still over the sea, the aircraft ran out of gas. In a calm voice, the pilot instructed the crew to take their prepared positions, as he was going to ditch the plane in the water. The gunner braced himself in the position for which he had been trained. A fearful thought flashed through his mind as he remembered that he could not swim. Still, his crew could come through anything! He heard his pilot say over the interphone, "This is it, fellows,—everyone get set." As he gripped his position tightly, there was a terrific long tearing noise, a wrenching jolt, and then everything became black and quiet. He awoke to find that he was struggling in water, thrashing about with growing despair because he was such a poor swimmer. Fortunately the pilot was nearby. He was a good swimmer and kept the gunner afloat while the plane sank. Neither of them could conceive how they had emerged from the plane. There were no other members of the crew to be seen and in a few minutes the plane sank out of sight. As he watched the plane sink, he realized that all his friends, with the exception of the pilot, were in there going to their death. There was no time to look in the plane and the pilot could not leave him. Luckily, they were only a short distance from the coast and in half an hour a boat picked them up and brought them ashore.

After the rescue, he and the pilot spent a week in a hospital recovering from minor wounds sustained in the crash. He felt weak and tremulous for the first few days and very sad about the loss of his crewmates. He could not sleep well at night, though there were no disturbing dreams at first. Although he hated the thought of returning to combat without his crew, he tried to be cheerful and looked forward to the time when he could return home after his tour of duty was finished. After ten days in the hospital, he reported that he felt fit for duty and was discharged.

When he reached his outfit, it was as if he had returned from the dead. He could read in the eyes of his friends the unspoken thought: "Your crew are dead—how could you have come back?" He could feel that the entire crew had been written off in the minds of his buddies; for them it did not exist. He was hurt by the fact that his crewmates' possessions had been divided up among the fellows before he got back to express what he felt would have been their wishes. Still he could not protest since he had done the same thing himself in the past. It was only the normal denial of sentimentality and affirmation of life shared by all the combat crewmen: we, the living, if anyone, deserve the watches, knives, cameras and small keepsakes of our friends. Yet it made him feel intensely alone. His pilot had been transferred almost immediately to a higher headquarters and only he was left. He was glad, therefore, when he was assigned temporarily to another crew and told he was ready to resume combat flying.

The night before his first scheduled mission he was very restless and had difficulty in falling asleep. In a terrifying nightmare he dreamed he was back in the plane with his crew, preparing to ditch. It was more frightening than the actual event. He saw himself in the plane, under water, trying to find a way out. The bombardier appeared and showed him a hole in the plane, motioning to him that he must get out. He awoke suddenly crying, with the realization that the bombardier never got out. After that he could not go back to sleep but lay quietly, smoking cigarettes, until it was time for the briefing. He could not eat breakfast and during the briefing felt strangely cold. His hands shook and he could not concentrate well on the details of the raid to come. He tried to shake off a growing feeling of dread and forced himself to get into the plane with an assumed nonchalance.

On the way out to the target, everything worried him. He mistrusted the pilot, with whom he had never flown before, and worried about every unexpected bump and shudder of the plane. He had a feeling of imminent catastrophe which kept him rigidly tense, listening to any change in the pitch of the motors for signs of failure, constantly looking for an indication that his fears would be realized. When the plane passed over the sea on the way to the target, he fought off rising panic by crouching on the floor of the plane with his head clenched between his fists. Over the target, he felt more controlled and was able to stand by his guns and look for fighters, though his knees shook and his hands trembled. On the way back he continued to feel helpless, trapped, doomed, but still determined that he must not show how he felt to his crewmates. The mission was uneventful, but on his return he was weak and exhausted from the prolonged tension. He went immediately to his tent to lie down, hoping to get some relief from the iron grip of dread and fear. He had not eaten that day and wanted nothing except sleep and relief. But he slept only fitfully, each time being awakened by the dream of his bombardier showing him how to get out of the sinking plane. Instead of bringing peace, the night was as full of anxiety as the day's mission.

The next morning he arose feeling weak, fatigued and haunted by anxiety. His abdominal muscles were tense, as if tied in knots, repudiating the idea of food. When his tentmate suddenly uttered a loud curse over having to get up, he jumped involuntarily, surprising himself and startling his friend. He found that he started in a similar fashion over every sudden sound or movement. He began to worry about what was happening to him. Could it mean he was losing his mind? While he was brooding whether to fight this reaction and fly until he overcame it, or to see his Flight Surgeon, his friends, who could not help noticing his condition, reported it to the medical officer. He was accordingly summoned for an interview, in which he tried as well as he could to put into words his consuming dread while in the air, and his present, unaccountable anxiety while on the ground. He could not explain why he felt so nerve-wracked and was afraid it would be taken for cowardice. The Flight Surgeon assured him that it was an ordinary reaction to his traumatic experience and suggested a week at a rest camp to see if relaxation and a good time would help him. He accepted this idea gratefully and said, "Captain, there wasn't nobody more eager than me when we started. And there's nobody going to call me yellow. My crew would want me to fly and finish their missions for them. If what's wrong with me is like you say, I'll do anything I can to get over it. I was afraid I was going nuts. I appreciate what you've told me."

During his stay at the rest camp, a beautiful spot with ample opportunities for diversion, he was unable to enjoy himself. Anxiety and tension continued, though they were less marked. The dream of the bombardier recurred every night unless he drank himself into a stupor, a method of relief to which he frequently resorted. When he returned, the Flight Surgeon noticed the persistent tremor, restlessness and startle reaction. Although the gunner asked to be allowed to fly some more missions to test out his ability to re-establish control, this did not appear to be a wise procedure and he was referred to a Medical Disposition Board for return to the United States. When he was interviewed psychiatrically prior to his appearance before the Board, he still showed many signs of sympathetic overactivity and appeared mildly depressed. Subjectively he felt much less tense. He attributed this to the fact that he was away from his outfit and under consideration for return home. He complained of insomnia, of the monotonously recurring anxiety dream and of a feeling of insecurity and lack of confidence in himself. Since his symptoms were no longer severe and seemed to be improving, he was not held for treatment but was immediately evacuated. His ultimate degree of recovery and disposition are not known.

. . . . . .

This case illustrates the gamut of reactions so frequently seen in previously competent men after a highly traumatic event. The anxiety appears to be well tolerated until the individual is returned to the precipitating situation. Then the ego is unable to control it and rapidly succumbs. The anxiety is free and is stimulated by the entire environment, including enemy activity, the plane and the men in the group. There is partial insight, but the individual can easily misinterpret the meaning of his symptoms unless properly guided. In spite of the severity of the symptoms, motivation remains good at least at the conscious level, leading to a desire for rapid recovery and restoration to flying. That recovery is so difficult is due not only to the persistence of fear resulting from the narrow escape from death and the physical injury, but even more to the violent disruption of personal relations caused by the death of friends. This is the deepest trauma and the most difficult to adjust to. The survivors of lost crews nearly always have difficulty. They feel the loss of their friends, and are seriously disabled by the deprivation. They miss the emotional support, the companionship and the secure feeling they had as a member of a competent team, and in point of fact frequently become orphans in their group. They tend to be used as substitutes, filling in various positions on different crews, but never again finding a stable and secure relationship. An increase in anxiety is the usual result, and when, as in this case, the physical loss is accompanied by a profound emotional reaction to the death of a close friend, disabling anxiety is the rule. The dynamics involved in this emotional reaction will be elaborated in a later chapter.

An interesting feature of this case is the moderate degree of regression undergone by the ego. This is characteristic of the effects of combat on flying personnel, in contrast with the severe regressions seen in ground force personnel. In fliers, the regression reaches a point where the ego reacts with free anxiety to any environmental stimulus but does not lose its capacity to deal with a protected environment in a rational manner in spite of the anxiety. It may break down in the combat environment, resulting in panic, freezing at the controls, momentary disorientation or some other bizarre behavior. In the environment of the airdrome, however, which would be equivalent to the environment of a rear area for an infantry soldier, the only signs of disturbance are the free anxiety and associated symptoms. Such men are always ambulatory patients and need no special care other than rest and psychotherapy. Thus they are comparable to the moderate anxiety states seen in ground force soldiers. In the severe anxiety states occurring in ground combat troops, the ego has regressed to such an extent that it is incapable of dealing with any environment, and such men need hospital care. Cases of this sort are only rarely seen in flying personnel. They are characterized by varying degrees of mutism, stupor, amnesia or bizarre behavior, and are sometimes accompanied by signs of somatic regression involving loss of normal coordinated muscular activity and release of old motor system (extrapyramidal) activities. For the sake of comparison, a severe case previously reported in our studies of war neuroses in the Tunisian campaign is included here (26). In the following case, there was extensive shattering of the ego in a young officer who had been pinned down with his men in foxholes for twenty-four hours by severe German mortar fire in Southern Tunisia.

CASE 11: *Severe, long-lasting free anxiety in an infantryman, accompanied by psychosomatic regression.*

The diagnosis on this 26 year old infantry officer's emergency medical tag was schizophrenia. The only additional information stated that the patient had been under severe mortar fire in the Kairouan Pass, and that a shell had fallen within a few yards of him, producing a semistuporous state in which he was found wandering around the fields. This had occurred on February 2 and admission to our hospital was on February 28, at which time he was still semistuporous. The patient was agitated and trembled constantly. His face betrayed persistent fright and bewilderment. He was unable to talk, producing only syllables in a whisper or low voice. He could not give his name and was apparently unable to recall what had happened to him, or even to make the effort to recall. His only word was "Who?" He started with terror at any sudden noise or motion made toward him by the attendants. His hands were stained brown from cigarettes, which he smoked chain-fashion. Since he appeared to be considerably exhausted from the long journey in ambulance convoy, it was determined to give him two days of rest, sedation and adequate nourishment, in order to see how much improvement resulted from this type of therapy alone.

Considerable success attended this regime. After two days he was much calmer. The constant coarse tremor had disappeared, although there were still spasms on stimulation. He ate eagerly, and had been able to sleep with moderate sedation. His face still showed much fear and apprehension on stimulation, but, when the atmosphere was quiet, he appeared calm and somewhat dejected. Speech was still impossible except for a few words stammered out with difficulty. He appeared to be worrying about the safety of people he had known. He asked after his wife repeatedly and recognized her picture, which he kept at his bedside, but continued reiterating, "Wife?", as if in constant need of assurance that she was all right. He recognized an officer from a different battalion of his regiment who happened to be in the hospital at the time. He did not talk to this officer but attempted to express himself through signs. When shown a roster of the men in his company, he pointed to two names again and again, looking at the officer with a worried and anxious expression as if eager to know whether these men were safe. The patient also showed a specific repetitively stereotyped behavior which seemed to be the wordless re-enactment of an actual event on the battlefield. He would start violently with fear, tremble all over and then hold his hands to his face, covering his eyes as if to shut out some horrible sight. Then he would appear to recover from this, and stare and peer intently at the ground. Finally he would heave a deep sigh, smile sadly and shake his head in a resigned fashion.

During his treatment with pentothal, the patient recovered the battle scene in detail, living it through again with great emotional release. The stereotyped performance just described proved to be an actual piece of his traumatic experience. He also recovered his memory of the past. Speech and rational behavior reappeared immediately and he improved rapidly, though much residual anxiety and some depression remained for a long time. However, after four weeks of psychotherapy, he was relieved of most of this depression, and for the most part was free of his anxiety. He gained weight, and was free of physical symptoms, yet he could not be returned to combat.

. . . . . .

Somatic regression, even more serious than this patient typified, was observed not infrequently in ground troops. They demonstrated fragments of extrapyramidal syndromes and even parkinsonian tremors and rigidities. That these were not the result of morphological changes within the central nervous system produced by blast was proved by their reversibility through narcosynthesis and psychotherapy.

Not all exposures to the repeated psychological traumata which constitute combat stress result in the production of continuous free anxiety. In a great many instances the anxiety is circumscribed and limited to isolated aspects of the total flying environment. This results clinically in the appearance of *phobic states*, conditions characterized by the development of anxiety in previously stable fliers only when exposed to a particular situation. Anxiety, for instance, may be associated with flak but not with enemy fighters or any other aspect of the combat environment. A particular type of aircraft may be the source of a severe phobic reaction after a series of crash landings and accidents in that plane. Although the anxiety may be so severe as to incapacitate the flier completely while he is flying the plane to which he has the phobic reaction, he may get along without difficulty in another type of plane. The content of the phobia varies in accordance with the multiplicity of threatening experiences to which the flier may be exposed. The most typical situations productive of isolated phobic responses are night flying, bad weather, over-water flights and formation flying. However, many other details of the flying environment may give rise to these reactions. All have in common the subjective conviction of the individual that he would be free of anxiety if he could avoid the specific phobic situation.

Some consideration must be given to the use of the term "phobia" in this connection. "Phobia" means fear and describes a symptom rather than the underlying situation giving rise to it. The word, however, is customarily used to indicate that the intense emotion associated with the consciously feared situation is actually derived from other unconscious sources. The evidence for this in civilian types of phobic reactions is obvious, inasmuch as the patient exhibiting this type of neurotic reaction is frequently unable to account rationally for his fear. The fear, moreover, seems unreasonable, or at least out of line with the ordinary experience of most individuals, who have never felt intense fear in crowds, in open spaces, in small rooms, on trains or in any of the typical situations associated with civilian phobic reactions. In contrast with these unreasonable fears, the isolated anxiety reactions in combat seem reasonable enough, since they are precipitated in previously well adjusted men by an especially threatening experience. A flier would seem justified in having strong fear in a plane after one or two crashes, and certainly after three or four.

Nevertheless, there is considerable merit in using the term phobia to describe this reaction. Wherever the anxiety in a specific phobic situation is severe enough to become incapacitating, a careful analysis shows that it covers strong anxieties due to unconscious trends which have been mobilized by the traumatic situation. This is of the greatest practical importance to treatment and disposition, because in evaluating the individual case it is necessary to determine whether the anxiety will actually disappear if the phobic defense is gratified. There is considerable temptation to deal rationally with this defense, if it is practically possible, in order to maintain the individual in some useful flying occupation. Aside from the practical considerations, such as the difficulty of providing flying assignments overseas that will exclude the possibility of the phobic situation arising, the important factor in evaluation is the question whether the anxiety will remain limited to the specific phobia or will spread to include larger segments of the flying environment. How can it be guaranteed that anxiety, now only aroused by a certain type of airplane, will not later include all aircraft and the act of flying itself? This question is always difficult to answer, since it depends upon the intensity of the underlying anxieties and the continued ability of the ego to limit them to the specific situation.

For this reason, each case must be treated individually and the factors involved in the formation of the phobic reaction must be analyzed, no matter how reasonable the symptom or how traumatic the original situation giving rise to it may be. In the cases presented below, it will be noted that the phobic reactions have in general two types of origin. In the first type, there has been no definite trauma, but the ego simply finds itself unable to manage pre-existing anxiety evoked from unconscious sources in relation to the personal significance of a certain aspect of the combat environment, whereas it can successfully deal with it in a different set of circumstances. In the second type, anxiety appears to be associated with a definite trauma, which has been repressed except for one or two aspects of the traumatic situation. At the point at which repression fails, the phobia appears. In either type of origin, the proper disposition of the patient is difficult to decide. The following case is representative of the first type of origin, in which there was no traumatic event and the phobia seems to have depended upon the deficiency of the ego in relation to a certain type of insecurity.

CASE 12: *Specific phobic defense developed against severe anxiety.*

A 23 year old night fighter pilot had always been somewhat high-strung. He had had no particular difficulties during his flying training in the United States or overseas, when for the first time he began to fly a Beau Fighter, a British plane that was considered the best night fighter at the time. Shortly after entering upon his combat missions, he began to develop anxiety. This symptom was subjectively felt as a lack of confidence in the ground controllers. He believed that those who were responsible for instrument location of enemy aircraft were inadequately trained and not sufficiently familiar with their equipment. Furthermore, he had no confidence in the accuracy of their instructions to him while he was flying on a mission. After he had been in combat for three months, one of his closest friends was shot down during an encounter with an enemy aircraft at night and this officer felt that the responsibility for his friend's death lay with the ground controllers, who had directed him improperly. After this episode his anxiety increased so that he could not sleep and was constantly preoccupied with gloomy thoughts and apprehensions. He therefore requested a transfer to daylight flying. The pilot was then seen by us for the determination of a possible psychoneurosis. He appeared to be very tense. His past history was not particularly significant, and he repeatedly made the request that he be kept in combat flying, only asking that he might not have to fly at night. He showed marked concern and guilt at the possibility of being removed from combat. He felt that he would hate to think of himself as a failure and just wanted a chance to prove that he was a good combat flier, but that he could never do this if he had to be dependent on the ground people telling him where to fly.

The request made by this officer posed the common problem: whether the flier's statement should be regarded as a rationalization of a far reaching underlying anxiety which would appear in any hazardous circumstance, or whether the anxiety might be controlled or absent in other circumstances. Flying at night is admittedly an insecure situation, which is felt more keenly by some than by others. Feelings of security in many individuals are dependent upon a constant contact with the environment through the sensory organs. In an airplane, loss of contact with the ground is not felt as an anxiety stimulus because of the adequate sense of contact with the plane, which is appreciated as a firm support or platform. Feelings of spatial relations in an aircraft, especially with reference to gravity, exist only with visual reference to the earth. At night, such visual reference is almost completely lost. The instrument panel remains the only means of determining one's position in relation to the ground. This factor—that is, the position in space with reference to the earth— is of no subjective importance as long as one has contact with the plane, but is of the greatest practical objective importance in relation to landings or possible collisions. If, on the basis of practical experience, such as crash landings at night or the deaths of friends under similar circumstances, confidence in the instrument panel or the flier's ability to interpret his position in space from it is lost, a great deal of anxiety is apt to be mobilized. Provided there is no other underlying anxiety, the fears specifically related to night flying can then be removed simply by transfer of the flier to day flying. In the case under discussion, in addition to the anxiety relating purely to flying at night, there was anxiety relating to being under the strict supervision of the ground control. In night flying, the flier has no will of his own, being completely directed by the ground operator who sets the course, speed and altitude. The night fighter pilot must faithfully follow these instructions until he is close enough to his target to operate his own equipment. There are some individuals who are unable to put confidence in anyone but themselves when faced with hazardous situations. No matter what may be the underlying source of this lack of trust in others, they cannot defend themselves against anxiety unless most of the defensive weapons are in their own hands.

In the case under discussion, it was considered that the pilot was one of these individuals. Because he had such strong motivation to continue in combat, it was determined to test out his ability to fly as a day fighter. He was accordingly given training in P-38 type aircraft and transferred to another squadron. Here he fully justified this recommendation. He became the crack pilot of his outfit. He shot down four enemy fighter aircraft within a short time. He completely lost all traces of anxiety and depression and in spite of moderate losses in his outfit was able to carry on without difficulty until he had completed his tour of duty.

.   .   .   .   .   .

It should be pointed out that the outcome is not in all cases so fortunate when the phobic defenses are gratified. This will be further discussed in the section on treatment and disposition. The following case illustrates a residual phobic reaction resulting from an intensely traumatic experience.

CASE 13: *Phobic defense precipitated by a specific catastrophe.*

A 19 year old B-17 top turret gunner had taken part in ten missions without undue anxiety. He was a well balanced boy, who had never experienced any emotional difficulties, and had a lively, pleasant personality. On his eleventh mission, there was heavy antiaircraft fire over the target and his plane received a direct flak hit in the bomb bay. There was a terrific explosion which momentarily stunned him, after which the plane went into a dive. When he recovered, he had difficulty in extricating himself from his turret position but finally tore himself loose. He opened the bomb bay door and saw a solid wall of flames. At the same moment, the pilot ordered the crew to bail out of the falling, burning plane. He went forward to the nose where he was met by another blast of fire. Through the flames he could see the pilot and copilot attempting to escape through the two cockpit windows.

He was trapped. The bomb bay seemed the only faint hope. He plunged through the flames and fell out through a large flak hole, assisted by an explosion in the bomb bay, being literally exploded out. After a delayed fall, he landed safely but only narrowly avoided falling on the burning plane, which had hit the ground ahead of him. He was immediately found by enemy soldiers, who took him to a hospital for treatment of second and third degree burns he had sustained when going through the bomb bay. During the seven weeks that he remained in the enemy hospital, the area was almost continuously bombed by the Allied Air Forces so that there was no security either during the night or during the day. The hospital was never hit and at the end of that time the area was captured by Allied troops before the patients could be evacuated by the enemy. Thus, the gunner eventually found his way back to his own squadron.

Although he had recovered from his burns and the initial shock of the experience, he exhibited on his return a moderate anxiety state similar to that in case 10. He was restless, sleepless, had anxiety dreams of falling in the burning plane, and showed a constant tremor of the hands. However, he had a strong desire to return to combat. He was accordingly sent to a station hospital for psychotherapy. Here he underwent pentothal narcosynthesis and ventilated his intense anxiety. After three weeks, all free anxiety had disappeared. He had no more anxiety dreams, was sleeping well and expressed a desire to return to combat. Although it was realized that considerable latent anxiety resulting from his traumatic experience remained, it was hoped that, in view of his strong motivation, he might be able to desensitize himself by gradual reintroduction to the combat environment.

This marked improvement persisted when he returned for the second time to his squadron. Although he was not so lively or spontaneous as he had been formerly, he had no free anxiety. Whereas prior to his treatment he had been unable to look at a plane without experiencing strong anxiety, he was now able to go on practice flights, experiencing only mild tension. It was planned to return him to combat flying, when, during a non-operational practice flight, he was informed that there were bombs in the plane. He suddenly developed severe anxiety and an overwhelming desire to bail out of the plane. On his return from the flight, he soon became calm but thereafter realized that he could not think of being in a plane loaded with bombs without feeling anxious. Although he continued to feel at ease on routine flights, he was never able to overcome this phobic reaction and was eventually returned to the Zone of the Interior for further treatment and disposition.

* * * * * *

The final outcome in this case is not known since the gunner's subsequent history could not be followed after his return home. It is quite possible that the phobic reaction would have disappeared with the passage of time and more therapy. This was not undertaken in the theater of operations, since it was considered that sufficient time had already been spent in the attempt to restore him to combat flying and because his determination to return to combat was wearing thin from lack of progress. Recovery in this type of situation is naturally determined by desire to recover, and, if this is absent, the secondary gain of the symptom defeats all efforts to help the individual. This flier had initially a sincere desire to recover. The formation of the phobia represents a failure of the ego to resolve fully the anxiety originally connected with the entire traumatic situation: the plane, the act of flying, the possibility of fire and of falling, flak, the caliber and skill of the pilot, and all the other factors upon which a flier's safety depends. He had managed to repress or overcome all conscious anxiety connected with these factors, but could not repress a conscious fear of bombs. Bombs undoubtedly represented the chief single traumatic factor, especially in view of the fact that he was bombed over a long period of time while he was helpless in the enemy hospital. Nevertheless, the fear of bombs also represented a condensation of all the fear connected with his entire traumatic experience, as if that fear were condensed and could now only be felt in relation to bombs.

The phobic reactions can be understood as one method by which the ego attempts to deal with strong anxieties. The anxiety is limited and localized to a specific situation. If this situation can then be avoided, the individual is free of anxiety (cf. case 18).

Another method frequently employed to get rid of anxiety is through the development of a conversion symptom. *Conversion states*, however, are not common among fliers, nor are the symptoms so florid or spectacular as among the civilian neuroses cases. The classic paralyses, anesthesias and peculiar gaits are not seen in flying personnel, although they are sometimes met with in the neurotic reactions to battle among ground force combat men. In fliers, the symptoms are almost wholly confined to the special sensory organs so necessary to flying: the eyes and ears.

Blurring of vision and difficulties with depth perception are the most frequent ocular complaints of functional origin. Vertigo, headaches, respiratory difficulties (cf. case 19), deafness and pain in the ears are the most common symptoms referred to the auditory and vestibular apparatus for which no organic basis can be found. Such symptoms arise quite naturally through the flier's intimate dependence upon these organs for security in relation to the flying environment. The secondary gain involved in not having the use of these senses, and therefore in being incapacitated for flying, is always prominent, though unconscious. Inadequate depth perception is an obvious bar to participation in formation flying, where safety depends upon accurately discerning distances between wing tips. Blurred vision and deafness are immediately disqualifying for any flying. The symptoms, however, do not arise out of a desire to escape. They always have a clear-cut connection with anxiety or with some actual previous injury to the organ, as is often the case with ear symptoms. For this reason, the conversion symptoms are not completely protective against anxiety and the most usual clinical picture is a mixture of anxiety combined with some form of conversion symptom.

In only one class of flying personnel have we seen an approximation of the "*belle indifférence*" so characteristic of the classic conversion hysteria. This was in the paratroops, who are not actually members of the Air Forces. These men, who face the highest casualty rates and the most difficult situations in combat, have a group attitude which does not permit free expressions of anxiety and fear. In an atmosphere where everyone is tough, rough and ready for the worst, anxiety cannot be verbalized or socially accepted. As a result, neurotic reactions among the paratroopers are apt to take the form of conversion symptoms involving the lower extremities. Weakness or paralysis of one or both legs is frequently seen and is accompanied by a total black-out of insight. The men lie comfortably in bed and show little or no distress concerning the severe disability. Although they may express a desire to be cured in order to return to their units, even the casual observer is not impressed with the sincerity of this desire in view of their obvious lack of concern for their symptom. In many instances the underlying anxiety can be brought to consciousness through psychotherapeutic efforts, although frequently the indifference will persist, in spite of all attempts to dislodge it, as long as there remains a chance that the individual may have to return to combat.

Among other classes of flying personnel, where anxiety is more freely accepted as a normal response to combat stress, the problem is not one of complete indifference to the symptom but rather one of deficient insight. The flier fails to understand the relation of his symptoms to the anxiety of which he is partially aware. Simple psychotherapy can often improve this insight and, if the motivation is adequate, can restore the individual to combat flying. The next case is an illustration of this situation.

CASE 14: *Hysterical conversion symptom related to the visual apparatus.*

A 23 year old fighter-bomber pilot, who appeared to be more serious than the average airman, had proved himself to be a fine combat flier. Although he was not inclined to enter into the usual rough and tumble arguments and mutual abuse characteristic of ordinary fliers, he was well liked. There were many losses in the squadron due to intense enemy action, and on his twenty-fifth mission his best friend was shot down by a German fighter plane. He was saddened by this loss and determined to do his best to avenge it on the enemy. After his thirtieth mission, however, he began to notice a blurring of vision during flights. He could not see objects distinctly, especially when diving on his target and when strafing. On some days this would be more pronounced than on others. In addition, he noticed that he was becoming restless and had vague feelings of apprehension for which he could not account. When he was told by his colleagues that his bombing was inaccurate because he failed to line up on the target for a perfect hit, he went to see his Flight Surgeon. His visual acuity was tested and found to be within normal limits. However, he showed a considerable defect in depth perception on repeated testing. Since there appeared to be definite psychological factors in this disability, he was referred for neuropsychiatric consultation.

On interview, he was quiet, well controlled and cooperative. He described the uneasiness he felt on missions but could not account for his apprehensions. He would not admit that he was afraid of enemy action or that he had been unduly disturbed by the deaths of his friends. Although he had the usual awareness of the dangers of combat flying, he could not connect this with his apprehension or with his visual symptoms. His conversation became much more detailed and lively when focused upon his ocular complaint. He stated that, a short time after he penetrated enemy territory on missions, his vision became blurred. The blurring would clear on active winking, but he would then notice that his eyelids felt heavy, as if he were sleepy. On occasion, this sensation would become so pronounced that he was alarmed lest his eyes should shut completely and not open again.

During this straightforward, if unusual, account of his difficulties, this flier gave the impression of being very sincere and earnest. It was felt that the lack of insight into his strong anxieties would respond most rapidly to a pentothal narcosynthesis. During the treatment he underwent a vivid emotional abreaction, freely acting out the anxiety which was his real response to the combat situation. He spoke of his friends who had been shot down and of his feeling that, if this had happened to them, it would certainly happen to him. He did not feel that he was as good a flier as they had been, so how could he get through without being shot down? He complained of all the things he had to watch for in enemy territory. There were so many dangers, so much to look out for, so much to keep his eyes on, if he were not to be taken by surprise. When he was in enemy territory, he used his eyes so much while looking for German fighters and gun positions, turning his head this way and that, that he sometimes referred to himself as "swivel-head."

As the effects of the narcosis wore off, and he became oriented to the present, he expressed considerable shame at having revealed such strong anxiety. He thought his reaction was very childish and weak, and asked what he could do about it. He was told that half the battle was in understanding it and that, now that he had insight into how he really felt, he could see for himself whether he could master his anxiety well enough to continue in combat. From this time on, he made rapid progress. He was sent to a rest camp for a week and on his return showed a new buoyancy and increase in confidence. His depth perception on repeated testing now was within normal limits. He was accordingly returned to his outfit, where he resumed combat flying and was able to complete his tour of duty.

. . . . . .

This individual had difficulty in accepting insight into his anxiety because of the common psychological dilemma in which he found himself. Because of dependent trends, he needed more protection than the combat situation could afford and therefore developed anxiety. But a strong superego reaction demanded an effort to persist in spite of any danger. In view of the superego's demand, it was more painful to admit anxiety than to deny it and hope that the pretense would work. It was as if the ego reasoned: once anxiety is admitted, all is lost. Then, in accordance with Hamlet's advice to "assume a virtue if you have it not," the ego proceeds to ignore all evidence of anxiety in so far as it can. However, the underlying revolt at having to endure so much insecurity and threat, makes itself felt through other channels. The eyes, already strained in the effort to forestall danger, now become the unconscious agents of this revolt. They blur, tear and refuse to look upon the scene, refuse to have anything to do with the bloody business. Such an isolated symptom is naturally overdetermined and all the factors that are concerned in the choice of the organ affected could not be elicited in a short time.

From a practical point of view, it was not necessary to make a detailed analysis of this situation in the combat area, nor was this indicated. All that was necessary was to reassure the flier that his dependent need for security was shared by everyone, that anxiety was therefore universal and acceptable as a reaction to the manifold dangers, and that the fact of its acceptance and admission into consciousness was in itself no threat to continued successful participation in combat. Aided by this support and the reidentification with his friends in combat which it provided, the flier was able to resolve his difficulties on the basis of his new insight. Not all men who develop conversion symptoms, however, are able to accept insight so easily. This is well shown in case 19, where the patient failed to develop insight in spite of intensive psychotherapy overseas and showed no change until his return home.

A method of dealing with anxiety very similar to that involved in the development of conversion symptoms is seen in the *psychosomatic states*, where functional impairment of the vegetative organ systems exists without consciousness of anxiety. Anxiety is such an ordinary occurrence among combat personnel and its somatic reverberations are such familiar phenomena that insight is almost a cultural property of the group. When death marches at his side, who can fail to appreciate the meaning of his cold hands and feet, his trembling knees, his racing pulse, his sudden need to defecate or urinate? These obvious somatic expressions of anxiety become incorporated in the language of combat troops, which has an inevitable physiological tone at best, and they are the subject matter of current jokes.

Although most combat men understand their psychosomatic symptoms and tolerate them as well as they can, some are immune to insight and appear at sick call complaining of stomach trouble, bowel distress or difficulties with their bladders. More commonly, there may be some admission of vague anxiety, but the somatic symptoms receive the chief emphasis and are actually so severe as to be incapacitating. The gastrointestinal tract is involved more frequently than any other organ system. Cardiovascular symptoms, which were expected to be found in large numbers on the basis of the experience during the last war, are of much less frequent occurrence. The "effort syndrome" as a clinical entity is comparatively rare among all combat troops and practically nonexistent among flying personnel. Fluctuating hypertension, similarly, may appear in isolated instances but is not a frequent finding. Genito-urinary symptoms are even less common. Nocturia and frequency during the day are standard accompaniments of anxiety in many individuals but they are seldom presented as isolated complaints.

In contrast with the other organ symptoms, gastrointestinal symptoms flourish in an abundance and variety that are surprising and sometimes confusing. Loss of appetite, loss of weight, epigastric distress, nausea and vomiting before and during missions, abdominal cramps and diarrhea occur independently and in combination. Whether some degree of anxiety is present or not, the symptoms may be confusing, especially in semitropical theaters of war, because of the prevalence of infectious diseases affecting the gastrointestinal tract. The differential diagnosis may then become a complex problem. This is especially true for intestinal complaints. The following case portrays the complexities involved in this situation.

CASE 15: *Diarrhea developed as the main symptom of severe anxiety.*

A 25 year old dive bomber pilot had a rigid personality and did not make friends easily. However, he was considered a dependable and efficient flier. During his first fifteen missions he experienced no particular difficulty. Combat losses of personnel were fairly high in his squadron but this did not affect him to an unusual degree. He experienced a moderate amount of tension while on missions, not severe enough to be a source of concern or to affect his efficiency. On his sixteenth mission, while diving on his target, he felt a sudden uncontrollable urge to defecate and lost control of his sphincter, soiling himself. He pulled out of his dive without trouble but on the way back to his base, he felt ill. He made a bad landing. The plane nosed over, the cockpit crashed to the ground and he was thrown partially out of it, dangling in an inverted position with his head partly thrust into the ground. He was extricated and found to have no injuries. The medical officer who examined him concluded that he had had a minor gastrointestinal upset due to some tainted food. He was mildly upset by the experience but in forty-eight hours felt ready to return to combat flying.

During the next three weeks, he continued to fly missions, occasionally noting some transient abdominal cramps. Then he suddenly developed a severe diarrhea, for treatment of which he was sent to a station hospital. After a five day course of sulphaguanadine, the diarrhea cleared and he was returned to his unit. In the hospital the stools were negative for amebae and no specific diagnosis was made. After he had flown two additional missions, subsequent to discharge from hospital, he developed severe headache and a fever, which were diagnosed as due to pappataci fever. He was treated for five days "in quarters." He then felt well and was about to be returned to combat flying when the severe diarrhea recurred. He was again given a course of sulphaguanadine and kept in quarters on the base. He improved rapidly and was scheduled for a mission. The morning that he was to go on the mission, the diarrhea returned and he was sent back to the hospital. Here it was determined to observe the flier without giving specific therapy. The stools were consistently negative for infectious organisms. Within five days, and without treatment, the diarrhea disappeared. During this time, he appeared to be restless and had some insomnia, though he denied having any anxiety. It was the opinion of the hospital physician that the diarrhea was of nervous origin.

During the next month the pilot was free of symptoms and flew five missions. In this time there were no losses in the squadron due to enemy action. Then he developed malaria owing to his own carelessness, inasmuch as he had not bothered to sleep under a mosquito net at the height of the malaria season. The illness was mild and he was returned to duty after three weeks, one of which he spent at a rest camp. He then flew one mission without difficulty. On this mission, however, he saw one of his companions shot down by antiaircraft fire, the plane crashing to the ground and scattering over the countryside. That night he slept poorly and the next morning, while on a test flight at 10,000 feet, he felt again a sudden overpowering urge to defecate. This time he managed to control his sphincter and got back to the ground without incident. That afternoon, however, while being briefed for a mission, he again experienced this urge to defecate, now also associated with a definite feeling of anxiety. He could not go on the mission. During the next few days he had five or six bowel movements per day but no real diarrhea. He was anxious and increasingly depressed. He avoided his friends as much as he could, and, since he seemed to be getting worse, he was referred for psychiatric consultation.

When he was interviewed two weeks later, this pilot was pale, thin, tense and anxious, and mildly depressed. There had been no diarrhea during the intervening time. He stated that he was terribly discouraged and disappointed because his constant physical illnesses had prevented him from completing his tour of duty. He had completed only twenty-six missions at this time, whereas most of his colleagues were reaching sixty-five to eighty missions. He thought that his difficulties were entirely of physical origin and that his tensions and anxiety were due to the continual frustration and disappointment. He categorically refuted the notion that his diarrhea could have any connection with fear associated with combat. When he was told that such symptoms commonly arose from combat stress and that both his Flight Surgeon and his colleagues were of the opinion that this was true in his case, he stated, without rancor, that he could not agree. Since there seemed to be so little possibility of establishing rapport with this flier or hope of developing insight, he was recommended for a return to the United States for further treatment and disposition.

·   ·   ·   ·   ·

This case illustrates the common difficulty in distinguishing the degree of functional involvement in individuals who have been physically ill or who have become debilitated under combat conditions. There was nothing in the patient's past history to indicate a previous overt emotional or psychosomatic disorder. He had experienced two definite physical illnesses during his tour of duty and the possibility of actual or toxic-infectious involvement of the gastrointestinal tract had always to be considered in that geographical area. Nevertheless, his intestinal symptoms began before the onset of the physical illnesses and their appearance coincided with exposure to combat stress, and the laboratory data were consistently negative. The preponderance of the evidence favored the psychological origin of his symptoms. The anxiety, however, although precipitated by combat stress, was deeply buried and only secondarily projected to his symptoms, where it was more acceptable to his strong pride. Probably the anxiety in this type of reaction would not be so difficult to dislodge if it were not so inextricably bound to strong hostilities, also expressed in the symptom. This flier was a cold, rigid and remotely hostile character, closely attached to his mother and an older sister. His characteristic faint negativism was portrayed in his refusal to sleep under a mosquito net, a flouting of regulations which could only hurt himself. It is probable that this mild character neurosis would never have led to outspoken symptoms except under a situation of severe stress and threat to his dependent need for security. It was only to be expected that the resultant fear and anger could not be brought to a full-bodied direct expression. The usefulness of the lower bowel for expressing these feelings is notoriously manifest in the four letter excretory profanities, which nowhere have a wider currency than among combat troops. When, as in this case, the usual verbalization of aggression and fear in terms of the excretory act has given way to the act itself, hope of effecting any improvement through psychotherapy in a short time is very dim.

Similar complexities are encountered in the many gastric neuroses seen among combat personnel. Food intolerance is a common complaint when the diet consists principally of C and K rations. Although controlled tests conducted by the army at home have demonstrated that healthy men can subsist for months on these diets without difficulty, such experiments do not take into account the gradual debilitation from which most men suffer overseas, or the recurrent attacks of malaria, infectious jaundice and other diseases which affect a large proportion of the personnel in many theaters of war. The treatment of these illnesses is effective, so that time lost through actual sickness is not great. Yet the aftermath of physical impairment, combined with the progressive loss of emotional control, results in anorexia, loss of weight and minor dyspeptic symptoms in many individuals. To separate the psychological from the physical factors in this common syndrome is an almost impossible task. One is content to recognize that both factors are involved, and that effective treatment lies in a total change of environment rather than in specific psychotherapy or physical therapy. As the diet has improved in the combat areas, many such functional dyspeptic syndromes have cleared up. Others have improved during hospitalization with its protected environment and increased comfort, only to recur when the individual is returned to his outfit. In a large proportion of cases, permanent improvement can be effected only by a return to the United States (cf. chapter 11).

Depressed states are not found among combat flying personnel as isolated entities but are always combined with varying amounts of anxiety. In several of the preceding case histories, depression has been one of the symptoms. However, depression in some cases dominates the clinical picture, and, if it is severe, may be the source of greatest concern to the medical officer (cf. case 17). In a few instances where the situation was neglected by the Flight Surgeon because the depression was masked or not sufficiently understood, a flier has quietly taken off in his plane without orders and never been seen again. The danger of suicide, however, is uncommon, since the depression is usually obvious and accompanied by seclusiveness and other personality changes strikingly different from the usual outgoing combat qualities. Its onset is later than that of the other neurotic reactions to combat stress. In the ordinary course of events, depression appears after a long period of struggle with anxiety, when it is clear that the fight to control the anxiety has failed. The flier then suffers much from his feelings of failure and of having let his buddies down, and is given no peace by his wounded pride. Failure is the most common but not the only content of the depression. If the casualty losses are very high, some men become at first fatalistic and then depressed, seeing no possibility of completing a combat tour or of getting back to their families. The feeling of doom may be so objectively justified by reality that not to feel depressed would be an unusual reaction. Depression is frequently precipitated by the death of a close personal friend or those of an entire crew. In the resulting melancholia are found some of the most difficult and perplexing therapeutic problems, the solution of which must usually wait until the flier is returned home for definitive treatment.

No matter what the conscious content of the depression, the background is always an intense and haunting identification with friends and close buddies, living or dead. In combat, the quick and the dead have a power to stir men to lengths of action and depths of feeling that are entirely undreamed of in the peaceful civilian life of the nation. So close are the men to each other, so bound together by a common purpose and a common fate, that one individual's combat career cannot come to a different conclusion from that of his comrades without pain. This leads to innumerable situations where a man must choose between a hero's death, without in the least desiring to be a hero, or life in the future with a bad conscience and a constant feeling of depression and guilt. If he chooses the first course of action, he may receive a posthumous decoration and a place of honor in that section of paradise reserved for airmen, but the act will have been due to the impossibility of leaving his friends or letting them down. A recent news story which was published in the press under the headline, "Greater Love Hath No Man," nicely illustrates how forcibly this devotion can govern men's actions. Four B-17 combat crew members, the two waist gunners, the tail gunner and the ball turret gunner, had often promised each other that, if one of them got into difficulties, the others would never abandon him, and they would all stick together no matter what happened. This was especially for the benefit of the ball turret man, who was in the most vulnerable spot. Their ship received a direct flak hit during a mission and was completely disabled, and the pilot ordered the crew to bail out. The top turret gunner, who was not in the compact, bailed out according to instructions and landed safely. The other four gunners stayed in the plane, which was out of control and crashed in flames and exploded. They were all killed. According to the top turret gunner, the flak had jammed the ball turret so that the gunner could not be extricated from it, but he was alive. The other three men were uninjured. They could have saved their lives and had been ordered to do so but they preferred to stick to their resolution and ride the plane down with him, knowing that the chances of a safe landing were hopeless.

This situation is reproduced every day in combat with endless variations. If the poignant dilemma of the individual who is faced with the choice of saving his own life, perhaps to fight again later, or of risking it for his friends, is solved in favor of the former, and especially if the decision is made out of his own anxiety, the result is often a severe depression. The guilt of abandonment cannot be banished, no matter how forcibly the man may try to put it out of his mind. Even when there has been no choice, and survival is due to the sheerest whim of fate, as in case 10 in this chapter, the "survivor's guilt" haunts the individual; he is "ghosted," as one man put it, by his dead friends, who will not leave him alone or give him peace of mind. The dead appear in dreams at night, happy dreams of former good times, which are now a mockery, or fearful dreams of dying, which are exact reproductions of what happened or fantastic elaborations of it. In the dream, the agony is the helplessness and suffering of the dead and the anguish of not having helped or not being able to help them. The dead also appear in waking reveries and in associations of places and people. The identification is too strong to be dissolved by the physical fact of death, and, since the dead live within the living just as they did before they died, they cannot be expected to remain in their watery or fiery graves.

CASE 16: *Severe depression resulting from repeated loss of comrades in combat.*

A 23 year old B-26 pilot flew his first two missions in combat as a copilot and then was made first pilot. He showed so much competence and initiative that he soon was made squadron operations officer. He was a warm-hearted, attractive individual, who had many close friends. He was inclined to worry a good deal and to take his responsibilities very seriously. Almost from the outset, he worried about the fate of the crews he controlled as operations officer. If a crew failed to return from a mission, he would be upset about it. He was not seriously affected, however, until he had witnessed and taken part in several crash landings which occurred within a relatively short space of time. First, a bomber spun in and crashed on the field while he was watching the return of a mission. He rushed out to the cracked-up plane and assisted in the removal of the body of the pilot, a good friend, who had been mutilated and killed in the crash. He was badly disturbed by the sight of his friend, torn and lifeless.

A few days later, while he was standing in front of the operations tent looking at the field, another bomber attempted to land and exploded, killing the entire crew and scattering fragments of their bodies about the field. The following day, he had himself to turn back early from a mission and make a forced landing at a strange field because of an engine cutting out. Loss of one motor in a B-26 was a serious affair at that time, but, although he was tense and worried, he made a skillful landing. A few days after he had returned to his own field, another plane crashed near his operations tent and several of the crew members were injured. On his next mission, he scheduled himself to fly as an observer, rather than as pilot. Over the target the plane was hit by flak and the pilot and copilot were both seriously injured. With the help of the bombardier, he got the pilot out of the cockpit and took over control of the plane. It was badly disabled, the hydraulic mechanisms were shattered and the landing wheels and flaps could not be lowered. He was able to bring the ship back to his base, where he made a crash landing. He was very tense for fear that the landing would be bad and that he would kill himself and his friends; he kept picturing the fatal crack-ups he had witnessed on the field. Nevertheless, he made a good landing, only slightly shaking up the occupants.

That night the pilot felt very nervous and restless and could scarcely sleep. He was alarmed at this reaction and, being afraid that he was developing a fear of flying, scheduled himself for a mission the next day. He believed that the only way to overcome a bad reaction to flying was to keep on flying, and that, if he stayed away from it, the feeling would become permanent. However, he did not feel sufficiently confident to fly as pilot and therefore again scheduled himself to go as an observer. He was tense and anxious throughout this mission, constantly expecting a mishap. His fears were justified. On the way back to the field from the target, a motor cut out and the second motor failed just as they were coming in to land. There was a bad crash. Although he was unhurt, two of the men in the plane were seriously injured.

From this time on, his fear of a disaster occurring while he was flying was fixed. He was certain that the string of crashes in which he had been involved so far without injury would catch up with him, and that the next time probably would be fatal. During the next two weeks, he left his name off the battle order and did not go out on missions. But it made him feel guilty to think he was risking the lives of other crews and was afraid to go himself. Every day he went through a severe inner conflict, in which he would try to persuade himself to put his name down for the next day's mission. Then the memory of the crashes would confront him and would be elaborated into a vision of himself and his crew injured and dying. The plane seemed like an evil force, bent on destroying, which had played with him as a cat plays with a mouse and now was ready for the kill. His resolution would then weaken and he would put off the mission for another day, but would feel miserable and beaten. Finally, unable to contain this inner torment, he confided his feelings to a close friend, whom he respected as a pilot and who was a warm and sympathetic individual. The friend's advice was to fly with him on several missions until he recovered his confidence.

Feeling encouraged by his friend's reassurance that he would surely overcome his fears, he scheduled himself to fly the next day as an observer with this friend. Just before the take-off, however, he had an overwhelming feeling of dread and weakened. He felt as if some irresistible force was holding him back. He made some excuse. The plane took off without him and never came back. It had been hit over the target by flak and the entire crew was lost.

When he learned of the loss of this crew, he was plunged into a descending spiral of fear and remorse, from which he never recovered. The knowledge that his presentiment of death had been correct confirmed all his fears. But that his friend, who had been so willing to help him, had to take the final punishment, while he had escaped only because of his weakness, was more than he could bear. Every night he dreamed of the crash of this crew. He could see the expression on his friend's face and in its suffering and pain he could read a terrible accusation. In the daytime, when he tried to concentrate on his work, pictures of the crash and of his friend blotted out the papers on his desk. Unable to make the important decision before, he now had difficulty in making even simple decisions. His mind became easily confused. At times he thought everyone was looking at him with an expression of contempt. Often he could bear this since he was equally contemptuous of himself. On occasion, however, if someone made a casual remark which he would interpret to refer to his fear of going on missions, he would become enraged, but be unable to speak, and would silently stalk off to wait for his anger to quiet down. Actually the attitude of his friends was extremely sympathetic, rather than hostile. They wished that they knew how to help him and were careful not to say anything which they thought might upset him. In spite of their attitude, his sensitivity, irritability and inefficiency became worse. On rare occasions, he would feel that his confidence would return and that he would go on a mission soon. Then for a while he would be gay and lighthearted. But these moments were fleeting and usually he was immersed in gloomy reflections. His Flight Surgeon was aware of the situation, attempting repeatedly to relieve his anxiety and depression by reassurance. When nothing came of his efforts and the pilot showed increasing despair and self condemnation, he determined to refer him for psychiatric consultation.

On interview, this pilot appeared retarded and severely depressed. He had no tremor nor other objective signs of anxiety, but there was considerable verbal blocking. He seemed to have difficulty in organizing his thoughts. Psychotherapy was directed chiefly at reducing the intense superego reaction and decreasing his sense of isolation. When these improved to some extent, he was returned for further treatment and disposition to the United States, where many returnees with the same problem are successfully treated (cf. chapter 12).

. . . . . .

The manner in which identification operates among combat fliers is clearly shown in this case. It is the source both of their greatest strength, supporting them in their resolution to face the stress of combat, and of their greatest suffering, if that resolution should fail. The reasons why the ego fails in the face of these stresses will be set forth in the next chapter.

CHAPTER 6

Psychodynamics

A<small>N UNDERSTANDING</small> of neurotic reactions to combat stress requires knowledge not only of the observable clinical symptoms and behavior which appear when the ego has begun to weaken, but also of the psychological mechanisms underlying *successful adaptations* to the combat situation. The psychodynamic processes entailed in such successful adaptations have the same relation to neurotic symptoms as the normal physiology of the body has to the abnormal physiology manifested in any disease process. Both must be clearly comprehended in order to institute a rational and effective therapy. Owing to the intangible and complex nature of psychological mechanisms, the psychodynamic processes are difficult to isolate, to measure and to describe. Even a lucid description is difficult, because so many processes involving separate parts of the personality at various levels of consciousness take place at the same time.

The present exposition cannot encompass all the factors involved in psychological health and illness in the face of combat stress. What is presented should be regarded as a working approach to the problem, derived from a study of actual cases encountered in the combat situation. There is much to be gained from such a study of fresh material: notably, a vivid realization of the feelings and reactions of men in combat, and the immediate origins of their symptoms. On the other hand, the all-pervading realities of the battle scene with its atmosphere of constant menace and insecurity tend to obscure individual differences of personality and to dim-out reactions that are wholly or in part based on previous personality trends. These can be recognized and have been brought out to some extent in the case material of early breakdowns. But they are difficult to evaluate in men of apparent previous stability, who show symptoms only after exposure to severe stress. The relationship of individual personality patterns to the effects of combat can be seen much more easily in returned combat veterans, to whom the passage of time and the distance from the combat scene give a much broader perspective. After the men have been home for a time, they can more readily be appreciated as individuals. Their combat experiences then shade into the sum total of their past experiences and can be seen in truer proportions. The lessons to be learned from the study of returnees in regard to the psychodynamics will be presented in chapter 15.

The universal stresses of combat tend to reduce all individuals to a common denominator, which we have called the combat personality. The reader will have noted that the cases presented in the previous chapter have a certain sameness. In spite of the fact that they were specially picked to illustrate different categories of combat reactions, there is considerable repetition of symptoms, attitudes and experiences. Indeed, the men are much the same, whether in health or in illness, as long as they remain in combat. Initially, they were all healthy, vigorous, aggressive young men, who had been stamped with the same imprint by months of training and combat activity. It is this universalized combat personality, this embattled "Everyman," whose psychological vicissitudes we studied in order to determine the psychodynamic principles involved in continued successful adaptation to combat stress, and in failure to adapt to it.

The principal way in which the combat personality is affected by the specific stress to which he is subjected is in the production of fear and, to a lesser extent, of hostility. We believe that in spite of its complexity, the problem of the appearance of fear can be reduced to two problems: Why does the individual develop fear to begin with, and what does he do about it after it has developed? The first problem involves the factors inherent in the combat situation which stimulate fear or protect the individual against its appearance. The second category entails the psychological defenses adopted by the ego to control or deal with this emotion, once it has arisen. The psychological mechanisms involved in each category sometimes coincide or overlap, and thus the distinction is not always sharp.

At this point it becomes necessary to establish the differences between fear and anxiety, although these terms are often used interchangeably. Fear is an emotion in response to a stimulus in reality that either threatens the individual at the moment or portends actual danger. The signal of fear is experienced consciously by the organism. Anxiety is an anticipation of danger. The signal is experienced by the ego, which is reminded of traumatic experiences previously endured and thus behaves as if the danger were present. The experience is thus an expectation of danger and a mild repetition of it. The signal of anxiety not only prepares the organism for danger, but also starts defensive maneuvers against it. The stimuli in reality, evoking anxiety, do so as symbolic situations to which the individual on the basis of past experience has learned to attribute dangerous results, and to which it reacts in a sensitized manner. The interpretation of these symbolic significances is unconscious, but the feeling of anxiety may become conscious and the defensive maneuvers or symptoms are expressed either in conscious thought or in behavior, although their connections with the evoking stimuli are lost. Yet anxiety is rarely accepted as a feeling without being attributed to some real outward source (projection). The above differences between fear and anxiety are less important than their similarities, since the feeling-tone and the physiological concomitants in anxiety and fear are identical. Furthermore, there are no pure fears inasmuch as all external dangers also have symbolic significance. How much is real (fear) and how much is apprehension (anxiety) is the problem.

There are obviously all sorts of fears: fear of personal injury or death, fear of harm or injury to or the loss of someone who is loved, fear of failure, of economic loss, of the loss of prestige, honor or reputation. All fears, however, have one thing in common. What is feared is the loss of something that is loved, highly prized and held very dear. Whether it is one's own person, another person, an inanimate thing or an abstract idea, fear will not develop unless this thing is intensely loved. If through a chain of circumstances a man loses his interest in life and his own self love, he will not care if he starves or dies, whereas in ordinary circumstances a serious threat to his life will precipitate strong fear. On the other hand, if he is passionately devoted to an abstract idea which is in danger, such as his country or his political creed, he will give his life to protect it with little apprehension.

It can be seen that apprehension or anxiety is related to the loss of what is loved most. Such love, affection, interest, care or attachment is the psychological aspect of a force which derives its energy from certain inner biological sources. The total quantity of this force and its objects are as variable in the life history of the individual from time to time as are the forces of somatic metabolism and energy.

In infancy and early childhood, passive intaking trends are prominent in relation not only to food and drink but also to love and attention. The child is concerned with its own somatic and psychological needs. This narcissism is gradually altered as the child grows bigger, older and more secure, after he has had sufficient gratification. He is then able to spill over his excess energy, his love and his attention toward objects external to himself—his parents, other members of the family and a gradually increasing range of interests—without demanding an equal return in kind. As he approaches satiation, he becomes more altruistic, less selfish and less self-centered. The degree to which he can love and give to others depends on his own inner security, based on having had enough for himself. If his security is precarious, love of others depletes him and he feels humility and inferiority. This is of no consequence, however, if he receives a return of interest and affection through possession of the loved object or by identification with it, thereby loving another as he loves himself.

If loss of the loved object, with which the insecure adolescent identifies, is threatened, return to frank self interest often results. The loss of the object of affection, however, is depleting to the ego and anxiety ensues. The more mature and secure men are less disturbed, although not unaffected, because their inner resources are greater and capable of withstanding more depletion. Yet every loved object has some degree of identification and hence of overevaluation, and cannot be given up lightly. When something that is loved is threatened, and the love cannot be withdrawn, then a severe emotional reaction is produced. The thing that cannot be tolerated is the loss of love invested in the object, and therefore loss of the object, whether a person, thing, idea, part or all of one's own self, cannot be tolerated.

The emotional reaction aroused by a threat of such a loss is at first an undifferentiated combination of fear and anger, subjectively felt as increased tension, alertness or awareness of danger. The whole organism is keyed up for trouble, a process whose physiological components have been well studied. Fear and anger are still undifferentiated, or at least mixed, as long as it is not known what action can be taken in the face of the threatened loss. If the loss can be averted, or the threat dealt with in active ways by being driven off or destroyed, aggressive activity accompanied by anger is called forth. This appraisal of the situation requires mental activity involving judgment, discrimination and choice of activity, based largely on past experience. If on the basis of such mental activity it is seen that the loss cannot be averted, the situation is hopeless and nothing can be done, then anxiety develops. This is, of course, most obvious where the threat is to one's own life but is applicable to a threat to anything dearly loved. However, only in the case of a threat to one's own life is strong fear an emotionally appropriate reaction, inasmuch as the only activity which fear leads to is withdrawal and escape.

It can thus be seen that the signal of anxiety has both emotional and mental components: emotional, in so far as it depends upon the threatened loss of something that is loved; and mental, in so far as it is predicated on the probability that the loss cannot be avoided. With these considerations in mind, it is necessary now to examine how the men in combat come to feel anxiety, what they love and hold dear, and what their mental processes are in the face of a threat of its loss.

As we have indicated in previous chapters, the American combat soldier is strongly attached and devoted to his group. The affection which he invests in this group is not lost and therefore his emotional economy is not disturbed for long periods of time because of several factors. For one thing, contact with the group is continuously maintained. Conversely, nothing is more painful than the necessity of leaving the group because of illness, detached service or transfer. In many instances, a man will refuse a transfer, even though it involves a promotion or a better job, simply in order to stay with his group. Secondly, his superego is strongly identified with the group, and, as he loves the group, he loves himself as a member of the group. Thus a part of his love is narcissistically reinvested in himself through the identification.

However much he loves the group, the average American combat soldier still retains a great deal of self love and of interest in himself and his own needs. From the point of view of the extensiveness of his needs he is dependent on others. On the other hand, American civilization is so constituted that he is able, in civilian life, to satisfy his personal demands through his own efforts, through initiative and work. Thus there is a kind of paradox implicit in the cultural and social organization of the nation: its citizens are dependent, from the standpoint of their individualistic demands, and mature and independent, from the standpoint of their aggressive confidence and ability to satisfy these demands by their own individual efforts. When the American, after a long period of training, becomes a member of the combat group, this paradox is exactly reversed. For the sake of the group, he gives up a large part of his individualistic demands. He simply has to do without many of the things he has always needed and is more or less content to do without them, on a provisional and temporary basis. From this point of view, in so far as he is able to give up immediate satisfactions and demands for larger interests and enjoyment in the future, he becomes more mature. It must be remembered, however, that he does not completely give up these demands but only puts them aside temporarily. At the same time, he gives up his own individualistic aggressive activity and becomes dependent upon the group. What needs he now has can only be satisfied by the group. From this point of view he regresses to a less mature, more dependent level. He is under strict authority and control and, like a child, is forever having to ask permission to have his needs gratified. If he becomes too aggressively demanding, he is punished or expelled from the group.

Thus, in the development of self discipline, self sacrifice and cooperation the combat personality has become more mature, but from every other standpoint he is in a more dependent and immature role than he was in civilian life.

Nevertheless, for what he has given up, he receives constant care and affection from his group as long as he plays his part properly. There is therefore no disturbance in psychic energy, and the individual feels in harmony with his group and has no anxiety. The status of the average combat crewman at the beginning of his combat tour can be schematically summarized in the following way: Most of his love and interest is devoted to his group and is satisfied as long as he remains in contact with it. The superego is identified with that of the group and will return some of this love to the ego as long as he fulfills the group ideals. A smaller portion is devoted to himself, but this is satisfied by the care and interest the group shows in him. Another small part is devoted to friends, family ties and interests at home. This last remains unsatisfied except in fantasy, and is given up on a temporary basis, though not without pain.

As long as the major portion of the man's interest and affection remains devoted to the welfare of his combat group, he will not develop strong anxiety over the possibility of his own injury or death. His chief concern involves the fate of his group. Then, if the group is strong and successful in combat, he has nothing to fear. But there are several factors which tend to break down this heavy investment of interest in the group, returning continually larger amounts of care and interest to his own fate. The chief of these is the loss of men in combat, especially of close friends. Although the group is partly an abstract idea, a symbolic object of attachment, it is also composed of individuals. When these individuals die or are removed through injury, the love and affection which were attached to them must either be transferred to newcomers in the group or be returned to the ego. Usually the latter takes place because of the identification with the lost friends, who, though dead, persist within the survivors, where they absorb continued affection which cannot be lightly transferred to new and untried men.

Another factor which contributes to an increase in self concern is length of time in combat. This factor is related to the development of anxiety in several ways and will be taken up again. But it is specifically related to the amount of affection devoted to the group. The longer the man remains in combat, the more the personnel in the group changes through attrition, so that eventually it may not be recognizable as his original group. For this reason, a large part of his original affection is withdrawn. Concurrently, as time passes, the affection for and interest in his family and close ties at home, which have had to remain unsatisfied, become increasingly impatient for gratification. Having only been set aside temporarily, they cannot be denied forever. As the man begins to think more and more of home, the combat group becomes an enemy which stands in the way of his achieving this gratification, and therefore more affection is withdrawn from it. The tremendous influence of this factor in relation to motivation is recognized by the armed forces, and in the Air Forces is solved by limiting the tour of duty to variable numbers of combat hours or missions. This provides a goal which appeases the demands of home ties, and, on the basis of the bargain, allows the man to continue to give his devotion to the group.

It is highly probable that this factor is more important with American combat personnel than with the fighting forces of many of our Allies, as well as of our enemies. In many countries abroad, military activity has so completely disrupted the home ties and extinguished the former way of life that all the interest and care which at one time belonged to them are permanently transferred to the combat group. Since they have nothing to go back to, such men can remain indefinitely attached to their combat units, where, in addition, they can vent their hostility on the enemy who has so severely deprived them. There are probably several other reasons why in such countries the combat troops' chief interest remains attached to their units for such prolonged periods. In Germany and Japan, for instance, where war has long been glorified as the ideal way of life, the combat units as objects of affection have less competition to face from other sources. In Russia the group, whether military or social, has achieved cultural significance far outweighing the importance of the individual, and in that country, even outside of political considerations, the fate of the individual has always been held of less value. Furthermore, for the Japanese, death does not deprive the individual of anything of great value, but initiates his entry into a new supergroup in a warrior's heaven, where all his needs are gratified in abundance (46).

Among Americans there are still other reasons for a steady withdrawal of interest from the combat unit. The mounting fatigue, combined with the effects of repeated physical illness or injury, enforces an increasing interest in the body and its well-being. Even in civilian life illness usually causes a withdrawal of interest from external things. After prolonged exposure to combat an actual physical depletion occurs, whether or not there has been overt illness or injury. If restitution can be made by means of rest camps, furloughs and other methods, the process may be reversed and the man can again devote most of his affection to the combat unit, other factors being favorable. There is a limit, however, to the amount of rehabilitation that can be accomplished by this method over a long period of time.

Another factor favorable to a return of interest to the individual and his fate is poor leadership within the group. Although initially only a small amount of energy is attached to the ego and its needs, this must be appreciated and fairly gratified by the group leaders. The combat personality wants what few needs he permits himself to be handled with justice and dispatch. Therefore, favoritism, absence of merited promotions, neglect or unnecessarily harsh discipline causes strong resentment. It is astounding what severe and revolting physical conditions combat men can live through more or less cheerfully as long as the group is a worthy object of affection. They will go through anything for a group they love. But if the leadership is incompetent or unfair, the group no longer is worthy of their love, and their interest centers once more upon themselves. That is why good leadership is so intimately connected with good morale.

For all these reasons, no matter how much affection was originally devoted to the group, continued exposure to combat and self depletion produces an appreciable withdrawal of love, which is returned to the self. The process may be long-drawn-out or may occur with dramatic suddenness; it is largely unconscious, and, most important of all, it is incomplete. Though a large portion of interest may be reinvested in the self, still a considerable amount remains attached to the combat group. Thus internal competition of interest is set up which is the source of the primary conflict of combat men: the fate of the group versus the fate of the individual. When the opposing forces of this conflict become established, the stage is set for the development of anxiety. A sufficient concentration of interest and love is now attached to the ego so that the possibility of injury or death can arouse the strongest emotional reactions, and these reactions themselves then come into conflict with the portion of the personality still strongly attached to the combat group.

What emotional reaction is aroused depends now upon the direct experience with the combat situation. Fear of injury or of loss of life is possible, but not unless the situation is recognized as threatening. The emotion which is called forth is related to the manner in which the ego interprets the combat situation. Many varieties of conclusions are possible. One man may feel from the beginning that the situation is terribly dangerous, so full of menace that his chances of living are hopeless, whereas another may not recognize much danger and feel calmly confident throughout his tour. Such variations are influenced by the past history of the ego in relation to trauma and insecurity, and can be seen more easily in the early neurotic breakdowns than in the men who are able to endure considerable stress. The ordinary reaction is a rather cool attempt to appraise the reality of combat and to learn how to make appropriate discriminations between real and fancied dangers.

This is an actual learning process. The situation may appear at first to be innocuous and the primary reaction to combat is usually detachment and objective interest. The antiaircraft fire may look like a spectacular but harmless Fourth of July celebration, entertaining but not dangerous. This attitude is soon changed by the repeated demonstration of the destructive effectiveness of flak bursts. Other possible dangers are only appreciated after some objective demonstration has alerted the ego. After a crash due to motor failure, the most vigorous attention may be paid to the sound of the motors, a sound which was never given any special emphasis before. Sounds, sudden flashes of light and other physical phenomena may become so intimately associated with a dangerous meaning that the interpretation becomes automatic and involuntary. A man who has been dive-bombed and repeatedly shelled automatically startles and looks for a foxhole or some cover at any sudden loud noise, even though he is out of the combat environment. Such learned automatic reactions persist for long times after removal from combat, only gradually disappearing. Because these interpretations of specific stimuli are so stable and persistent, the stimulus frequently becomes the focus for anxiety of wider origin and thus takes part in the formation of the phobic symptom. This is demonstrated in case 12, where the interpretation of an intensely dangerous significance in unexploded bombs in the plane could not be overcome after a traumatic experience, although previously the ordinary interpretation of a mild but real danger had been made.

When such automatic interpretations of severe danger are intense and not adapted to current reality, it is as if the ego had been so shocked and found itself so helpless that it could not wait to appraise each new situation where the stimulus recurs, but reacted automatically on the basis of its experience with the traumatic situation. Then, if the process is largely unconscious, no new learning can take place. A conditioned reflex appears to have been formed to the precipitating stimuli. The reflex will persist as long as the ego does not have sufficient confidence to appraise the situation anew to see if it is as dangerous this time as it was at the time of trauma. It is a conditioned reflex only because it is not available to the higher centers for modification by a fresh testing of reality. This is what makes the neurotic process interminably repetitive.

To interpret reality is difficult enough, although a lifetime is spent in learning how to do this. What construction is placed on the evidence of the senses depends upon past experiences and is always liable to error. Especially in combat, where the environment is so quixotic, unstable and overfriendly and at the same time overhostile, mistakes in interpretation of reality are easy to make. One sometimes sees men who err in the opposite direction and fail to interpret danger when they should. As a consequence, they are protected against developing subjective anxiety, but may become a source of anxiety to others. The defect in discrimination gives them the appearance of being unrealistic and slap-happy, illustrating the maxim that fools walk where angels fear to tread. Often this reaction is based on actual ego exhaustion from prolonged combat, or on mild but unrecognized cerebral injury due to blast or physical concussion. Many such cases were seen in infantry units kept too long in the lines, where it was known as the "old sergeant's syndrome," and also in fliers who had seen too much combat, but the majority of these cases are not seen because they do not live to tell the tale.

When to these manifold difficulties in interpretation is added the fact that the mental process has become automatic and unconscious, and therefore not susceptible to new learning, the reaction changes from a normal difficulty with reality to a neurotic process. The chief reason why the process becomes automatic appears to be the actual helplessness of the ego when faced with the dangerous situation. This brings up the question what emotion and what activity are called forth when the situation is recognized to be dangerous. As has been stated, the initial reaction is usually one of alertness and tension: the organism is mentally and physically prepared for trouble because there is a threat of losing something it loves and needs, and the actual emotion is an undifferentiated combination of hostility and anxiety. If the threat can be averted by activity, the reaction becomes differentiated into hostility and aggression, the degree of emotion depending upon the seriousness of the threat. If the threat can be mastered by counteractivity, whether by deception, persuasion or destruction, anxiety will not arise. Mastery, or its opposite, helplessness, is the key to the ultimate emotional reaction.

Thus, the problem of anxiety in this context centers about the position of the ego in regard to mastery, independence and freedom of activity. In the anxiety problems of early childhood which form the core of the usual neurotic process, the ego is peculiarly helpless because of its inexperience and its complete dependence on the family figures which constitute the threat. In combat, the ego is often helpless because of its position in the group and the nature of the danger situation. The combat personality surrenders a great deal of its freedom of activity to the group, which is then relied upon for protection. The efficient functioning of the team is the guarantee of safety, and this applies equally to the efficient functioning of equipment, such as the aircraft, which must be maintained by teams. As long as the group demonstrates its ability to master the dangers fairly effectively, the individual feels sufficiently protected and competent in the environment. But when combat losses are high and close friends have been lost, or when the individual has experienced repeated narrow escapes or a traumatic event, the group is no longer a good security, and the ego learns how helpless it is in the situation. There is no one to rely upon. At the same time, it cannot overcome the dangers by its own efforts because of the actual dependence on the group.

The ego is thus in a regressed and relatively impotent position, reminiscent of childhood. Its difficulties accumulate as it withdraws more affection from the group and develops greater concern for its own fate, only to find that this fate is less and less under control. Confidence in the activity of the ego is further shaken by the loss of friends with whom there is much identification, when the thought arises: "He and I were exactly alike; if it could happen to him, it can happen to me." Confidence is diminished in addition by physical fatigue and illness and loss of sleep. A vicious circle is established, leading to the progressive destruction of confidence in the ego's ability to master the dangers. Out of the ensuing helplessness is born the intense anxiety.

Thus severe anxiety is always secondary to regression and dependence of the ego, and its meaning is that in its regressed position the ego has been deserted by all the forces which could help and protect it; nothing can be done, and the only possible method of avoiding complete dissolution is by flight. It is little wonder, once this conviction has been formed and the ego has been crushed by its own impotence, that the reaction should become automatic and that it would be a long time before the ego might feel strong enough to re-examine the situation in the light of fresh experience, if indeed it could ever do so.

There are two methods by which the ego in some individuals can protect itself against development of anxiety, while clearly recognizing the dangerous meaning of combat and its helpless dependence on the group. The methods appear to be exact opposites of each other, although the underlying dynamics are not comparable. In the first, the individual believes that, although others may die, "it can't happen to me." The second is characterized by the feeling: "I'll probably get it on the next mission, but I don't give a damn." The ideas of personal invulnerability associated with the first method have various ramifications. Many men have this feeling at the beginning of a combat tour and in most of them it appears to be based largely on good previous experiences with reality. Their past has been so secure or any insecurities have been so well mastered that they enter combat with a large reserve of confidence and cockiness. However, as they lose friends in combat and have narrow escapes of their own, they usually become less convinced of their own invulnerability, and this type of protection against anxiety is not very reliable. In other men, the idea is based on faith in magical or supernatural power. Some men feel protected by God ("God Is My Co-Pilot"), or have a fatalistic notion that their span of life is predetermined by Providence and that such incidental details as enemy activity can have no bearing on the outcome. From a psychodynamic point of view, such men have exchanged an uncertain dependence on the group for a dependence on a more reliable, supernatural power. The most outspoken example of this type of dependence in a soldier is found in the Psalms of David, where the Deity is forever being petitioned for more help, thanked for what aid has been given or soundly scolded for having been remiss. In our time such personal relationships with a deity are uncommon, and, although

God is frequently appealed to during a war by various leaders in public pronouncements as well as by combat troops in the privacy of their personal agony (cf. case 3), the appeals lack conviction for the most part.

Related to this type of protection, but more archaic, is the reliance on superstitious devices and on "luck" frequently seen among the bravest and most competent combat men. All sorts of supposedly lucky objects are carried on missions—pictures, mementos, a particularly unsavory and outworn article of clothing, a charm, a dog or some other animal. Sometimes a member of the crew or a certain airplane is believed to be lucky or unlucky. Such occult importance is attached to certain days or periods of the month, and to certain targets or bivouac areas. Although these attitudes are usually expressed with considerable tongue-in-the-cheek, humorous detachment, it is a case of the true word behind every jest. In its search for a more reliable source of protection than the group, the dependent ego reverts to the period in its development when magic had a real significance. To the child, feats of magic are no more impressive or unbelievable than the wondrous accomplishments of the adults about him. Nearly everyone has a sufficient memory of the time when magic seemed true and indisputable to be tempted to try it out again when under severe stress. Then, if the magic formula or charm appears to work, the intense need for help and protection becomes concentrated and fixed upon it.

Many men are unable to place their confidence in the protective benevolence of magical or supernatural power, and, finding themselves deserted and without aid from any quarter, still do not develop anxiety. They accept the likelihood of death at any moment, not with the inner harmony of those that are still intensely attached to their group, but with a fatalistic and bitter resignation. Being certain of an imminent death, neither the past nor the future has any meaning to them; only the present moment is real. The absence of ties with the past or future may in such cases destroy some of their moral and ethical values, so that they may show a temporary psychopathic behavior. Their consumption of alcohol increases often to the point where it is limited only by the source of supply. Alcohol not only benumbs their loneliness and despair but also affords a substitute relief for their dependent cravings. They become aggressive and quarrelsome in their relations with others, taking out their resentments on any scapegoat. If women are available, they frequently satisfy much of their dependent need as well as their hostility in furious sexual activity. The "I don't give a damn" reaction is actually closer to a masked depression than to a successful adaptation, but it does protect the individual against anxiety. The protection, however, is unstable and often breaks down when the individual comes close to the end of his combat tour. The reaction is most often seen when combat losses are very high and the mathematical chances of survival very low. During the last few missions, hope of survival once more becomes realistic, and at that point concern for his own fate again returns to the individual. Once he begins to hope and to care, he may suddenly develop intense anxiety.

All the above considerations relate to the development of anxiety out of the fluctuating relationships of the ego to the external environment of danger. The ego, however, is menaced by other sources of anxiety, which are secondary to the above. Of these, the most important are its own hostilities and resentments. We have seen that anxiety and hostility are born of the same situation of threat and are always very closely related. In combat, as long as the ego feels fairly competent and protected within the group, hostile and aggressive activity is successfully directed at the enemy. There are a few individuals in whom this aggressive activity may come into conflict with long-standing superego attitudes opposed to such destructive and unethical practices, but in general the group attitudes on this point are adopted by the individual. The combat soldier can become a killer without guilt in spite of his past training by virtue of his identification with the group. There is some tendency for guilt to develop over bombing of cities, but this is usually well rationalized. As the ego regresses under combat stress, however, and the individual feels less attached to his group, the influence of the group military superego may also lessen. Then the individual begins to wonder about the sense of his destructive activities. As former civilian superego attitudes are re-established, a feeling of guilt and an expectation of retaliation from the enemy appear. Past conflicts over hostile-aggressive activity are revived, with the production of secondary anxiety. On account of the guilt arising from the present and revived past conflicts, some individuals develop a feeling of doom and a sense of impending catastrophe, which are less related to their objective, mathematical chances of survival than to their feeling that anyone participating in such destructive activity deserves to die.

Under the influence of this feeling, hostility can no longer be expressed toward the enemy but is now easily directed toward the group which has involved the individual in such a situation, the combat unit and the army as a whole. This hostility is reinforced by the resentments aroused by the failure of the group to be a good protection for the now dependent and frightened ego. The man then feels that not only did the army get him into this mess, over which he feels so guilty, but it fails even to protect him adequately and is ready to abandon him to certain death without any qualms. His hostility is further reinforced by any feelings of unfairness or neglect stimulated by inadequate leadership. Resentments of this type, however, are very difficult to express as long·as the individual remains in the combat group. If they were directly expressed toward the group, they would result in a counterhostility, and the individual would find himself completely isolated, perhaps punished, and certainly deprived of what support and affection he has been getting from the group. Furthermore, the hostility comes into conflict with that part of the superego which still remains identified with the group and wants to play the role of a good combat soldier. Depending upon the strength of the superego, then, a varying portion of the hostility may become self-directed, resulting in depression. The superego condemns the individual for being so weak, so anxious, so far from the ideal of a combat soldier. Then, if the ego is very regressed and dependent, its anxiety is further increased. The individual feels that no one is on his side or will support him, whether the group leadership, his friends or his own pride. He is completely isolated, alone with his anxiety, his failure and his depression. An example of the way such a depression accumulates is found in case 16.

The hostility may not be altogether turned against the ego in the form of depression. A large part of it may be expressed in the form of irritability and quarrelsomeness, so characteristic of the reactions to combat stress. The sudden fury over a trivial disagreement represents for the most part an outlet for resentments caused by frustration of dependent needs. The regressed ego is actually furious because it does not receive enough support and protection. And the superego reacts because of the dependence, which is an insult to the masculine pride. As a result, most of the arguments are over some real or fancied slur on a man's aggressive ability whether in combat or in other group competitive activities, or over some incident where the man feels he has been let down by a friend. The argument then is: "You're no friend of mine; you don't stick by me; you don't give me enough support."

A large part of the hostility, however, cannot be expressed at all, but must be contained or repressed. Some men repress their hostility from long habit and these are the ones who isolate themselves more and more from their friends in the group, lest their hostility escape the restraint, producing new troubles and fresh anxiety. The repression further increases the strain and tension of the ego, leading to the subjective sensation of an imminent explosion, or, as it is usually put to the Flight Surgeon, "If I have to take much more of this, I'm afraid I'll blow my top." There, in one concise statement, the individual's anxiety (afraid) over his repressed hostility (blow my top) resulting from his frustrated dependence (can't take it) is precisely expressed.

The foregoing description of factors involved in the production of anxiety is purely schematic, indicating general trends rather than a standard process which affects everyone alike. The human personality is so dynamic and fluctuating that any attempt to isolate and describe the underlying mechanisms at a given moment necessarily produces artifacts comparable to a beautifully stained and fixed specimen of cellular pathology. When viewed through the microscope, the technicolored anatomical relationships are interesting and informative, but they actually bear little resemblance to the living process. Human reactions and behavior are so overdetermined that a bare description such as the above cannot even approximate the actual situation but can only highlight some of the important features. For instance, it is impossible to show how the factors vary at different levels of consciousness, how the regression of the ego varies from moment to moment and day to day, in accordance with innumerable factors which support it or weaken it.

Suffice it to say that the regression is usually incomplete, and that a large part of the superego remains firmly identified with the group, no matter how severe the regression. This is the situation which compels the men to struggle against their anxiety, once it has arisen, and to find some way of controlling it. Anxiety is a painful emotion and a natural solution would be simply to withdraw from the situation which has produced it. Although this is the solution adopted by a few men, who have been described as showing "lack of moral fiber," and in whom the anxiety produces no intrapsychic conflict (cf. case 7), in most, the persistence of identification with the group and of personal aggressive ideals in the superego compels them to remain in combat until they are honorably released. The ego must therefore find some way of dealing with the anxiety.

The dynamic struggles of the ego against its anxiety lead to many of the outstanding neurotic symptoms. The ego has only a few weapons at its disposal. The method of choice with American troops in this war, at any rate, is simply to tolerate a large part of the emotion. This type of solution produces the clinical state known as free-floating anxiety. The ego makes every effort consciously to repress or control the anxiety. It thrusts thoughts of the dangers and of possible death firmly away. It does its best to inhibit the sympathetic signs of anxiety, the tremor and the sweating, and to remain, outwardly at least, as cool and calm as possible, so that the job in combat can be carried out. Though it has recognized the relation of the anxiety to the dangers of combat and thus has good insight, it is determined not to let the anxiety interfere. That the insight can be so good is due to a cultural attitude manifested by the group as a whole, an attitude of tolerance toward expressions of anxiety. The men as a rule feel that they have not too much to lose if they admit their anxiety since it will be understood and accepted, as long as they continue to make a firm effort to control it. The teachings of psychiatrists and the enlightened attitude of the army leadership are responsible for permeation of this tolerance throughout the services. A few outstanding exceptions are seen among some commanding officers, who become enraged at any admissions of anxiety, mistaking them for signs of confirmed irresolution and weakness. Although anxiety is a sign of weakness and regression, as we have indicated, the important point is that it is only partial and is opposed by other forces in the personality, demanding continued strength and mastery and capable of enforcing these demands. The ego is actually in a stronger position if it can freely admit its anxiety and deal with it as a reality than if it is forced to misrepresent the situation out of the need to feel itself like others. A repressive and hostile attitude toward free anxiety on the part of commanding officers does not cure anxiety, but only leads to less efficient techniques of dealing with it.

Many, if not most, combat crewmen go through their combat tours with varying amounts of free anxiety. It may be well that in soldiers of other nations the dynamic equilibrium is such that anxiety does not develop when the ego learns how dependent and unprotected it is in combat, but with American troops anxiety is the usual outcome. Nevertheless, in spite of the commonness of anxiety, with its plain implication that our combat troops are not hardened warriors who are afraid of nothing, the anxiety seldom interferes with the efficient performance of combat duties. Usually it is fairly well controlled as long as the men stay in combat, where control is so important. It is only when the ego becomes seriously depleted and weakened from the many strains it must withstand, and from the effects of illness, fatigue and lack of sleep, that the anxiety escapes control and becomes so severe that it interferes with efficient work. Because of the fine, technical nature of the work of air crews, they are removed from combat as soon as this happens, whereas ground force troops may be retained in battle in spite of equally severe anxiety. For this reason, one sees more seriously disintegrated and regressed anxiety states among ground force personnel, where, in addition, the stress accumulates at a faster rate and is often much more severe. Aerial combat attacks the ego with fine, chiseled blows, while infantry and severe artillery battles reduce it with the force of a sledge hammer.

In no matter what arm or service, the combat men carry on, as a rule, and endure their anxiety until they are relieved from combat or until the ego is so stripped of resources that it cannot carry on any functions at all. Then there appears not only the emotional regression to the dependent and helpless position of a child, but also a physiological regression. One by one various ego functions may disappear. Intelligent thought and action become impossible when the weakened ego can no longer appraise reality, and are replaced by panicky or bizarre behavior. In some, the ego cannot effect coordinated motor functions, which give way to severe tremors and wobbly, staggering gaits and stuttering speech. Sensory functions, such as sight and hearing, vanish when the ego can no longer tolerate the stimuli they subserve. The ego may even lose its connection with past and present reality entirely (cf. case 11), relapsing into an amnesia or a stuporous state. In the latter, intense quantities of anxiety acting upon the exhausted ego produce complete disintegration. As the ego's functions fail and especially when its inhibitory power collapses, various released reactions on lower neurological levels appear. Infantile attitudes and postures are exhibited in combination with signs of uncontrolled activity of the old (extrapyramidal) motor system, such as a continuous coarse tremor, muscular rigidity and a masked facies.

This process represents a progressive weakening of the ego in its relationship with the sources of anxiety and the mechanisms of its control. In this process, which begins with a small and partial regression and weakening of the ego, the final stages are an almost complete elimination of normal ego mechanisms. Only the now ungovernable anxiety and various released primitive psychological mechanisms are evidenced. In some individuals, however, the ego utilizes a secondary defense against anxiety, which frequently prevents such a severe shattering of all its resources. The defensive maneuver immobilizes, limits or binds the anxiety, which is then replaced by a neurotic symptom. Although the symptom itself then represents a sacrifice of part of the ego's function, it is a relatively small part and permits the remainder of the ego to function in a stable and efficient manner. This is the meaning of the phobic and conversion symptoms.

By concentrating the anxiety it feels on account of its generally insecure and dependent position, and limiting it to one or two specific aspects of the combat situation, the ego manages to relieve itself of strong anxiety in relation to other aspects of the situation. Thus a phobia, while substituting for a much wider range of anxiety, allows the ego to function efficiently except when in contact with the specific phobic situation. The phobic situation is always the one in which the ego feels most helpless, whether the threat is internal, as with the long-standing repressed hostility underlying the phobia of death in case 5, or external, as with the recent traumatic experience in case 13. Whatever its origin, if the phobic defense can be gratified so that the individual is not exposed to the phobic situation, the ego is capable of carrying on and has thus achieved a compromise which often has considerable practical merit. The defense, however, is not too stable, inasmuch as many of the phobias in combat cannot be defended against without removal of the individual from the entire combat situation. Furthermore, should the ego become weaker owing to other causes, such as fatigue or new trauma, the whole phobic defense may break down, with the appearance of generalized free anxiety. For this reason, any practical decisions as to disposition on the basis of a phobic defense against anxiety must only be made after careful consideration of all the factors involved in the symptom. Case 12 is an example of a phobia which protected without subsequent further breakdown, but there are many similar cases which do not have such a successful outcome.

In the phobia, the ego applies a specific meaning to a portion of the environment which is interpreted as being highly dangerous, and in relation to which the ego regards itself as extremely weak. The anxiety resulting from this weakness is openly admitted, and is frequently accepted by the superego as a reasonable justification for avoiding or withdrawing from that part of the anxiety-laden combat situation. If it is not accepted by the superego, or if it is not accepted by external authorities, such as the group leaders or the Flight Surgeon, and withdrawal is not permitted, the phobic defense has no value and the individual exhibits continual anxiety. At any rate, the intent of the symptom is to placate the authority, whether external or internal, demanding continual exposure to the whole anxiety situation, with the formula: "I can't stand this part of the situation (this type of plane, these bombs) because I'm too weak, but I can tolerate some other part of it (I hope), if you give me the chance." This compromise is meant to impress the authority with the ego's good intentions, and thus to preserve the affective relationship with the group and with the superego while sparing the ego the intense anxiety. In the formation of a conversion symptom, the same intention is accomplished in a different manner. The ego, in this case, explains its weakness on the basis of a physical defect and thus does not have to admit its anxiety. The advantage obtained by this maneuver is just as obvious as in the case of a phobia, if not as frank. The physical defect, the blindness, the deafness, the deficient depth perception, the pain in the ear, will operate by removing the individual from the anxiety situation.

This, however, is not a conscious or deliberate deception. The actual physical symptom is always based either on an antecedent real defect resulting from illness or injury, or on a functional symptom resulting from anxiety. The functional difficulties with depth perception in fliers, for instance, are due entirely to intense anxiety, which interferes with accurate interpretation of visual stimuli. The pilot who has seen his buddy killed in a midair collision, resulting from too close formation flying, becomes extremely anxious when he finds himself in too tight a formation. At the same time he notices that he cannot distinguish very well the distance between his wing tip and that of the next plane. He then attributes his anxiety to the visual difficulty. When he is tested by his Flight Surgeon, the difficulty in depth perception persists, although the anxiety is no longer obvious. Most conversion symptoms among combat personnel are similarly obvious combinations of anxiety and a physical defect, in which the ego puts the cart before the horse. The physical symptom binds the anxiety and the superego is appeased. For this reason, if the physical symptom is removed by persuasion, threats or psychotherapy, the anxiety which it covers is released. This type of defense is usually adopted by specially predisposed, immature and unrealistic individuals whose superegos appear to be easily fooled. Because they have such a strong need to act the part of efficient combat men, they cannot afford insight. Case 3 is an example of such a reaction, in which it was not hard for a weak and regressed ego to convince the superego that it would be strong as a lion if it were not for the physical defect. In this connection, the problem of insight posed by this case is interesting because the psychological blindness which allowed this individual to explain his difficulties as being due to "nerves," meaning an organic nervous ailment, is more common in civilian neuroses than in the reactions to war. Most combat soldiers, as we have stated, have a fairly good insight into the connection between their somatic symptoms and the anxiety situation which produces them. A few, however, have no insight into the emotional origin of their tremor, restlessness, irritability and the associated subjective feelings, but regard them as signs of an organic disease process. Thus even anxiety itself, if its emotional meaning is not understood, can function as a conversion symptom, presenting the same dynamic problem in regard to treatment.

The purely psychosomatic symptoms function in precisely the same manner. The same reversal of role which is seen in conversion symptoms is evident in the psychosomatic states, where the individual attributes his anxiety to his symptoms, rather than vice versa, and worries because he is "sick." The difference lies in the fact that the involved structures are innervated by the autonomic nervous system. The emotional origin of most of the symptoms lies in anxiety. This is true of the sweating, the nocturia and frequency, the dry mouth and dilated pupils, the rapid pulse and pounding of the heart, the diarrhea and the sudden failure of sphincter control. Some of the symptoms, however, are due to repressed hostility. These include headaches, hypertension, vomiting and abdominal cramps and diarrhea in some instances. It must be emphasized that anxiety and hostility have a common, undifferentiated origin and therefore affect some organs in the same way. The gastric disturbances and dyspepsia, on the other hand, being a perversion of the normal responses to hunger, appear to represent a somatic expression of a hunger for more love and care than the combat situation can supply. It is interesting that this symptom is so frequently accompanied by an inordinate craving for milk, a food that is difficult to obtain overseas. Although drinking milk is a cultural trait of most Americans, it is suggestive that the particular food so intensely desired is that associated with the earliest signs of maternal affection and care.

Psychosomatic symptoms, the dynamics of which are discussed in chapter 11, like the conversion symptoms, substitute for conscious anxiety, deceive the superego and at the same time accomplish a withdrawal from the anxiety situation, since, if the symptoms are severe enough, the individual cannot carry on his duties. Frequently withdrawal does not take place, either because the superego continues to demand more or because the external authorities will not allow it. In that case the anxiety then spills over as free anxiety. It can thus be seen that none of these defenses against free anxiety are permanently effective. They are simply maneuvers which may stem the tide for a time, after which the ego is once again faced with the problem of severe anxiety and its intensely crippling regressive effects.

Thus the central problem in the neurotic reactions to combat remains that of anxiety and its relation to a regression of the ego functions. We have already outlined what appear to us to be the chief psychological factors involved in the regression and the concomitant appearance of anxiety. But in dealing with these processes, a description in terms of the psychological apparatus is only a one-sided approach to a problem that is also definable in physiological terms. The physiological processes underlying the ego regression and the production of anxiety are the same phenomena as the psychological processes, approached from a different frame of reference. Although we may perhaps look forward to a happier time, when the distinction will be simply one of words, at the present time the distinction is based on a different technique of investigation and therefore must be adhered to. Nevertheless, the semantic distinction is already outworn and this is nowhere more apparent than in the foregoing descriptions of the neurotic reactions to combat, some of which are stated in psychological terms, others only in somatic language.

To recapitulate the problem in psychological terms, the ego experiences anxiety in relation to the loss of a loved object when it appears that it cannot defend itself successfully against such a loss. In combat, the object which is chiefly threatened is the life and existence of the individual. Although, as we have shown, there are other sources of anxiety, this is probably the most acute. The reaction to the stimuli of combat depends upon the meaning given to these stimuli in terms of recognizing them as a threat and of feeling confident of the ability to neutralize the threat. Both of these are matters of interpretation based on past experience, and, when this has been a bad experience in which the ego has found itself dependent and defenseless, anxiety is liberated. Neurotic anxiety is therefore a last-ditch emergency mechanism biologically oriented toward a flight from the threatening situation. However, other forces, located in the superego or in the external environment, demand a continued attempt to master the threat, and at their behest the ego attempts to inhibit or control the anxiety. The ego may be able successfully to accomplish this until it is further weakened by fresh traumatic experiences plus the continual strain of repression, fatigue, physical illness and denial of basic emotional and physical needs. Then, as the ego loses its inhibitory power, anxiety dominates more and more, becoming an ungovernable force which swamps the ego and disintegrates its function.

Thus anxiety passes through the stage where it is a relatively appropriate biological response, serving to alert the organism and prepare it for flight, to a pathological phase, where it is no longer appropriate or is actually self-destructive. After a removal from the precipitating environmental stimuli, the ego may recover sufficient strength to enable it again to inhibit the anxiety and gradually recover its functions. If it has been severely disintegrated, it may continue to be bombarded by anxiety and may fail to recognize the difference between the stimuli of the new environment and those of combat. The degree of recovery depends upon a change in the reciprocal relations between the intensity of the anxiety and the strength of the ego. The more unconscious and automatic the reaction of the ego is, the greater will be its difficulty in recognizing its renewed strength and testing its capacity against the new situation. Treatment, therefore, involves introducing the whole anxiety situation into consciousness and encouraging and supporting the ego in its attempts to make this test.

To understand these psychological processes in neurophysiological terms, it is necessary to understand the relationships between the higher cortical centers (the cerebral cortex) and the lower centers which integrate, regulate and reinforce the motor visceral expressions of emotion (the diencephalon). This is a complex phasic relationship. The latter is a central regulating apparatus, which effects the coordination of many responses within the sympathetic nervous system and the endocrine glands that characterizes *emotional expression*. It receives its afferent stimulation from the thalamus, which is the central collecting nucleus for external and internal sensations, and from the cerebral cortex, directly or indirectly. Crude sensory stimuli, such as pain, sudden loud noises or sudden loss of a stable support, stimulate automatic reflexes, resulting in an alerting or startle response, which is effected without the intervention of the cerebral cortex. The reaction, therefore, is not dependent upon an interpretation of the meaning of the stimuli, but is purely reflex. It then may reverberate to the cerebral cortex, causing secondary feelings of anxiety. In this way, the lower centers stimulate the cortex through its afferent innervation.

Another main source of stimulation of the effector portion of the diencephalon is through its connections with the cerebral cortex. Such stimulation consists of requests for alertness or preparations for flight of the organism, dependent upon cortical interpretations of the dangerous meaning of environmental or intrapsychic stimuli. Response to the latter is especially interpretive since it anticipates an external danger subsequent to a possible act of its own, a sequence which it has learned to expect on the basis of its past and especially its childhood experiences.

Thus the reciprocal relationship between the cortex and the diencephalon for emotional expression can be well seen. Each can stimulate the other. The stimulation of the cortex by the lower centers, however, could be carried to excess, if it were not for a powerful inhibitory control by the cortex. The driving power of the lower centers on the cortex has been demonstrated by the evidence of electroencephalography (recording of brain-waves), and by the same technique the tremendous power of the cortex to stimulate them has been shown. What happens when this inhibition is removed is illustrated by the automatic and excessive "sham rage" reaction to any stimulus, seen in an experimental animal when the cortex has been surgically re-moved. Through its inhibitory innervation, the cortex is able to damp down excitations in the diencephalon and thus can control the intensity of the alerting or anxiety response. This explains the peculiar double role of the ego, which is able through the stimulating cortical innervation to excite apprehen-sion and through inhibitory innervation to control anxiety.

Viewed in the light of this phasic relationship between cere-bral cortex and diencephalon, the intensity of an anxiety re-sponse at any given moment depends upon which phase is dominant. Intense or pathological anxiety could be due to (a) an intense reflex stimulation through the thalamic sensory path-ways because of pain, loss of stable support or the sudden impact of many stimuli associated with a physical trauma; (b) excessive stimulation of the lower effector centers by the cortex when the latter anticipates or is in contact with environmental or intrapsychic stimuli which are given a highly dangerous interpretation; (c) loss of the inhibitory control over the effector structures by the cortex when the latter becomes weakened by fatigue, disease or concomitant bombardment from the diencephalon. As the inhibitory control is lost, the diencephalon may become continuously active, producing a constant neural excitation manifested as constant severe anxiety. As the cortex loses its inhibitory control under the intense stimulation, it may lose many other inhibitory and modifying activities, mani-fested in the release of lower-level neurological mechanisms as well as in failure of learned functions.

It is now necessary to relate these neurological mechanisms to the psychological mechanisms previously described. Psychologically we say that anxiety is experienced when the ego learns how helpless it is in relation to an interpreted threat, and that this is a learned reaction based on past and present experience. Neurologically, we say that the original or primary anxiety experience is the result of a reflex through the sensory thalamic pathways, and that the cerebral cortex is not involved in this reflex, only becoming secondarily aware of the reaction. Such lower level responses are seen not only in decorticated experimental animals but in infants, who react to most environmental or internal stimuli with an undifferentiated alerting, anxiety or rage response. As the cortex becomes better developed with the process of growth and maturing, it establishes increasing inhibition over these indiscriminate responses. At first only secondarily aware of the reflex response to the stimuli, it attempts on succeeding repetitions of such stimuli to modify the response, segregating those stimuli which are truly dangerous from those which can be dealt with, and learning by trial and error how to deal with the former. Thus the maturation of the cortex is associated with an increasingly selective treatment of incoming stimuli, these being more and more long-circuited through the cortex, which continuously inhibits the primary reflex responses to them. For those stimuli which on the basis of experience to date are still regarded as dangerous the inhibition is called off, and the effector responses are stimulated. No matter how mature and firmly in control the cortex may be, certain sudden and sharp stimuli may still evoke purely diencephalic reflexes. This is especially true if their effects are accomplished quickly enough, before the cortex can be alerted and can take effective action. This is often what happens in the case of the traumatic stimuli of combat, the sudden explosions, the fall from a burning plane, the unexpected struggle in icy water after a ditching. In these cases, since the reflex response does not reach the cortex, except later and secondarily, one may say that the ego, psychologically, was in the most helpless situation of all, being completely ineffective in relation to the response. Psychologically the ego, and neurologically the cortex, are regressed by the circumstance to the initial situation in infancy before the cortex began to establish its control. When the cortex secondarily receives the excitations from the diencephalon and the external sensory pathways, a cortical reflex is formed, so that on a repetition of the traumatic stimuli, even though now mild, the cortex immediately stimulates the diencephalon to evoke the biological alerting mechanism. Or to phrase it psychologically, when the ego becomes aware of the initial shock of anxiety, and of its relative or absolute helplessness, it reacts to the possibility of a new exposure to the traumatic situation in the future with anxiety. This is what is meant by the power of the ego to evoke apprehension through interpretations of stimuli based on past experience.

However, this cortical reflex may be modified by the cortical inhibitory influences on the diencephalon, so that, although the repeated stimuli set up reflexes which would activate the diencephalon, the response of that apparatus is limited. This is equivalent to the ego control over anxiety. If the stimuli are continuously operative but the inhibition is maintained by the cortex and fresh diencephalic reflexes do not occur because the cortex can now initiate appropriate activity, the original cortical reflex may disappear altogether. This would be equivalent to a mastery of the traumatic situation by the strengthened ego with the disappearance of the anxiety response, a newly learned reaction. The cortical reflex, however, may be reinforced if the continual exposure to the stimuli evokes fresh diencephalic reflexes, corresponding to the increase in anxiety when the ego is repeatedly exposed to the traumatic situation without being able to take effective action. Similarly the cortical reflex will be facilitated if the inhibitory pathways from cortex to diencephalon are weakened by exhaustion of the cortical centers through fatigue or illness or simply through continued neural activity. This corresponds to the manner in which fatigue, illness and the strain of continued repression weaken the ego. On the other hand, the fatigue of the cortical centers may not affect the inhibitory pathways as much as the diencephalic stimulating pathways. This would account for those cases where the individuals, after long exposure to combat, fail to develop anxiety reactions in any circumstances, no matter how potentially traumatic, and because of lack of the capacity to remain alert are usually killed by enemy activity or their own mistakes. In the usual instance, the cortical inhibitory centers fail first, so that the cortex is flooded with excitation from the diencephalon. This further weakens the already fatigued cortical structures, which eventually can no longer conduct appropriate discriminatory and inhibitory activities in any direction. Psychologically this is equivalent to the severe disintegration of the ego under the pressure of fatigue and intense anxiety, in which all incoming stimuli evoke an undifferentiated anxiety accompanied by bizarre behavior, infantile attitudes and old motor system activities.

Thus we can see that the regressive failures of adaptation underlying the signs and symptoms of neurotic combat reactions can be explained in terms of ego dynamics or in terms of corticodiencephalic interrelations. It is the same psychological process, however, no matter what set of terms is used. The descriptions have relevancy only in so far as they increase our knowledge of what is happening to the individual. For such a knowledge there is a crying need, if we are to know how to treat therapeutically the difficulties of the men who are in combat or who have returned from it.

CHAPTER 7

Treatment and Results

THE TREATMENT of neurotic combat reactions in the theater of operations is conducted in two phases. The first phase operates at the level of the combat group and is concerned with prevention and early treament. The second phase occurs when these initial efforts have failed to prevent the formation of disabling neurotic symptoms, necessitating the removal of the individual from his combat organization for definitive psychiatric care and disposition. Prophylaxis and early treatment are of necessity in the hands of the tactical medical officers; in the Air Forces the responsibility is assumed by the unit Flight Surgeons, and in the Ground Forces, largely by the Battalion Surgeons and the Divisional Psychiatrists. The more specialized psychiatric treatment given after the combat soldier has been removed from his unit is conducted by the psychiatric consultants assigned to the headquarters of the particular Air Force concerned and by psychiatrists in the ground force general and station hospitals. Since this study concerns principally the effects of combat on air crews, the following discussion of therapeutic methods will be confined to those practiced by the Air Forces. Although the details of the organization of psychiatric therapy in the Ground Forces differ somewhat, the general principles remain the same.

The Flight Surgeon assigned to the tactical combat groups is roughly comparable to the family physician in civilian medical practice. He is responsible for the general health of the combat personnel. In the pursuit of his objective, to maintain the men in as fit a condition for combat flying as possible, he functions as a public health officer, concerned with the social problems of hygiene, sanitation and morale, and also as a personal physician concerned with the individual mental and physical ailments of his men. Like the general practitioner, he is called upon to diagnose and treat a great variety of illnesses and to apply with reasonable competency a wide range of therapeutic techniques, medical, surgical and psychological. Superimposed on this broad range of interests, he has a special field of interest, that of aviation medicine, which is concerned with the characteristic effects of high altitude flying, under conditions of low oxygen tension, low atmospheric pressure and rapid changes of velocity. Since these environmental stresses exert their effects primarily upon the ear, nose and throat, the cardiovascular system and the nervous and mental apparatus, the Flight Surgeon is by way of being a minor specialist in these fields. Nevertheless, like the family physician, if the resulting symptoms become very disabling or of grave import after attempts at therapy, he refers his patient to specialists for consultation and treatment. It must be emphasized that this has less to do with the personal tastes or skills of the individual Flight Surgeon than with exigencies of the military medical setup.

In this role of family doctor to the combat personnel in his organization, one of the Flight Surgeon's chief responsibilities is the mental and emotional health of his men. He holds the first line of defense against the stresses of combat. From a practical point of view, because of the numbers of men he is in contact with and the immediacy of his care, his work is of much greater potential importance and effectiveness than that of the specialists in the rear. For this reason, it is imperative that he have a good working knowledge of the principles of psychiatry and psychotherapy, a training that he should be able to use with as much confidence as he places in his surgical and medical technique. In simple language, this means that he must understand the patient as a human being, understand his needs, his conflicts and his defenses, and know how to help him solve his problems. In this connection, the Flight Surgeon is again in the same position as the family physician who, from time out of memory, has recognized the relation between the stress of circumstances and the patient's health, and whose ability to handle successfully the emotional and personality factors in illness is called the art of medicine. Fortunately, in our time, it is possible to substitute for the intuitive and trial-and-error source of knowledge implicit in the concept of an art of medicine a systematic body of knowledge which should render this important therapeutic aid more a matter of training than an accident of personality.

In one important respect, however, the Flight Surgeon cannot be so easily compared with the physician in civilian life. In addition to his interest in protecting and helping the individual in relation to the effects of combat stress, the Flight Surgeon as an army officer is dedicated to the success of the military mission. Because of this responsibility, he must require his patients to continue to expose themselves to a stress which he knows is responsible for their symptoms. In this fashion his therapeutic interest may come into conflict with his military obligations. At times the military situation plus a shortage of replacement crews and reserves may enforce the use of all combat personnel, no matter how tired or emotionally disturbed. This conflict, however, is only a reflection of the primary conflict of all his men, and its solution is the same. The Flight Surgeon must find ways of raising the tolerance of the men for the stress. Only when he has been unable to accomplish this and the symptoms have become crippling, does his medical obligation require him to remove the affected individual from the stress.

The problem of maintaining the individual tolerance for combat flying stress resolves itself into the control of these factors which are important in the precipitation and management of anxiety, outlined in the previous chapter. Naturally, not all these factors are susceptible of control. The Flight Surgeon can do nothing about the intensity of enemy activity, but he can bring his influence to bear in other ways. Specifically he can modify group attitudes and deficiencies through his special relationship with the group leaders, and he can strengthen the ego of the individual through his personal contact with the men.

In the miniature authoritarian social and political organization represented by the combat group, the Flight Surgeon is not only the disinterested family physician. He is also the public health official, and, as such, is vitally concerned with all matters of group policy and practice which have an effect on the morale of the men for whose emotional and mental health he is responsible. In this matter he must also be his own lobbyist, since, as in any political-social state, his function is advisory rather than legislative. According to army rules and regulations, the Flight Surgeon has no direct authority either in medical or related policies affecting the health of the individual, or in the disposition of an individual case. He may only make recommendations to the commanding officer, who may or may not follow such recommendations. The extent of his influence therefore depends upon the extent to which he can obtain the confidence of his commanding officer. This requires tact, skill in human relationships and a demonstration of a sincere and balanced interest both in the accomplishment of the military mission and in the health of the individual. Especially important is the last-mentioned, since, if he thinks only of the military mission and adopts an unsympathetic attitude toward the problems of the individual, he soon loses the confidence of the men. They quickly sense that they are regarded as expendable robots, who can expect no help from the Flight Surgeon. Although he may stand in well with certain elements in the command leadership, such a super-rugged Flight Surgeon arouses strong resentments among the men and eventually becomes ineffective. On the other hand, if he sees nothing but the problems of the individual, and continually presses protests and demands upon the group leaders designed to decrease the stress on the men at the cost of military success, he will alienate the trust of the leaders, and as a result will have no influence with them. The middle line between these two extremes is sometimes difficult to determine and will be defined differently by various personalities. Inasmuch as it is to everyone's interest to establish a reasonable policy concerning the health and morale of the combat personnel, if the Flight Surgeon exhibits moderately good judgment, persistence and sincerity, he will usually obtain the cooperation of group leaders and men.

Once the Flight Surgeon has established a good working relationship with both the group leaders and the combat men, he is in a position to function with considerable effectiveness in matters of general health and morale. Since he has the confidence of the men, he will know of their resentments and annoyances over real or fancied injustices in the outfit. Although many of these matters may not be in his province, they are repeatedly brought to his attention, and, since they have an important bearing on the motivation of the men for combat and on their capacity to adjust to combat stress, he should be able to discuss them dispassionately with the group leaders in the effort to reach a fair solution. Such resentments decrease the individual's identification with the combat group, resulting in a withdrawal of love and facilitating the development of anxiety. They must therefore be ironed out so far as possible.

The most provocative problem in this realm, and one that is never completely solved because of its very nature, is the question of the amount of combat stress which should be endured by the average individual in the group before being relieved. This problem is so complex and has so many unpredictable angles that no hard and fast policy or regulation can ever be set to cover it. At any time a change in the activity of the enemy may require more or less combat activity from each individual. Changes in the strategic plans of our military leaders, or the nonarrival or too abundant arrival of replacements, may throw out all previous calculations of what will be required from the individual soldier. On the other hand, exhaustion of the personnel, ill health, bad leadership or overwhelming enemy activity may materially cut down the amount of further stress each individual can absorb. In general, it is found that the men can withstand more stress than they think they can. Under inspired leadership or through sheer necessity they are able to fortify their ego defenses against anxiety and fatigue, and by tapping their ultimate reserves hold themselves intact for unbelievable lengths of time. They will continue mechanically long after their conscious motivation for combat has been destroyed, carrying on as long as friends remain by their side because they are required to, for there is no way out, and because they have become habituated to the control and repression of anxiety. It is in some of these old combat soldiers that the anxiety-alerting mechanism becomes exhausted ahead of the anxiety-control mechanism, resulting in the schizoid, detached and tactically inefficient ignoring of dangers, which usually leads to their death in action. In most, the anxiety-control mechanism eventually breaks down, resulting in a stable soldier being overwhelmed with anxiety and ending up as a psychiatric casualty. Thus, although it is true that combat troops can always stand a little more stress, the question arises whether it is wise to require them to do so, from the standpoint of their present military efficiency or of the effect of the psychological injury on their future lives.

The ultimate solution of this ever present and constantly vexatious problem is in the hands of the Command, not of the medical officers, and the doctors are sometimes criticized for concerning themselves too much with the future of the individual. It is true that the medical officer is on more solid ground when he makes his recommendations purely on the basis of the immediate fitness for combat, and on this basis the men can usually be brought to tolerate a little more stress. The tactical commander is concerned with the carrying out of his mission, and the possibility of a severe psychological injury being inflicted in the process concerns him no more than the possibility of a severe physical injury. He accepts it as inevitable that war is destructive of men and material, and, assuming that there is a general agreement in regard to the expendability of personnel, expects his Flight Surgeon to "keep 'em flying," regardless of future consequences. This accordingly becomes the primary aim of the Flight Surgeon. It is tempered, however, by long-standing concern for the individual and his problems and by a knowledge of the tremendous economic and social waste and personal misery incident to psychological illness. Then, if there is a good relationship between the tactical command and the Flight Surgeon, the latter's judgment will be given due consideration in the formation of policies related to the rotation and relief of flying personnel from the stress of combat.

In the formation of any such policy, the chief consideration is that it should be applied with uniformity to all combat flying personnel. Since they are making so great a sacrifice, combat troops are extremely sensitive to discrepancies in the amount of stress they are required to withstand in comparison with others. Though it is obviously difficult to compare one type of stress with another, and such comparisons, when applied between one branch of the service and another, frequently reach a point of absurdity, nevertheless gross and clearly obvious discrepancies produce a strong resentment, which is destructive of good morale.

In this and many other matters, large and small, the Flight Surgeon can exert a beneficial influence on group morale through his contact with the men and his recommendations to the group leaders. As we have stated before, many of the commanding officers of the squadrons in the Air Forces are very young, inexperienced in the handling and administration of a group of men, and interested primarily in flying and tactical problems. Impressed by the authority of his age, training and profession, some of them lean heavily on the Flight Surgeon for guidance or give him a free hand in many matters. If this is the case, the Flight Surgeon must be careful not to abuse his authority, remembering that final responsibility always rests with the commanding officer. Others, possessing a large amount of self reliance, may completely disregard the Flight Surgeon and spurn his recommendations as unwarranted interference. In this event, the Flight Surgeon is called upon to exercise all his talents as a salesman.

It is in his role as a personal physician in intimate contact with combat crew men that the Flight Surgeon can perform his best work. His aim is to help the men control the anxiety resulting from combat stress, and this prophylactic and therapeutic goal meets the needs of both the individual and the group. In order to fulfill this aim, the Flight Surgeon must have, in addition to an adequate understanding of psychiatric principles, a thorough understanding of himself—of his own weaknesses and capacities—and a complete familiarity with his men. Neither of these prerequisites is passively achieved but each must be pursued with vigor. No matter how sincere his devotion to the military mission, and no matter how strong his therapeutic intent, the Flight Surgeon who lacks adequate insight into his own anxieties and methods of dealing with them will go astray in trying to help others. He may fail completely to understand the whole problem of anxiety and lose interest in helping the individual, developing intolerance and annoyance toward the men's symptoms, or he may overidentify himself with the men, becoming too sympathetic, too much the advocate in the cause of their suffering. Innumerable variations of these two extremes may occur as a result of lack of insight, all of them missing the therapeutic happy medium of a tolerant and permissive attitude toward anxiety combined with an insistence upon control. On the other hand, the medical officer who can frankly face his own anxiety of whatever origin, clearly evaluate it and take effective steps to control it, is in the most effective position to demand control in others without becoming irritated at the necessity of making such a demand.

Self knowledge, however, is no more important than a knowledge of the men whom he is charged with maintaining in psychological health. Many Flight Surgeons assume that such a knowledge can be gained simply through social intercourse with the men. Since the Flight Surgeon lives in such close contact with the men, and, if he is alert, mingles with them on all possible occasions, it is true that much can be learned in this fashion, particularly if he is an acute and intuitive observer. It should be remembered, however, that in the completely uncontrolled social environment an individual's real attitudes are apt to be concealed. Furthermore, on such occasions the Flight Surgeon himself is usually too emotionally involved in the social situation to be capable of objective evaluations. The diagnostic mirror in which are reflected the transference attitudes and ego capacities of the individual is steamed up and gives distorted images in this situation. It can only be clear and bright in the controlled atmosphere of a personal interview and from this point of view an initial interview soon after the individual enters the group is of the greatest value. The Flight Surgeon is then at the greatest advantage, since his personality is unknown to the new-comer and any attitudes that are displayed will be purely transference reactions. Thus, if he is skillful, the Flight Surgeon at such an initial interview will be able to obtain a clear picture of the new man's personality and be able to form an estimate of assets and make a prediction of his expected combat career. Details of the individual's past history should be elicited not by a formal question and answer technique, but in a leisurely "bull session," which, though directed into certain channels by the interviewer, does not put the individual "on the spot" nor give him the impression that he is required to exhibit any definite attitudes. In this fashion the Flight Surgeon should be able to form an opinion in regard to the man's motivation for combat, his capacity to identify himself with the group, the degree and kind of insecurity which he has been able to tolerate in the past without anxiety, and the methods by which he deals with anxiety and other unpleasant emotions or situations. It is a good idea for the Flight Surgeon to record his conclusions and the prediction of the expected combat reactions based upon them in each case. In many instances his preliminary conclusions will be shown by later developments to be wrong. Whether he has underestimated or overestimated the individual, he will be able in any event to profit from his mistakes. His own insight, knowledge and skill will be thereby increased. In the performance of his duties from this point on, the Flight Surgeon should not wait, if possible, for the individual to come to him complaining of certain symptoms, but should follow each man, entering in his record the pertinent facts in regard to his combat reactions, his accomplishments, promotions, citations and exploits, and all positive events tending to build up his self confidence and increase his ego span. Similarly he should make a note of negative events, such as crash landings, bail-outs, loss of combat crewmates and injuries and illnesses, which tend to weaken the ego and promote anxiety. He should then record the individual's reaction to these events, based upon his own observations and the comments of friends and colleagues. Whenever such observations show that the individual is losing ground in his control of reactions to combat, an interview is indicated to see what should be done. In some instances, the Flight Surgeon may feel, on the basis of the man's method of dealing with anxiety, that he is better off left alone. In most cases, however, it is well to undertake some direct intervention in advance of the individual's seeking a consultation with the doctor on his own initiative. Pride and fear may prevent the individual from seeking such help until the optimum time has passed.

This raises the pertinent question in regard to what the Flight Surgeon can do in the way of direct prophylaxis and therapy. Two points of attack are available to him. He can to some extent manipulate the flier's environment, easing the pressure on him when this is indicated; and he can increase the efficiency with which the individual handles his anxieties. Both of these points merit elaboration.

As we have pointed out in previous chapters, physical and emotional fatigue and physical illness exert a real strain upon the ego, reducing its capacity to cope with the threatening aspects of the combat situation and its power to control or suppress the resulting anxiety. Before fatigue has accumulated to the point where a serious weakening of the ego ensues, it can often be relieved by appropriate maneuvers. These include more adequate spacing of missions, without removal from the combat group, or a temporary removal from combat for a period of temporary duty at some other assignment or at a rest camp. The efficacy of rest camps in relieving the fatigue of combat crewmen has been established by the experience accumulated in the various theaters of operations. This experience has also established that, once serious neurotic symptoms have become evident, the rest camp is futile as a therapeutic device and may even cause an aggravation of symptoms. (*Note:* This statement does not apply to the treatment of neurotic reactions among infantry and other ground force personnel in so-called "exhaustion centers." In these cases the degree of physical exhaustion is frequently overwhelming and much is achieved from sheer rest, no matter how serious the symptom. In addition, psychiatrically trained personnel in these centers conduct the psychotherapy which follows the period of rest.) The rest camp, however, is extremely useful as a prophylactic measure. The rest camps are usually located in pleasant surroundings, having adequate facilities for sports and recreation and good food. Discipline is greatly relaxed, so that the men are more or less free to do what they want, and, depending upon the locale, may be able to lead a life somewhat similar to that at home. This is very beneficial to those who are not too emotionally disturbed to enjoy themselves and to obtain adequate relaxation. With those who are, the opportunity to rest merely mocks their sleeplessness. The contrast with the grim realities of combat, rather than affording relief, reminds them of what they must return to. Rest and enjoyment are inaccessible and they remain preoccupied with gloomy thoughts of flying and dying. For this reason, it is important that the prophylactic value of the rest camps be utilized at the right time, a responsibility that only the alert Flight Surgeon can fulfill. Tactical necessities or lack of adequate facilities at the rest camps may prevent him from carrying out this responsibility, but nothing can excuse him for not recognizing its importance at the proper time.

Control of a flier's sleep by adequate sedation when necessary is as important as the periodic vacations from combat at a rest camp. The men often resort to alcohol to get a good night's sleep. Many are shy of the barbiturates, which they consider as "dope," and are fearful of forming a habit. Such misconceptions are easily corrected by the Flight Surgeon whose aim is to protect the ego from the effects of anxiety during the night, so that it can take up the struggle somewhat refreshed in the day. The barbiturates are also useful in providing a more intensive sedation for acute anxiety states resulting from intensely hazardous missions or traumatic events. When a flier returns from such a mission, in which he has had a severe shock and exhibits uncontrolled behavior, excessive tremulousness or mental confusion, he can be greatly benefited by moderate sedation under sodium amytal for a period of twenty-four to forty-eight hours. The medication should be given orally in such amounts that the individual will sleep when not stimulated but can be easily aroused for meals. The aim is merely to relieve the ego from the acute anxiety produced by the recent trauma, until it becomes strong enough to digest the experience. The period of sedation should be followed by a psychotherapeutic interview, in which the anxiety is allowed expression under more controlled circumstances. This is not to be confused with the "deep narcosis" therapy, which has not proved successful, or with "narcosynthesis," which will be discussed later.

To see that the fliers remain in good physical health, taking adequate steps to combat their fatigue and any physical illnesses they may suffer from, is the earliest task of the Flight Surgeon. As the men get on in their combat careers, varying amounts of anxiety will develop in accordance with the process which we have outlined. As anxiety appears, the Flight Surgeon will recognize how each individual is dealing with the problem. On the basis of his own observations and corollary information obtained from others in the group, he can determine whether or not it is being handled successfully. If there is evidence that the ego is weakening under the stress, no matter what particular form this takes, some kind of intervention on the part of the Flight Surgeon is indicated. This may take the form of a psychotherapeutic interview or a less formal contact on any suitable occasion. In this connection, anything that the Flight Surgeon says to a flier concerning his reactions to combat and to flying, whether in jest or with serious intent, has a psychotherapeutic implication. Such remarks, therefore, should not be uttered carelessly but with specific intent.

Because of his real position of authority and his training and experience as a doctor, the Flight Surgeon evokes definite transference attitudes in the flier, which are not concerned so much with the impact of his particular personality as with the symbolic meaning of his authoritative position as a possibly helpful, possibly threatening figure. These attitudes vary with the personality and present emotional configuration within the individual, but the degree to which the Flight Surgeon is sensitive to them and can utilize them intelligently will determine his effectiveness as a therapist. He will see that some of the men will expect him to be a kindly father, others, a friendly brother. Some will want mothering and comforting, while yet others will look for scolding and punishment. He will note that in anticipation of his expected reaction to their more or less unconscious needs and attitudes, some will show aggressiveness and resentment, others will display anxiety or shame or make appeals for help and forgiveness. While listening to the flier's complaints or description of his feelings, the Flight Surgeon should keep a psychic ear cocked for these underlying and usually unstated attitudes, continually asking himself, "What does this man want or need from me?" The flier will always say that he wants relief from his symptoms or complaints or from a certain situation, which is true enough as far as it goes. But beyond that, what?

In dealing both with the flier's symptoms and with the transference attitudes, the Flight Surgeon should follow his intuition. If he is sincere, sensitive and open-minded in regard to himself as well as to the flier, he will instinctively take the right psychotherapeutic path. It is well, however, if he has a definite notion of precisely which path he is taking and how he means to accomplish his objective, which is to strengthen the ego in its struggle with anxiety. As an aid in clarifying thinking on this score, it is possible to organize a simple psychotherapeutic plan, designed to cope with the most pertinent dynamic factors. The chief points in such a plan are: (1) to increase insight, (2) to neutralize ineffective or crippling methods of dealing with anxiety, (3) to permit abreaction of anxiety and hostility, (4) to modify the superego, (5) to support the dependent needs and (6) to estimate the limit of tolerance for anxiety. There is nothing new or intricate in any of these psychotherapeutic maneuvers, since they are only what the Flight Surgeon does naturally, by instinct. There is something to be gained, however, by a clarification of certain issues, especially those involving the unconscious transference attitudes.

(1) The matter of insight is of the first importance. In the course of his therapeutic career, a doctor may frequently find situations in which a patient loses a neurotic symptom without becoming aware either of the meaning of the symptom or of the reason for its disappearance. Cure without insight is always possible, especially if the external circumstances can be changed. A marriage or divorce, or a change of job, may effect a miraculous disappearance of a neurotic symptom. Similarly, removal from combat because of a broken leg may cure a pronounced

functional diarrhea without the individual's becoming aware of what cured him. But the Flight Surgeon's task is to maintain men in combat. He can change the circumstances only as a last resort, when he has to remove the individual from combat. If he is going to master this situation, therefore, the individual must clearly realize how it affects him.

He must understand his own anxiety, and what he can do about it. Misconceptions concerning the nature of anxiety and its meaning are quite common. To some, the existence of anxiety threatens a loss of control or even impending madness (cf. cases 5 and 10). Others mistake its somatic manifestations for signs of physical illness. The range of misinterpretations is very wide, but, whatever its particular form, the Flight Surgeon is called upon to explain to the individual what is going on within him. Such explanations can be couched in simple physiological terms, everyday analogies being used to show the effects of strong emotions upon the body. The aim is to establish a very simple and practical insight which recognizes the biological importance of anxiety, placing it in the sphere of an ordinary reaction which everyone has to control (cf. case 10). No deeper insight is looked for, since it is not necessary and usually not possible to uncover the unconscious sources of anxiety during the time an individual is in combat. There are sufficient anxiety-provoking stimuli in the combat situation to account for any quantity of anxiety. It is enough if the individual understands his anxiety as the biological response to a threat and takes up the problem of its control on that basis.

(2) Inefficient or crippling methods of dealing with anxiety are closely allied to the matter of insight. The two are not mutually exclusive, since an individual with insight may be crippled by an overwhelming intensity of anxiety. But, in general, the greater the insight, the more efficiently will anxiety be dealt with. This is especially true in regard to the conversion and psychosomatic symptoms. Among combat fliers, conversion symptoms are usually simple devices based upon some original functional or organic difficulty serving to conceal strong charges of anxiety (cf. case 14). It is usually possible to relieve the symptom by an explanation of its function and purpose, and by adopting a permissive attitude toward the underlying anxiety, encouraging its expression. If these measures fail and the conversion

symptom interferes with successful participation in combat, then the individual must be referred for psychiatric consultation.

Psychosomatic symptoms represent similar protections against anxiety, which spare the individual the necessity of dealing with the anxiety itself, yet result in an inefficient solution of the problem. It is somewhat more difficult to establish insight into this situation and to wean the individual away from the symptom than is the case with conversion phenomena. In either case, however, the symptom cannot be given up without the liberation of the anxiety. In many instances the symptoms will not disappear no matter how clear the insight, since they represent the visceral concomitants of anxiety and, as long as anxiety persists, the symptoms will remain. This may mean that the symptoms will persist as long as the individual is exposed to combat. On the other hand, an immense advantage is gained simply from the individual's having learned what kind of problem he has to deal with, and it may well be that the symptoms will at no time be so severe that he will not be able to endure them until he has finished his combat tour. In this, as in every other aspect of psychotherapy in the combat situation, the aim is to enable the ego to endure its psychological and somatic pain, yet maintain its motivation for combat.

(3) To permit an expression of anxiety, hostility, guilt or whatever strong emotion the flier is struggling with, is a delicate maneuver which the Flight Surgeon must handle with skill and wisdom in order to achieve the therapeutic goal. In most men the ego struggles to suppress these emotions, whose very intensity threatens its efficiency. The ego would like to remain cool and not preoccupied or distracted by such intense feelings. Since emotions, however, are characterized by charges of energy seeking some form of expression, the ego may become weakened by the very process of suppression, or else may adopt one of the compromises discussed above, which results in a neurotic expression of the energy. The problem, therefore, for both the flier and the Flight Surgeon, is how to effect some expression of the emotion without the ego's becoming overwhelmed in the process or giving up its desire to endure further the painful situation. To express one's feelings is often quite painful. Moreover, they are felt by the pride to be weak and shameful, and the natural tendency is the self instruction: "Keep it to yourself—forget

about it!" Expression or abreaction of emotion for these reasons is usually facilitated by any maneuver which reduces the pride's reaction and which enables the individual to share his pain with someone else, who can support him and give him help. The two processes must go hand in hand, since ordinarily a flier's pride will prevent him from seeking someone else's help in this way, no matter how great the need. These considerations will be discussed below in connection with the Flight Surgeon's handling of the transference situation. Here it is desired principally to emphasize that the ego can be vastly relieved and strengthened by such an expression of emotion. The therapeutic value is twofold. First, the simple expression of the energy is a relief, a load off the chest, in the sense of the time-honored value of emotional catharsis. Secondly, though this has an equal general applicability, it is specifically appropriate to the combat situation, and it is a relief for the ego to discover that it can afford such an indulgence of emotion without sacrificing its strength, without being overwhelmed or losing desire or face. In other words, the ego learns that abreaction in itself is not a danger.

On the other hand, whether or not this is true depends upon the attitude of the therapist and again is directly concerned with his handling of the transference situation. Men may give way to their emotion in other circumstances and, because of the reception or effect of their behavior, regret it later. They know they must control their emotions on missions both for their own sakes and because of their crewmates. But the effect of loosening the control when back from a mission may be either happy or harmful, depending upon the attitude with which it is received. A flier who, after a particularly hazardous but expertly performed mission, begins to pour out the details with much emotion to his commanding officer on returning and is silenced with the remark, "Stop moaning like a baby—what the hell did you think you were out there for?," will not feel that there is anything to be gained from expressing his feelings. Later, the Flight Surgeon will have to deal not only with his accumulated anxiety, but also with his increased resistance and resentment. Still, if he is skillful, the Flight Surgeon may obtain an expression of both the anxiety and the resentment, while yet maintaining the ego's strength and motivation for combat. The core of the matter lies always in the way he manages the transference situation, and in this case the wounded pride should not present too great an obstacle.

(4) Modification of the superego involves dealing with a pride which is either too strong or too weak. Strong pride can be both the most serious obstacle to therapeutic success and the most powerful factor in its favor. It is to a large extent the flier's pride which prevents him from understanding his anxiety and from giving expression to it in order that he may deal with it in a logical manner. On the other hand, it is also his pride which largely forces him to endure the anxiety of combat and to carry through his tour of duty. In this tricky, though not paradoxical situation, the Flight Surgeon again is dealing with strong transference feelings involving the pride's reaction to his position of authority within the group. However, what a flier might not be able to express to his commanding officer, or even to his friends in the outfit, he may be able to communicate to the Flight Surgeon. Here the Flight Surgeon's dual role as a doctor interested in the individual and a medical officer interested in the military mission works to a therapeutic advantage. As a doctor, he can listen to the flier's difficulties without criticism. The ego can afford to expose its weakness and dependence without fearing an affront. As a military figure, the Flight Surgeon will be interested in maintaining the flier in combat. The ego therefore can assume that an exposure of its weakness will not automatically result in a removal from combat or in censure, but in some helpful procedure. This theoretically advantageous situation must be backed up by the expressed attitudes of the Flight Surgeon. His attitude must convey to the flier the conviction that expressions of anxiety involve no loss of face. Thus, by a single stroke he may reduce an overintense pride to a level where it can accept anxiety and may prevent it from falling to the level where it gives up the struggle. An outright attack upon the superego may not be necessary, once the flier appreciates the Flight Surgeon's attitude. In severe depressions in which the superego is very hostile and there is much self accusation, it may be necessary to point out to the flier how unrealistic and rigid his pride actually is. If the Flight Surgeon is sincere, a certain degree of identification with him will be effected, inducing the superego to give up its severe and harsh ego-ideals for the more moderate standards advocated by the

Flight Surgeon. Sincerity is categorically necessary inasmuch as the flier, none too trusting to begin with, is very sensitive to false patronizing attitudes.

The moderation of the superego which is accomplished through identification with the Flight Surgeon tends to reduce both anxiety and depression. In this way one source of hostility and pressure upon the ego is eliminated and this increases its potential strength. If the maneuver has been successful, the flier will feel less isolated, less shamed, less unloved and still willing to continue in combat in spite of his symptoms. On the other hand, the flier whose pride is so weak that he is considering methods of escaping combat because of his anxiety must be approached from the opposite direction. Here it is a problem of stimulating the superego to make a greater demand upon the ego. Again, this can only be done by identification. As we have pointed out previously, the difficulty in such cases revolves about the weak capacity of some individuals to form strong identifications, especially with the combat group. The military figures may be completely rejected as objects with which these fliers can identify themselves, because they are too harsh and demanding, not giving enough in return. If anyone in the group has the capacity to stimulate identification in these men, it is the Flight Surgeon. His interest in the individual as a physician, combined with the traditional aura of support associated with this role, may be something around which interest and identification can be built. At any rate, it is always necessary for the Flight Surgeon to try to work with these men in the attempt to increase their self demands, and by continued interest and support to try to counteract their resentment at having to endure so much pain and anxiety. The fact that pride can be so intimately connected with the passive-dependent needs leads directly to the following maneuver.

(5) At no point in the management of the transference situation is so much tact called for as in the handling of the flier's dependent needs. The management of this problem ties together all the psychotherapeutic maneuvers previously discussed, since it is the degree of dependence that pricks the pride, which then forbids the development of insight and the expression of anxiety. In this situation a flier cannot be directly faced with his dependence. If he has any pride at all, nothing can be gained

by pointing out his weakness and calling him a "baby," as was done by the repressive commanding officer who asked the flier what the hell he thought he was sent out there for. The flier's anxiety and his seeking of help are sufficient admissions of dependence in themselves. In the heat of combat, if an individual suddenly loses self control, giving way to panic and undisciplined behavior which render him useless and disturb others, rough and repressive measures may be called for. It is then sometimes necessary for someone in authority to order the individual to pull himself together and to forbid any further giving way to anxiety. Such repressive measures may be completely ineffectual but they sometimes work. If they are successful, their effect is short-lasting, since they are merely emergency devices which stimulate the already exhausted ego just as a "shot" of adrenalin stimulates the heart muscle in the case of cardiac arrest. Rather than the false vigor which can be aroused by a tongue lashing, an insult or a command, what the ego needs is firm and continued support.

How to give such support without antagonizing the flier's pride, on the one hand, and without increasing his dependence, on the other, is the crux of the therapeutic problem. The solution must always be adjusted intuitively to the individual case. The weakness and dependence derived from the actual helplessness in the combat situation cannot be relieved by the Flight Surgeon. He can, however, on occasion recommend some change in a flier's position in the combat team, designed to provide more support from his associates. Since the human factor is so important, any personality differences tend to increase the difficulties facing the weakening ego.

Conversely, a sympathetic and supporting attitude on the part of a strong friend on the combat team may see a man through a most difficult combat tour in spite of a weakened ego and much anxiety. If such a friend is lost in combat before the end of the tour of duty, the man's unsatisfied dependence again becomes a problem, now very likely complicated by depression or guilt. The Flight Surgeon may still be able to satisfy some of this dependence simply by his continued interest and obvious desire to help. His repeated assurances, his acceptance of the flier's anxiety and hostility without criticism, and his steady insistence on a continued exposure to further combat act as a strong prop to the ego. In the majority of cases, this will sufficiently strengthen the ego to allow it to endure anxiety over the required length of time in combat without becoming incapacitated.

(6) Whether or not the ego will be able to endure the anxiety without becoming incapacitated is a point which the Flight Surgeon has constantly to consider. Even though he may not be able to recommend a removal from combat, and even though, if he makes the recommendation, it will not be carried out because of tactical considerations or a poor relationship with the commanding officer, nevertheless to estimate as accurately as possible the individual's limit of tolerance for anxiety is always the Flight Surgeon's responsibility. In doing this he performs a service both for the group and for the individual. In the ideal circumstance, the group is interested in utilizing fliers who are at the peak of their performance and is eager to get rid of those who are likely to crack because of anxiety. Many practical considerations make this ideal impossible, and, as has been stated, it is necessary to maintain the men in combat even though they have begun to slip. In this event, the best that can be asked is that the flier be kept in combat till just short of the point where his anxiety may lead to the loss of his crew, himself and his equipment.

The individual is naturally interested in the same way in being removed from combat before his anxiety leads to his death or that of others. He is, however, more seriously in conflict over the issue. From the standpoint of his anxiety, he cannot be removed from combat soon enough. From the point of view of his pride, he wants to carry out his obligation and not let his friends down. In view of this conflict, he is in a poor position to make an objective evaluation of the limit of his effort and of his capacity to control his anxiety. He therefore feels more comfortable if the responsibility for a decision in this matter is taken out of his hands. For this reason, the flier likes to have a fixed tour of duty, limited by a definite goal of hours and missions, to shoot at. By the same token, he is immensely reassured if he knows that the Flight Surgeon is carefully watching him to see that he does not exceed the limit of his tolerance for anxiety before he reaches this goal. The flier does not know what this limit is and is inclined to worry about it, thus adding to his anxiety. If he has confidence in the Flight Surgeon, he will depend upon him to keep alert and remove him at the proper time if this is necessary. This then is another way in which the Flight Surgeon can support and strengthen the ego by satisfying a dependent need.

Unfortunately there is no simple method by which the Flight Surgeon can evaluate this factor. There exists no precision instrument designed to measure the ego's capacity to control anxiety or to predict when this capacity will be exhausted. It must remain a matter of clinical judgment based upon past experience. That is why it is so valuable for the Flight Surgeon to keep a record of each individual, noting his actual performance as compared with the initial and subsequent predictions. He can only learn from his mistakes, hoping that his mistakes will not be serious. Rare is the Flight Surgeon who does not have moments of doubt and remorse occasioned by the loss in combat of a pilot whom he had determined to ground after the completion of that mission. He can never be absolutely certain that such a loss was due to pilot failure resulting from anxiety, but neither can he rid himself of the tormenting suspicion that he failed his medical responsibility and should never have permitted the man to fly. Beset by this kind of responsibility and the necessity of supporting so many fliers and tending their physical and emotional needs, the Flight Surgeon himself may become depleted. Yet this is his contribution and small it is in comparison with what the combat crews are giving.

When the Flight Surgeon's therapeutic attempts have been unavailing and the flier becomes unsuitable for further maintenance in combat because of his neurotic symptoms, the individual is grounded and removed from the combat group. Prompt removal is necessary for the sake both of the flier and of the group. If he is kept in the group, he soon becomes discouraged and disgusted because of failure to improve and because nothing is being done for him. He exerts a disturbing influence on his friends, who grow to resent having him around, since he reminds them of what may happen to them, while at the same time he is not running the risks to which they are daily exposed. If he has completed or almost completed his tour of duty, he is returned to the United States as rapidly as possible. His subsequent disposition and treatment will be taken up in the next section of this book. If he has not completed his tour of duty, he then becomes a problem for further treatment and disposition within the theater of operations. For this purpose, he is referred to the psychiatric consultant at the Air Force headquarters or to a psychiatrist at a ground force hospital, if the former is not available.

This second echelon of treatment has a different and more complicated therapeutic aim than the first. The Flight Surgeon has a simple and practical goal: to maintain the flier in combat for as long as possible and to remove him at the right time. The psychiatrist must evaluate a wider range of possibilities. He must determine (1) whether the Flight Surgeon has correctly evaluated the situation and the flier is actually unable to tolerate any additional combat stress; (2) if this is true, whether further psychotherapy can so strengthen the ego that the flier can return to combat in a short time; (3) if he cannot be returned to combat, whether he can carry out a noncombat flying assignment or must be grounded and reassigned to some other form of duty; or (4) whether the flier is so ill that he must be returned to the United States at once for more prolonged treatment.

In the performance of all these tasks, the psychiatrist functions in accordance with the same principles as were outlined for the Flight Surgeon. He is aided, however, by the skill which comes from experience and by the wider range of possibilities for disposition which are open to him. In evaluating the degree of "operational fatigue," he serves as a check on the Flight Surgeon, who may be new or overcautious, and for this reason becomes alarmed at the first sign of anxiety. The flier may simply require a little stronger support in order to master his anxiety sufficiently to carry on in combat. On the other hand, more detailed psychotherapeutic work may be called for. In particular, pentothal may be required in order to effect a sufficient release of anxiety to enable the flier to control a specific symptom. On the basis of the results of pentothal treatment, which will be described below, and the work accomplished in psychotherapeutic interviews, the psychiatrist determines what disposition to recommend for the flier.

The wide range of dispositions itself poses a peculiar problem in relation to psychotherapy. If the aim of therapy were only to do away with the flier's symptoms, a change of environment would appear to offer a simple and rapid solution. The symptoms being the result of stress, the obvious answer should be to remove the individual from the stress. Although this is true for many individuals, in actual practice it has been found that an equally large number do not behave in accordance with such a simple view, for in them the effects of combat stress cannot be wiped out simply by removal from the combat scene. This latter group becomes an important problem for rehabilitation on their return home. Overseas, however, the psychiatrist's aim is not simply to attempt to cure the symptoms of "operational fatigue" by a removal from stress. The men he sees are those who have not yet completed a tour of duty, and who therefore still have an obligation to serve in some capacity, preferably combat. Only when the evidence obtained on investigation shows that the individual has completely exhausted his capacity to deal with any further stress, or will rapidly reach this stage after any further exposure, is the psychiatrist justified in recommending a change of environment. In reaching a decision as to what the aim of therapy should be and what psychotherapeutic steps can be taken to achieve it in the individual case, it is always necessary to estimate the degree of concealed or repressed anxiety, the strength or weakness of ego forces which can be opposed to this anxiety, and the quantity of motivation for a return to battle stress. The amount of anxiety which is clinically observable at an initial interview is highly deceptive and is apt to be no indication of the actual intensity of underlying anxiety. What can be seen in the form of tremor, other signs of sympathetic overactivity, restlessness and the stated complaints of the flier depends upon the degree of ego control at the moment. Thus it depends partly upon his motivation, since a flier who wants to get out of further stress will make no attempt to conceal his anxiety, while one who is determined not to leave his comrades, no matter how badly he feels, will make every effort to hide it. Furthermore, the ability to conceal anxiety depends upon the strength of the ego at the moment, upon whether it is still fatigued from the combat experiences recently endured or has had some time to recuperate. Most important of all, it depends upon what type of phobic, conversion or psychosomatic defenses has become established in order to control free anxiety. For all these reasons, the psychiatrist is prepared to take with a grain of salt the degree of clinical anxiety he can observe at the moment.

The strength or weakness of the ego forces available to control anxiety is also difficult to estimate. This depends upon the degree of regression to dependent and helpless attitudes which has taken place under the impact of the combat stress, the amount of dependence which was present prior to combat, and the character of the compensations or overcompensations which had been developed against such dependence. Again, this cannot be read as if from a book by looking at or talking to the flier for a short time. It must be put together from all the evidence that can be obtained: from a consideration of the precombat history, the intensity and type of combat experience, including how much stress he has been able to withstand up to the moment, the observations of his close associates and his Flight Surgeon, and the observable transference reactions.

The motivation for a return to combat stress is the easiest of these three factors to determine, but even here the apparent situation may be deceptive. Although many fliers will talk frankly of their ambivalent feelings on this matter and describe how their desire to escape further stress is inextricably mixed with a desire to stay with their buddies and carry out their obligation, others cannot be so frank. The latter profess a strong desire to remain in combat and in truth this is their chief conscious attitude. They are not aware of the strong force of their urge to escape, which remains buried, repressed into a back alley of their minds (cf. case 3). A very small number are aware of their desire to escape further stress but to various degrees attempt to conceal it in order to fool others concerning their intentions (cf. case 7). Such individuals have been discussed in relation to the problem of "lack of moral fiber" (cf. chapter 3).

How is the psychiatrist, faced with this confusion of false fronts, able to distinguish the real from the apparent for the purpose of determining what should be done in regard to treatment and disposition? For the most part, the ability to discern the real dynamic forces within the personality depends on his skill and his experience in dealing with many cases. As the flier tells his story during the initial interviews, the psychiatrist directs the conversation toward an account of traumatic or painful events in combat, crash landings, narrow escapes, deaths of friends, noting any reverberations of anxiety as these incidents are recounted. Frequently, however, because of the strength of superego attitudes or the stability of a defensive conversion or a psychosomatic or phobic symptom, it may be impossible to bring the anxiety into focus in the consciousness of the flier. In this event, the psychiatrist may rely simply on his clinical judgment in regard to further treatment and disposition. He has, however, a diagnostic and therapeutic weapon at his disposal which in a large proportion of cases will rapidly clarify the underlying dynamic situation. This is the intravenous use of sodium pentothal to secure a brief narcotic state in which the concealed emotional situation can be exposed, abreacted and synthesized into consciousness.

We have previously described the use of sodium pentothal to effect a *narcosynthesis* in the treatment of severe and moderate anxiety states among ground force combat personnel (26). The severe states in which an actual synthesis of repressed traumatic material into consciousness almost always occurs with a dramatic improvement are not seen among Air Forces personnel. Among combat fliers sodium pentothal can be used in two ways. It is a good diagnostic tool, enabling the observer to gain a clear view of the intensity of anxiety, the degree of regression, the strength of dependent trends, the superego attitudes and the dynamic relation of all these factors to each other. The knowledge thus gained can be of great advantage to the psychiatrist in relation to further treatment and ultimate disposition, even in the absence of any clinical gain to the patient. The repressed emotional situation may be clearly exposed and abreacted in the narcotic state without its achieving any synthesis. Since the material in this event is lost when the individual arouses from the effects of pentothal and no change has occurred in the relative strengths of the dynamic forces (cf. case 3 and the first pentothal treatment in case 19), narcosynthesis cannot be said to have occurred and there is no symptomatic improvement. In this context, the treatment is identical with the "sodium amytal interview" or "narcoanalysis," long used in civilian psychiatry, in which the benefit results almost entirely from the insight the therapist gains concerning the patient's concealed difficulties.

A second and the actual therapeutic gain accrues from the use of sodium pentothal when repressed painful or traumatic events and the repressed anxieties and hostilities connected with them are not only exposed during the treatment, but accepted by the flier's ego. He then is able to deal with them in a more economical and realistic fashion, giving up the neurotic compromise which has resulted in his symptoms. This is the process which we have called narcosynthesis, since under the action of the drug and with the aid of the therapist the previously repressed or forgotten feelings and memories are synthesized by the ego. If this process has taken place, whether or not the individual can return to combat, or what further disposition should be made, will then depend upon the new grouping of forces within the ego. How this takes place can best be illustrated by a description of the details of the treatment.

Sodium pentothal is issued in ampoules of 0.5 Gm. and 1.0 Gm. and may be administered in either a 2.5 per cent or a 5.0 per cent solution. The dosage required for a satisfactory narcosis is usually between 0.25 Gm. and 0.5 Gm., though in some very marked anxiety states in large individuals more than 1.0 Gm. may be necessary. The individual is placed in a semidarkened room and is told that he is going to receive an injection which will make him sleepy. For some individuals, who are afraid of the treatment, of receiving an injection, of the "needle" or of the deleterious effects of a drug, further reassurances may be necessary. However, it is our experience that once explanations are attempted in order to reassure an apprehensive individual, further questions follow which require further explanations, so that one must be prepared either to say very little about the treatment or else to give a lengthy dissertation on the subject. In general it is wisest not to initiate the treatment until some degree of confidence has been established in the therapeutic relationship and some transference attitudes have developed, although this is not always possible or necessary. If the treatments have been in progress in a hospital or some other institution, the easily observed clinical benefits and the lack of harmful or unpleasant reactions will have produced a general acceptance of the procedure, and individual resistance to it will be minimal.

The drug is injected into the antecubital vein at a slow rate (0.1 Gm. per minute), while the flier is asked to count backwards from the number 100. Shortly after the counting becomes confused and before actual sleep is produced, the injection is discontinued, although the needle may be allowed to remain in the vein until it is ascertained that the proper depth of narcosis has been achieved. This may be deceiving. Some individuals suddenly fall asleep in the midst of their counting, only to become wide awake and alert on slight stimulation. In such cases more of the drug must be injected. If the individual is mute or stuporous and therefore cannot count, a corresponding depth of narcosis must be estimated from the tonus of the eyelids and the pupillary reflexes. In rare instances the injection is difficult because of a violent tremor of the arm. In almost every case there is some increase in the symptoms of anxiety as the injection is initiated. As it proceeds, however, the tremors subside and the individual becomes quiet. Speech may be somewhat thick and there may be spasmodic coughing but we have not seen any serious pulmonary difficulties with the doses and technique described.

By the time a satisfactory level of narcosis is reached, a few individuals will begin to talk spontaneously, and, if they are on the subject of their battle experiences, they are allowed to continue without interruption. In the greater number of cases verbal stimulation is necessary. The flier is told in a matter of fact manner that he is in his plane with his crew in flight. Depending upon the amount of known history, specific details are added corresponding to the most traumatic parts of his combat experiences. If little or nothing is known of the painful combat experiences, a typical scene is depicted. The flier is told that he is on a mission; that he is approaching his target; that flak is bursting all about; or that enemy fighter aircraft are attacking and that he must tell what is happening. The amount of such stimulation which must be given in order to start the individual talking and to bring him into contact with the painful experiences varies tremendously. Some react with the first few words, selecting the crucial stimulus such as "flak" or "target," and launch into a vivid account of the action. Others resist for various periods of time. When such resistance is maintained, the stimulation can be made more dramatic and realistic. The therapist can play the role of a fellow crewmate, calling out fighters or flak in various positions, warning of an imminent ditching or asking for help with a wounded buddy. Persistence is rewarded in almost every case by an account of the scene in progress.

The individual reactions during the progress of the treatment are extremely varied. In some men the situation is relived with such intensity that the activity requires a motor rather than a purely verbal outlet. They may wander about the room as if about the plane, or, using the pillow or bedclothes as armor plate or some other protection, may wince and cower at flak and cannon bursts. Others live through the scene verbally and emotionally without much motor activity. The tendency to live through the various combat episodes in the present tense, talking to unseen buddies, or to react with various emotions to unseen events, without talking, leaves large gaps in what the therapist can grasp of the situation, as if he were listening to one end of a telephone conversation. The latter, therefore, is constantly moved to ask the flier to tell what is happening. Many fliers, however, recount the episodes in the past tense, giving a clear picture of what took place. The minuteness and wealth of detail which flood the memory, even of events which took place many months and even years before, is always impressive.

The events which are depicted with the realistic impact of an expert dramatic production are probably always true counterparts of what actually took place, rather than fantasies such as are produced in dreams or hypnotic states. The emotional reactions, however,. do not necessarily represent the actual behavior of the flier during the original episode, but rather what he repressed and controlled in order to carry on his job. The terror exhibited in moments of supreme danger, such as during explosions within the plane, the falling of a plane, the mutilation or death of a friend before the flier's eyes, is electrifying to watch. As the event approaches, the body becomes increasingly tense and rigid. The eyes widen and the pupils dilate, while the skin becomes covered with fine perspiration. The hands move about convulsively, seeking a support, a protection, a weapon or a friend to share the danger. Breathing becomes incredibly rapid and shallow. The intensity of the emotion sometimes becomes more than can be borne and frequently at the height of the abreaction, there is a collapse. The individual falls back in bed and remains quiet for a few moments, usually to resume the story at a more neutral point. Some men return over and over again to one short traumatic scene, living it through repeatedly. In such cases, more than one pentothal treatment may be required, each one bringing out new pieces of repressed material as if the ego's tolerance for the painful memories increased in the interval before each treatment.

During the time that the flier is in a close emotional contact with the traumatic situation, the therapist may play an active or a passive role in the performance to the degree required by the process of the abreaction. No attempt should be made to produce a hypnotic situation, or to direct the material into any definite channels, unless there is a clear indication that resistance has developed to the communication of some thought, event or feeling which was on the point of emerging. In this case, the therapist may encourage or exhort the flier to communicate the painful material. In most instances, if the resistance is still powerful under the influence of the drug, no amount of work on the part of the therapist will be of much avail, although another pentothal treatment at a later time may accomplish the desired result. The therapist usually remains as a vague background figure, from which vantage point he can step into other roles as it becomes necessary. Many men, especially those with free anxiety, a stable ego organization and a firm contact with reality, are aware of the psychiatrist's presence throughout the treatment. They talk to him directly, telling their story in the past tense and relying on him only for moderate support and sympathy during moments of strong emotion. Others, in whom there has been more dissociation of feeling and who "live through" their experiences under pentothal with great intensity, need more active support. The therapist may be called upon to play a variety of roles. If the flier becomes convulsed and blocked with the violence of fear, he must step in as a protective and supporting figure, comforting and reassuring him. When intense grief and anger are exhibited over the death of a buddy, or guilt because of a personal connection with his death, a forgiving and supporting attitude is required. At the same time, some steps may be taken here to point out the irrationality of the guilt, although this is usually best left to a later point in the session when the individual is no longer under such strong emotional stimulation. Some men who talk constantly to their friends throughout the session become blocked at certain points either because of the intensity of the emotion or because they seem to get no response from their friends. The therapist may then play the part of the friend, stepping into the combat scene proper in an active role. He can discuss plans of action, the treatment of wounded buddies or whatever is called for to further the progress of the events at hand.

As the effects of the drug wear off and the depth of narcosis decreases, the flier enters that twilight area in which he is still strongly in contact with painful combat situations and the feelings aroused by them, and yet is increasingly in contact with his immediate environment, the therapist and the present reality. It is at this point that the therapist begins to play an increasingly active role. His immediate concern is to make sure that the material which has just been abreacted is actually synthesized into consciousness. Because of the short-acting effect of sodium pentothal and the absence of the prolonged period of sleep seen with other drugs, the circumstances are mechanically favorable. Nevertheless, in some instances, where the resistances are too strong, a synthesis cannot be established. In such circumstances, the individual usually snaps out of the narcosis into an alert or partially confused state, but completely amnesic for what he has just been saying. A review of the material may bring it back into memory, in whole or in part. On the other hand, efforts to effect a recall may fail and the individual's memory may remain completely blank regarding the entire experience.

In the majority of instances the transition is smooth and the material is spontaneously synthesized into consciousness. Then, because the dynamic forces at work are at the moment so labile and freshly stirred up, the therapist has an ideal opportunity to effect a modification by active interference. Superego attitudes can be easily influenced at this time, either in the direction of decreasing motivation and effecting a new identification with precombat personalities, if the problem is a depression, or in the direction of increasing motivation and reinforcing desire to withstand more stress, where the anxiety is not too severe and there is a good chance of re-establishing confidence. In those with conversion symptoms or those in whom the ego has for the first time faced the full intensity of the actual anxiety, the symptoms spontaneously disappear, since they have lost their functional purpose. However, the ego is in need of encouragement and support for its new frankness. Although in losing the protection of the symptom the ego must suffer the pain of free anxiety, actually in many instances considerable gratitude and relief are expressed as the individual finds that he can do this without suffering too much or losing too much prestige. If motivation is good and there has not been too much regression to dependent attitudes, such individuals may be returned to further combat stress (cf. case 14). During the abreaction, the pharmacological effect of the drug plus the presence of the therapist has enabled the ego to face the painful situation and express its anxiety. The very act of abreaction reduces the pressure upon the ego, so that it can continue frankly to face the painful combat situation after the effects of the drug have worn off. With the pressure relieved, and aided by the therapist, the ego finds that it is stronger than it had anticipated. For the vicious circle which had perpetuated the neurotic compromise in which the ego was continually weak and incompetent, a "benign" circle is substituted. The ego can afford to look squarely at the situation, which it has been unable to master and had therefore avoided, in part at least, and to find a new strength. It is encouraged to find new and more efficient techniques in order to master the situation or at any rate control its anxiety. How does this gain through narcosynthesis come about?

We believe that the opening wedge is the pharmacological effect of pentothal on the diencephalon. The barbiturate drug decreases diencephalic activity to a greater extent than it damps down the activity of the cerebral cortex. This results in a corresponding decrement of emergency expressions. Since it is no longer so forcibly stimulated, the cortex can re-establish its inhibitory function more easily. In other words, the ego, no longer harassed by such an overpowering intensity of anxiety, can re-establish its appraising functions and can now afford to face the traumatic situation. Although this immediately evokes an expression of the anxiety itself, with its new strength the ego can control it, digest it and synthesize it. Once this has been accomplished, the ego can continue to dominate the emotion and can initiate new steps to control the situation. New learning can now take place. This constitutes the benign circle.

However, the change in the relative strength of the dynamic forces which is seen in narcosynthesis exists principally in relation to past traumatic events. The future strength of the ego in facing new stress, involving the possibility of repetitions of the painful situations coincident with a return to combat, can only be estimated. For this reason, an evaluation of the depth of regression and the strength of dependent attitudes, usually starkly revealed during the course of abreaction, is crucial to the goal of therapy. As he sees the dependent trends and the weakness and strength of the ego clearly exposed during the treatment, the therapist tries to determine whether or not further psychotherapy, rest and more adequate support on returning to the group will enable the newly strengthened ego to cope with more stress. If the flier has revealed himself under treatment to be almost completely helpless in dealing with the stress already undergone, then a return to combat is out of the question and the therapeutic problem consists in determining what other type of duty he will be able to handle. The way the ego approaches the past traumata under pentothal should give a clear indication of what can be expected of it in the future. If dependence and helplessness are too marked, then, no matter what the aims of the superego or the needs of the military situation are, the external stress on the individual must be reduced.

If pentothal has not been used in treatment, the psychiatrist must make a similar evaluation from what he can learn in psychotherapeutic interviews. Fliers whose dependence is revealed not only in the way they have reacted to their recent stress but in a past history of neurotic symptoms and insecurity (cf. case 2) may require removal not merely from combat but from any type of flying stress. When this is required, the therapeutic problem frequently consists in dealing with an outraged superego and the resulting depression. On the other hand, grounding the flier and reassigning him to other duties may not solve the problem for an ego which has been too weak to begin with or too badly damaged by combat stress. In this case, treatment over-seas can only make a beginning in restoring the ego's strength, and for further recovery the individual must be returned to the United States (cf. case 13). If such men are returned to any form of duty overseas, for the sake either of their pride or of the military needs, they continue to have symptoms. On their return home, recovery may proceed spontaneously, but in many instances further treatment is necessary.

Neither pentothal narcosynthesis nor brief psychotherapy can be regarded as a certain cure for the flier's difficulties or an infallible technique for returning an individual to further stress. A fairly accurate evaluation of the weaknesses and strengths of the ego and a change in the direction of increased strength are all that can be expected. The latter may be sufficient to abolish the symptoms resulting from the recent stress but not enough to warrant any further exposure. On the other hand, it may well be that the increased strength, especially in the case of minor phobic and conversion symptoms, is sufficient to warrant a new trial at combat. What can be accomplished in this regard then depends upon the interplay of the three main factors: the initial weakness and dependence of the ego, the amount of increased strength gained from treatment and the degree of stress which will be encountered in any future assignment. The psychiatrist must juggle these three factors and extract from the mixture a disposition which is a reasonable compromise of the needs of the flier and the needs of the military situation.

A disposition which allows the preservation of the individual in some form of flying duties, or even in combat flying duties, is often possible by a reassignment to some slightly different task but one that is more in line with the ego's capacity to handle specific stresses (cf. case 12). Bomber pilots, for example, sometimes feel so keenly their responsibility for the other men in the plane that this added anxiety weakens the ego in its struggle with other anxiety factors. Many such men, if transferred to single-seated fighter aircraft, can carry on well in combat, having only the responsibility of their own life and the plane at stake. Furthermore, some men can carry on in an anxiety situation fairly well if they can be active. The maneuverability of the fighter aircraft satisfies this need for activity, whereas bombers must fly in rigid formation, maintaining a straight and level course which renders them much more passive against enemy action, especially flak. On the other hand, a fighter pilot may feel uncomfortable and isolated in his small plane, preferring the company and support of other men in a crew and the security of a large plane with more than one engine. The details of these individual reactions to the specific environment of combat flying vary tremendously. It is the task of the psychiatrist to determine whether a sufficient stability of the ego is initially present or has been produced through treatment, so that, if such demands are satisfied, the flier will be able to carry on successfully. Even with the help of pentothal, mistakes will be made in reaching such a decision, but, like the Flight Surgeon, the psychiatrist can learn from his mistakes, increasing his knowledge of the relation between ego dynamics and combat stress.

Although he is allowed a free hand in carrying out his treatment, the psychiatrist can only recommend the disposition of the flier who is referred to him. The actual disposition is approved by a medical board and carried out by the responsible military command if the latter is in agreement with the disposition. There is usually little difficulty concerning dispositions, if the psychiatrist has established good liaison with the military commanders and if his work demonstrates an alertness both to the needs of the individual and to those of the military situation. The results of psychiatric treatment in an active theater of operations have adequately demonstrated its contribution both to the success of the war effort and to the well-being of the individual.

PART IV

The Reactions after Combat

CHAPTER 8

The Return Home

WHEN THE COMBAT SOLDIER overseas is asked what he is fighting for, the usual answer is short and pointed: "So I can go home!" This is no war of idealism with lofty slogans and stirring patriotic songs. It is a necessary but dirty business, far more arduous and long-lasting than most of our citizens foresaw. Although there are many exceptions, the average soldier is not well informed as to the final causes for the war or its ultimate necessity. The Atlantic Charter, The Four Freedoms and postwar aims do not stir the soldier to his best efforts; only good morale within his own small group and the hope of getting home soon can do that.

Even those who were most eager to go overseas and get into the fight, either openly or secretly begin calculating their chances of being rotated home before they have passed many weeks on foreign soil. The gigantic numbers of men inducted into the armed services impress the soldier overseas, and he wonders where those millions of other men could be. Why has he been selected to do the dirtiest and most dangerous work, while others at home are employed on safe base jobs, living in civilized style often with families nearby? He estimates his "share of the war" and seeks for promises of goals to be reached in terms of time or number of missions. Even the most adverse conditions can be tolerated, sometimes almost cheerfully, if the soldier has the definite promise of rotation home after a specified time. But what a drop in morale, what unleashed resentments against the army and its officers when no goals are set, the percentage of rotations turns out to be infinitesimal or the early ill-advised promises are broken! From an idea, to a wish, to an all-embracing, increasing and overpowering longing, thoughts of home, home, home finally dominate the soldier's whole existence.

The thought of home intrudes itself disagreeably on the soldier's mind, when there are special causes for worry which increase his preoccupation with the subject and decrease his fighting efficiency. Lack of mail, worrisome letters, suspicion of wives' unfaithfulness, broken engagements, financial troubles and a host of other problems far away at home make the flier feel helpless and impotent in solving his important personal problems and stimulate his anxiety and insecurity. These create powerful forces that augment thoughts of home till they become persistent obsessions.

It had been learned from peacetime aeronautics that fliers could not continue their occupations beyond a certain time without rest, if they were to avoid the hazards of "flying fatigue." The British had been unable to rest their fliers even for a brief period during the emergency of the Battle of Britain when their country was in extreme peril. But after that battle had been won and the toll of the living, irretrievably damaged fliers counted, provisions were immediately made for a limited tour of combat duty, to be followed by rest and rehabilitation before return to the fight.

The American Air Forces soon adopted this system. In the early days of American participation in the war the capacity of the average flier was not estimated correctly, so that the first tours of combat duty were not long enough. The expected number of combat missions was then set and maintained for each type of plane in each theater of operations, since the stress and danger varied with each of these factors. Until these goals were stabilized, fliers reacted to each change as to a broken promise, with lowered morale and mobilized hostility to the Air Forces.

Later, a new system was put into effect, based on the logical conclusion that no set number of missions could be expected of every one. The individual is never the average man. Fliers are human beings and not airplane engines manufactured identically in quantity on a production line. If the flier cannot complete the minimum number of missions, formal medical proceedings are necessary to ascertain whether he is suffering from a war neurosis or gives up because of fear. In the one case he is sent home as a psychiatric casualty for rehabilitation; in the other he is subjected to administrative action. The new system provides check-points after a certain number of completed missions, for example, thirty-five or fifty, at which time the Flight Surgeon examines the flier and determines if he is capable of continuing. Every man is expected to continue to the threshold of his personal tolerance for fatigue. The results of this system should be gratifying if it is executed according to plan.

An attempt has been made to send some men home for thirty days' leave because they are not too exhausted to return to combat after a short rest, whereas others need an indefinite stay. Actually the Air Forces, like the other armed services, discovered that once a man has returned home from combat it is difficult to get him back overseas. The returnee sees too many soldiers at home who have not had their turn at the privations and dangers in a combat zone; he does not see a manpower shortage. The British, who rotated their fliers to the mother country for duty as instructors or ground officers, found that about 50 per cent were able and willing to return to combat after six months of such alternate duty.

With all these uncertainties as to whether a man will be able to go home and remain there when he reaches the promised goal, he "sweats out" his last few missions. The flier no longer has a defensive fatalistic attitude concerning his missions because his potential removal from his group has already recrystallized his individuality. His personal anxieties rise to the surface no matter how indifferent he tries to be. The possibility of going home is too wonderful, too good to be true, so that he expects something awful will happen to mar it. The soldier is afraid to think too much about home for fear of bringing the wrath of fate upon himself. He resorts to tricks of self delusion, purposely miscounting his number of missions so that he may not anticipate too greatly the accomplishment of his goal.

Other emotions also tend to offset his happiness. Waiting gives him time to reflect in retrospect on what he has been through. Leaving his crew, the mess and tentmates and the squadron creates a sense of guilt; the thought of those who died and can never go home intensifies this feeling. It is this feeling of guilt that is the basis for considering the last mission to be so dangerous. It is the projection on fate of the accusing finger of the flier's own ego-ideal, which cannot tolerate his desertion of his dead and living comrades. All these emotional reactions, stimulated by the anticipation of returning home, probably decrease efficiency and make the fliers more vulnerable to disaster on their last mission, which superstition has it is the most dangerous—"the jinx mission."

After a soldier receives orders to return to the United States, any triviality obstructing his immediate departure and travel becomes magnified to gigantic proportions. The slightest frustrations create anxiety. It is as if he must hurry, hurry, hurry before his orders are rescinded, or perhaps he will not get there in time —for what, he does not know. Delays in obtaining transportation, the slowness of the boat and the formalities at a port of debarkation are tremendously annoying. If he has been permitted to leave the theater of operations before the completion of his tour of duty by decision of a medical board, he must enter a hospital of some type immediately on arrival in the United States before getting a leave or furlough. This he takes as a personal affront, and is extremely antagonistic to the doctors. The unfairness of his attitude from a rational standpoint is obvious, since it was a medical officer who enabled him to leave combat without disgrace under the label of illness. In this frame of mind he is difficult to treat psychiatrically, so that, if at all possible, an initial furlough at home is granted prior to institution of therapy.

If he returns to the United States through a rotation policy, the flier automatically goes directly to his home. Before we follow the flier to his home, let us discuss what he expects there and why. We have already learned of the normal overpowering desires for home. Added to these are certain excessive and neurotic wishes that develop out of disturbances in their personalities in many men who have suffered the stress of combat. These individuals suffer from a psychic bankruptcy, an exhaustion of the energy which they are capable of putting out in aggressive and independent action. They need replenishing affection, consideration and attention, as a small child needs to be praised and comforted after a particularly strenuous and exhausting activity (cf. chapter 10).

As the neurotic and regressive reasons for the wish to go home increase, the concept of home becomes more unrealistic. As a haven from the dangers of combat with the enemy and from the threats of discipline on the part of superior officers in case of failure, home assumes the characteristics of a magical fairyland. All the faults and difficulties in the economic and social structure of the individual's home environment seem to fade away. The people at home become endowed with unrealistic attributes of beauty, kindness, generosity, and are considered to have the soldier's return home as their only desire. Mothers become the most loving and kind individuals, wives assume a beauty and character far from real, and children are model and have no faults. To a lesser extent this rosy hue surrounds the figure of the father or the brothers. For a time at least, there is an attempt to envisage their fathers without the role of authority, fantasying them as equals or pals. They think of going on fishing or hunting trips or sitting in "bull sessions" with them. All in all, anticipation of the return home is extremely unrealistic since the returnee expects the perfection of paradise in the "new life." Actually the return home to a "brave new world" is fantasied as a rebirth after the personal psychological death symbolized by repetitive combat missions.

At last the soldier is home but in a peculiarly dissatisfied and often disturbed state of mind. This, of course, should be expected because his desires are unrealistic. No place nor person in reality can reproduce his fantasies. He dreamed of being treated as a hero with great popular acclaim but the later returnees find that the early heroes have exhausted the adoration of the civilians, whose capacities to become excited over and deeply interested in the returned soldier decline, as more and more men return home and their own postwar problems loom dangerously ahead. The individual therefore finds that his welcome, unless he has been an outstanding hero, is largely limited to the circle of his small social group. The fuss and excitement outside the home soon die down. The soldier has a negativistic, dissatisfied reaction to civilian responses, no matter what they may be. If the soldier receives a great deal of attention, he often becomes annoyed because he does not have enough time to spend alone with his family, but, if enough attention is not given to him, he resents the indifference of the civilian community. Any suitable rationalization is utilized to justify his antagonism to people not in uniform.

The returned combat soldier's attitude toward civilians not only causes serious interpersonal difficulties but is the nucleus of a serious social problem. He has read much in the newspapers and army publications about the high wages and the luxurious life of war workers and civilians who have not entered the army.

He has read overemphasized stories about strikes and of his government having to exhort people to take war jobs or to continue their work, while he has risked his life and endured innumerable hardships. While overseas, he and his buddies have built up a hostility toward civilians, with little factual knowledge of the changed economic and social setting at home. There can be no doubt that his hostilities are not entirely rational.

In reality the soldier envies the civilian his freedom, his work and his financial status, and envy creates hostility. When he arrives home and sees how people actually live and prosper, his resentments are tremendously stimulated. He blames them for lack of war supplies overseas and for the inconveniences of lack of food and cigarettes. There are no rationalizations that enable him to reconcile the civilian attitudes toward war with the deaths of his buddies. The soldier is disturbed by the mercurial and unrealistic reactions of civilians to the good and bad news of the war, their optimism regarding an early end of the war or their impatience for quick action, the cost of which he knows but they do not. He hates the romanticizing of war, the illusions and legends originated by our fantasy makers of the press and radio, who give the public what they like to hear. When the commentator of a motion picture newsreel states, "There is nothing combat crews love better than a tough fight," the men who actually fought for life wonder whose world is real—theirs or the civilians'.

Women with new furs, jewels and luxuries, couples crowding into night clubs and theaters, incite them to fury. Unfortunately in order to give returnees the best of accommodations and a luxurious reception, our redistribution stations are in resort and tourist towns, where money flows freely for luxury hotels and exotic entertainment. Many soldiers, especially under the influence of alcohol, either verbally or physically attack these "bastardly 4-F's." There are many versions of the following story. A civilian with only good intentions approaches a soldier in a bar with the question; "How was it over there, buddy— pretty tough?" The soldier looks at him with contempt and answers, "Why don't you go there and find out?"—and walks away, after calmly punching the questioner on the nose. Patronizing offers to buy him drinks are distasteful and are often rejected with violence.

At first the soldier centers all his attention and interest on his loved ones at home, and this is fully reciprocated. However, his people have their own jobs and numerous duties, and life does not stand still because a boy has returned home. He must refamiliarize himself with his old possessions alone and with his remaining friends at their convenience. Mother has a multiplicity of domestic duties or responsibilities, including caring for her other children, to which she must attend at the sacrifice of the full time attention which her returned son expected. Brothers have their individual school work and domestic duties; if they are younger, they treat the hero with adolescent indifference and even with resentment for disturbing their possession of mother, after a first burst of enthusiasm. Wives, who were fantasied to be the most beautiful and wonderful women in the world, soon are unable to measure up to such unrealistic dreams on the part of the returning husbands. They too have often changed because of their own deprivations during the period of separation and need more than they can give. If the family has moved to new quarters or another neighborhood, the new physical environment has an even greater anxiety-provoking strangeness. Many readjustments have to be made in manner of dress, in the proper use of clothes within the home and particularly in social gatherings. The pungent army language has to be modified for civilian ears and cleanliness has to be maintained at a much higher level. The soldier who returns from overseas duty has slowly to learn and relearn the multifold civilized customs and attitudes of life in the United States, despite his annoyance at these "nonessentials."

Re-establishment of sexual life is not easy or rapid, especially if nervous reactions from combat have affected the soldier's libido. Often he finds his wife, unused to a husband, difficult to adjust to his sexual activities, which often are excessive. On the other hand, psychological factors and physical disturbances may have made him temporarily impotent, which is a source of anxiety to both the soldier and his wife. In many cases he married just before departure overseas and he knows his wife only slightly. This creates a marital situation even more difficult than usual, since their relationship must be started afresh with little in the way of common past experiences or interests. A large number of divorces result. Many soldiers attempt to confirm real or unrealistic suspicions of their women's unfaithfulness. Often enough it has been a fact, and it is surprising how open many of these defections have been and how easy they are to detect. Many married soldiers, who themselves have been unfaithful overseas, adopt an unforgiving attitude toward their erring wives. The narcissistic injury is more than they can endure in view of the already existing injuries to self esteem caused by combat. The reality of the soldier risking his life while his wife had pleasure with a civilian or a stay-at-home soldier is overpowering. If a child has been born while he was overseas, the problem of a second honeymoon is complicated by the necessary drudgery of care for the infant. Sometimes the soldier finds that there is not even adequate room for him at home. These are but a few of the normal and natural frustrations that the returnee must endure in contrast with his own anticipation of a reception like that of a "prodigal son."

It should not be understood that there are no gratifications at home. There are far more than enough for a normal person, but the hungers and needs of many men are so tremendous that they seem insatiable and impossible of satisfaction. Furthermore, many soldiers have left homes in which the interpersonal relations were conflictual and were responsible for discomfort and disturbances to his peace of mind long before combat. Overseas he forgets these difficulties and builds in his mind an illusory peaceful and happy family life. When he returns, his old conflicts are revived and even accentuated, because he returns to their source in an even more intolerant mood.

Return home thus becomes productive of emotional disturbances by virtue of the disappointment that a regressed personality must experience in an environment that cannot satisfy his fantasied concept of home, and because old conflicts are revived on return to the situations where they originated. As time goes on, the normal adaptive functions of the ego synthesize the conflicting tendencies and the soldier is reintegrated into American life. If conflicts persist, anxiety increases and the patient often becomes so disturbed that he is referred to the hospital by examining psychiatrists at stations to which he reports for redistribution.

After his twenty-one days' leave or furlough at home, the returnee proceeds to the redistribution station nearest his home. Here he goes through a series of thorough physical examinations and laboratory studies and a psychiatric survey. He is interviewed in detail by personnel reclassification officers for a new assignment in the army within the United States. When physical or emotional disturbances are noted, he is sent for proper treatment to appropriate installations. During this process of redistribution, anxiety regarding his new assignment begins to develop in the soldier. Many men have military specialties that are of no use except in combat, since there is only a limited need for instructors. The questions where he will be assigned and what he will do and how he will get along in his new unit are problems that bother him day and night, because he still lacks a feeling of security and the assurance that there are other than hostile and destructive forces in the world. Many returned soldiers feel that the war is over as far as they are concerned, and see no need for remaining in the army. Some try in every way possible to get out, including exaggeration of nervous symptoms and provocative behavior. The redistribution program furnishes the returnee with several days of indoctrination lectures concerning life in the United States and his role in the army in this country. But more important should be the instillation in these men of the certainty that they will not be sent overseas again until after a definite period, and that they will receive fair and equitable treatment in a task of some significance for the war effort. Otherwise why should they work or, for that matter, even stay in the army?

The soldier receives his new assignment and arrives at his new base, and here additional problems and burdens are put on his shoulders. He has a hostile attitude toward the stay-at-home soldiers. They should be out fighting the war too. Why haven't they gone overseas? An interesting reaction was observed in a group of flying officers and enlisted men returning home by plane. As they flew away from the war, living quarters, food and comforts became increasingly better, so that the soldiers stationed at these quiet bases lived comfortably and safely. The universal, disgusted reaction was: "A hell of a war *they're* fighting!" As they encountered increasing luxuries, these returnees stroked white table cloths and fondled gleaming silverware as if they weren't certain of their reality. They gorged on steaks and chops, often eating two dinners in rapid succession. They bought all sorts of jewelry for themselves and their families. Finally, at one stopover close to the United States the officers' club was found to be built and run at the acme of luxury. The sneering depreciation was just about to break through again, when one officer stated, as if he'd just discovered the fact, "But after all that's what we've been fighting for—to keep things at home like we used to know them. What are we griping about?"

In his new assignment the soldier often finds himself having to do things or to teach methods that have been abandoned by combat outfits long ago. He finds himself under the direction of officers who know far less than he. He has to abide by rules and regulations which are much stricter than those he has been accustomed to overseas. It is rather difficult for him to readapt himself to the army as he knew it before he left. The farther a man has gone from home, the less rigid has been the army discipline. In some overseas theaters, an enlisted man has lived much like an officer. Now he returns home after having jeopardized his life and finds himself involved again in the caste system of the army, which sharply discriminates enlisted men from officers.

The army attitude toward him is no less hostile. When he enters an outfit in this country, he upsets the promotion gradient and disturbs its smooth-running organization. The soldier may have a rating which is incompatible with his ability to function in the United States. He often has to be given "on the job" training. His very presence jeopardizes the safety of the other men, because the more soldiers return home on rotation, the more will have to go overseas to replace them. This in itself is enough motivation for antagonism. In addition, the stay-at-home soldier unconsciously feels guilty on seeing the returnee because of his own deficiency in the war effort even though it may be through no fault of his own. The result of hostile attitudes on both sides does not make for ease of adaptation for the returnee. The returnee needs a purposeful function in the army and rapid reincorporation into a group with good morale in order to facilitate his adaptation to army life in this country.

Through all the vicissitudes that have been described most men successfully develop emotional stability. Those who react with disabling anxiety during their last missions, their travel home, their overseas furloughs, or during the first weeks of reassigned duties, are referred to a special convalescent hospital for treatment. They demonstrate an excessive or prolonged reaction, present to some degree in every man, and are not qualitatively different.

Up to this point we have considered the vicissitudes of all men returning home from overseas duty. Most of these have finished a full tour of combat duty. Many soldiers are returned to the United States by medical disposition boards because of incapacitating symptoms, before they have finished their tours of duty. It will be observed that the change of environment has a profound effect on them.

When reference is made to the results of treatment and disposition of patients recognized and treated overseas, described in chapter 7, it will be seen that many patients are sent home by medical disposition boards for rehabilitation requiring more than ninety days. Many of these patients are unsuccessfully treated for shorter periods in the combat area. Others are kept overseas and reclassified for ground duties at bases that are relatively safe, and they seem to make a satisfactory adjustment. The fact that anxiety seems to disappear when a man is removed from combat flying, grounded or sent home as an instructor, has convinced many administrative officers that anxiety states are akin to malingering and should be punished by some disciplinary action, such as loss of rank or, as advised by the most intolerant, sent to the infantry front lines. It is difficult for them to accept phobic mechanisms which protect against anxiety by keeping the patient distant from the anxiety-producing stimulus as anything but malingering. Unconscious and conscious motivation are not considered as separate forces.

Goldstein (22) has emphasized the term "neurotic reaction" as a result of war in contrast with the diagnosis "war neuroses." He believes that symptoms due to war events are not neuroses because with the former there is usually no permanent personality change and no fixation of symptoms takes place. Personality change occurs only when causes are effective in maintaining insecurity. According to this thesis men who develop neurotic reactions should recover on returning home to a place of safety and security. We have good evidence for believing that this occurs in an unknown number of cases, but like all generalizations it overemphasizes only one aspect of an extremely complicated picture and is based on a particular type of case.

We have no detailed data concerning men who have promptly recovered on return home. While one of the authors was still overseas, and the other was at the Don Cesar, the only AAF convalescent hospital receiving cases of war neuroses, many patients sent home were not hospitalized. They were "lost by spontaneous recovery." We therefore cannot give the case histories of these men and have no statistical data regarding their numbers. On the other hand, both of the authors have received and studied at this hospital patients whom they had sent home while they were still doing psychiatric work overseas a month or two previously. These patients did not recover on return to a safe and secure environment. Three typical histories are presented to illustrate various sequelae occurring after the men had returned home.

CASE 17: *Anxiety and depression necessitating return to the United States, which effected considerable relief—complete recovery by further psychotherapy.*

A 22 year old B-25 pilot was first seen overseas after he had completed forty-seven missions. At that time he showed a marked anxiety, gross tremor of the hands and a severe depression. His face appeared haggard and masked and he looked much older than his 22 years. His speech was slow, with much blocking, so that he had difficulty in expressing himself. He complained of insomnia, with terrific anxiety dreams, and loss of appetite. He had lost 15 pounds in weight in the last few months.

It was difficult to elicit a story from him because of his verbal blocking, which increased when he was asked about his depressed feelings. He had entered combat in June 1943 and had originally participated in low-level sea sweeps. His outfit was equipped with planes for use on targets from minimal and low altitudes. He apparently had no particular difficulty on these missions. His symptoms began when he was transferred from this squadron to one employing medium altitude tactics on routine targets. There was no evident precipitating factor in regard to his symptoms. He gradually found himself becoming anxious. During his last few missions the anxiety was so severe that it interfered with his efficiency, and he found himself worrying about his responsibility to his crew, afraid he might be responsible for their death or injury because of his shakiness. He became irritable and then increasingly seclusive. His inefficiency became so marked that on his last two attempts to take off on missions he was involved in aircraft accidents due to his poor judgment.

Although it was not possible to obtain much information concerning this pilot's depression because of his blocking, it was clear that he was suffering from a feeling of having failed to perform his duty. He had not been able to complete a tour of duty because of his anxiety and resulting inefficiency. His reaction, however, was markedly inappropriate, since he was only three missions short of the official quota and his record had been very good. He appeared to obtain some benefit from verbal assurance that he had performed his job well, that many others were similarly affected and that he would undoubtedly recover so that he could fly again and possibly return to combat at a later time. Although he gave the impression of being fairly ill, it was thought that he would benefit more from a rapid return to the Zone of the Interior than from psychotherapy at that time. He was seen by the Medical Disposition Board, which recommended a return to the United States for treatment.

On his entry into our hospital in the United States after his three weeks' leave at home, this officer showed a remarkable change. He had recovered from all his symptoms and looked young, fresh and eager. The change in his appearance was so striking that the medical officer who had seen him overseas scarcely recognized him. His speech was spontaneous and he stated that he slept and ate well and had no dreams and no depression. He attributed his improvement to the beneficial effect on him of his wife and home.

In interviews with him, it became evident that he still had some tension and a trace of his former depression. He could not talk freely about this; however, he showed an exaggerated superego reaction. It was discovered that an intense sense of duty had been characteristic of him all his life. There was nothing else remarkable in his past history. His father had died of cancer at the age of 30, when the patient was 7 years old. His mother had remarried, and, although at first he had experienced some friction with his stepfather, he rapidly established good relations with him. With an older brother and two older sisters he had always been on the best of terms.

When this pilot had received his commission, he had made a resolution to be at all times an exemplary officer. In combat he was perpetually harassed by his sense of duty. A feature of the sea sweeps to which he was first assigned was the elective nature of the targets. He was free to attack a variety of targets depending upon his judgment of their value and the extent to which they were defended. On several occasions he had failed to attack a choice target, when flying in the lead of an element, because of worry about the safety of those who were following him. Whenever this occurred, he would feel depressed for several days. However, he would feel equally depressed if any of his friends were lost when he was leading a flight. On several occasions this happened. One of his best friends was shot down off his wing as he was leading the flight through an intense flak barrage. After this he felt depressed for many days and blamed himself for his friend's death. But the most depressing event was the occasion on which he was leading an element of three planes off the Greek coast and found a German merchant vessel. The other planes were piloted by green pilots. As they were going in on the bomb run at deck level, the patient realized that the other two planes were too close behind him and that the delayed action bombs which he was intending to drop on the ship would have blown the other two planes out of the air. At the last moment, therefore, in order to save the other two crews, he swerved off his bomb run and headed home without attacking the vessel. For days after this, he would awaken at night with a great feeling of guilt and depression to think of the ship which he had not sunk still at anchor in the Greek harbor. When he was discussing this incident, the patient became somewhat tense, experiencing a slight revival of his original reaction of guilt.

Psychotherapy in the hospital was confined to testing such traces of guilt reactions against reality in an attempt to modify to some extent his very strict superego and prevent a repetition of the depression following future experiences. He demonstrates the type of neurotic reaction found so frequently in persons with compulsive characters. He was able to obtain considerable insight and became completely relaxed, so that he was shortly discharged to return to full flying duty. At the time of his discharge, he had no anxiety connected with flying and was eager to return.

. . . . . .

Although this patient was not entirely well after his return home, he was sufficiently improved to present, at least superficially, an entirely different clinical picture. He typifies a large number of patients who are sent by Medical Disposition Boards to the United States for rehabilitation, but who are not sent to hospitals on their arrival because of a delay in receipt of their papers or because of some other administrative error. They spend their overseas leaves at home and, on reporting back to redistribution stations for reassignment, show so few signs of illness that they are returned to duty at once at a Continental base. Yet, as this patient demonstrates, they are not entirely well, even though on the road to recovery. They probably would be able to work out their own psychological solutions to a residual conflict with time and through the processes of living. They do not have neuroses in the sense of a permanent deformation of the ego structure; there is only a temporary neurotic reaction to a specific external stimulus which does not necessarily cause crippling of future function or repetition of the same pattern of behavior.

CASE 18: *Severe anxiety state, developed in combat and persisting on return home, relieved by psychotherapy.*

An upper turret gunner was an eager and capable combat crew member for his first thirty missions, although many of his missions were over very rough targets. Between his thirtieth and fortieth missions, he began to feel somewhat fatigued and slightly irritable. He also experienced some anxiety when over the target but no reduction in his efficiency. On returning to base from his fortieth mission, during which his whole flight had been severely damaged by flak, he had to assist in extricating a friend from another plane. This man, also an upper turret gunner, had been severely injured and was covered with blood. After this episode, the patient developed marked anxiety, which increased steadily on his last ten missions. He also developed severe insomnia, loss of appetite and frequent headaches. He became rather seclusive during this time. He experienced such intense anxiety that he could not stay in his turret. He had a feeling that he would certainly be killed if he got into the turret. While he was over the target on his last mission, he was seized with an overpowering urge to go to sleep.

In spite of the accumulation of anxiety and interference with his operational efficiency, his Flight Surgeon, when he went to see him to complain of how he felt, told him that he was "yellow" and a coward. It was a fact that at the time medical officers and all personnel were under pressure to maintain everyone on a flying status because of shortage of replacement crews. The patient reacted with great bitterness to his Flight Surgeon's attitude and went to see another Flight Surgeon, who grounded him and referred him for psychiatric consultation. He appeared at that time to be moderately depressed, irritable and anxious. In a brief psychotherapeutic discussion, an effort was made to bolster his ego in relation to having completed his job overseas, in order to decrease his depression, some of which was due to the attitude taken by his Flight Surgeon. It was felt at that time that he would need no particular treatment other than a return to the United States, since he had been previously a stable personality with no neurotic trends.

On his return to the United States, the patient showed continued anxiety and moderate depression. He complained of difficulty in concentrating, insomnia and lack of appetite. Because of these symptoms, he did not enjoy his leave at home. On entrance into the hospital, he appeared rather ill and depressed. He said that he did not want to be discharged from the army and that he was uncertain about any return to flying. He still had a marked fear of aircraft. From discussion of his experiences in combat, it was clear that the principal traumatic factor was his identification with the wounded turret gunner whom he had extricated after his return from his fortieth mission. He said the turret gunner, Dave, was hit in the face by a 20 mm. shell. One eye was lost and one arm and one leg were paralyzed. It was a terrible sight. The wounded man was covered with blood. After the patient's plane landed, he was the first one on the scene. He carried the wounded gunner out of the plane—"I figured that both of us were turret gunners. The same thing might happen to me, and then I wanted to be sure of being helped fast, so I couldn't let him down. Now he is back here in the United States but disabled."

In the course of a few psychotherapeutic interviews, the patient rapidly improved. He abreacted his anxiety and developed insight into the factor of his identification with the wounded turret gunner. After he had developed this insight and relieved himself of some of his anxiety verbally, he began to sleep well, his appetite improved and he gained weight. His battle dreams disappeared completely and he was eventually discharged for return to full flying duty. At the time of his discharge, he had no fears of flying.

. . . . . .

It was judged that this patient would recover by the simple expedient of returning home, but subsequent events did not confirm this prognosis. Although the soldier was a stable person, he did not improve and only recovered after being given appropriate help in the form of psychotherapy. He had had more than a superficial reaction and had developed a definite change in his personality which influenced his whole attitude toward life. Yet with appropriate therapy, he made a good recovery.

The next case is outlined with considerable detail, because it clearly indicates the difficulties of psychotherapy overseas as contrasted with its possibilities in this country.

CASE 19: *Anxiety state fixed by conversion symptoms, loosened by return home, and only then amenable to psychotherapy.*

This patient was first seen overseas. He had been referred for medical disposition because on his last two missions he had fainted when the airplane had reached an altitude of 10,000 feet. He was a B-25 bombardier, who had a good record of performance during his first eight combat missions. On his ninth mission, while approaching the target, his plane had been caught in prop-wash and thrown into a dive. The patient was thrown against the bomb sight, sustaining an injury to the left anterior chest wall. The plane fell for a long time before the pilot luckily managed to obtain control and pull out of the dive. The patient had much pain in the chest and was coughing up blood; nevertheless, when the pilot got back into formation and continued on over the target, he was able to drop his bombs successfully. On returning to the field, he was seen by his Flight Surgeon, who sent him to a hospital. He remained there for over four weeks, during which time his cough and hemoptysis cleared up. He was then discharged back to full duty.

It was on his return to flying duty after this hospitalization that the symptoms of fainting appeared. The patient stated that he had no foreknowledge of impending syncope. He remembered feeling cold and sleepy, and the next thing he knew he would awaken to find himself leaning on the bomb sight. Other members of the crew, who had been trying to communicate with him over the interphone, were aware that something was amiss. In order to investigate the situation, his Flight Surgeon took him up for a check ride. He noticed on this occasion that the patient became pale, breathed rapidly and had a rapid pulse when a height of 10,000 feet was reached, and that shortly thereafter he fainted. The Flight Surgeon assumed that the cause of the fainting was anoxia and administered artificial respiration. On returning from this flight, the Flight Surgeon referred the patient for disposition with a diagnosis of organic injury, and fainting due to anoxia.

This diagnosis appeared manifestly unjustified and it was considered that the patient was more probably suffering from a hyperventilation syndrome with an anxiety background, since anoxia after a few minutes at an altitude of 10,000 feet would be rare indeed. It was accordingly determined to investigate possible sources of anxiety leading to hyperventilation. From the beginning, the patient denied having any conscious anxiety or fear. Although he did not directly show hostility when told that his troubles might be due to fear, he constantly rejected this idea, laughing and joking at such a possibility. He stated that he had never been afraid of anything. He described himself as one of the best bombardiers in his outfit, and talked about his activities in combat with a great deal of pride and jocularity. He attempted to produce the impression of the typical carefree, aggressive combat crew member. There was something about his attitude, however, which was not wholly convincing. The effect was theatrical and overplayed. He spoke of the tremendous importance of the work of a Tactical Air Force and persistently demanded to be returned to combat flying, only asking that he be assigned to an organization which would not fly above 9,000 feet. Although he was repeatedly told that such an assignment was not practicable since there were no organizations which always flew at low altitudes, he continued to demand such work in a rather childish fashion.

Because it was impossible to establish any insight into his underlying anxieties in psychotherapeutic interviews, a pentothal interview was undertaken overseas. He was told that he was in his plane with his crew going to the target. He then related in the present tense the story of this mission, describing the way the plane got into the prop-wash, the dive and the continuation on to the target. He spoke to various members of his crew as if actually going through the mission; however, his attitude was completely unemotional and calm and he showed no anxiety whatsoever. On one occasion, however, when told that he was going on another mission, he made the following remarks: "It's all right, fellows, keep on going—don't turn back on my account. I know I won't last if you go on—I'll die—I can't make it—but I don't want you to turn back for me—it's no good to be a straggler." These remarks were delivered in a similar unemotional tone of voice. Shortly after making these remarks, he awoke and looked about in a dazed fashion, asking where he had been. The pentothal interview was reviewed with him and he was asked what could be the significance of his remarks about not turning back for his sake. He stated that he could not understand what he might have meant by these remarks and appeared to think that the whole thing was rather foolish. It was obvious that the pentothal treatment had failed to elicit any actual anxiety, although his statements about not turning back for his sake appeared to indicate a deep conviction that he would die on a combat mission. Inasmuch as no anxiety could be realized either in interviews or under pentothal, it was decided to accompany the patient on a flight in order to observe his actual reactions in the air. Accordingly the therapist went with the patient on a practice flight in a B-25. On the way up to the field, patient showed more than his usual amount of jocularity and aggressive humor. The theatrical aspect of his personality was particularly apparent. On several occasions he commented on the possibility of distant unidentified planes in the neighborhood turning out to be German fighter aircraft; although he joked about this, the joke was unrealistic, since German aircraft had never penetrated to this area. In the plane the patient appeared to be in good humor and cheerful. He got into the copilot's seat in order to help the pilot take off, since there was to be no actual copilot. His talkativeness at this time, more than ever, gave the impression of a frightened individual whistling past the graveyard. When the plane neared an altitude of 9,000 feet, the patient came into the section of the plane behind the pilot's compartment, where further knowledge of the altitude was kept from him. The pilot had been previously instructed to fly about for some time before ascending to 10,000 feet. Just before actually reaching this altitude, the patient began to tremble. His face then appeared to be pale and drawn. His respirations began to increase and the tremor slowly spread until it involved his entire body. The patient stated that he did not feel scared but that he was sleepy, and he actually shut his eyes for long moments. He was forcibly instructed to breathe slowly and deeply, and, although the altitude was maintained for fifteen minutes, he did not faint. The pilot was then instructed to descend. At 8,500 feet the patient suddenly looked alert, his tremor ceased and he stated that he felt good. He was then allowed back into the copilot's seat, where he carried on the ordinary duties and appeared to be cheerful and jocular.

In subsequent interviews it was pointed out to the patient that the tremor he exhibited in the air was very similar to the tremor of nervousness. He admitted then that his nerves might have been somewhat affected by his injury and subsequent illness, but strongly denied that this reaction had anything to do with fear or anxiety. He took the attitude that the therapist, if the latter wanted to, had a right to think that he was scared but that he, the patient, could never be convinced that this was the source of his trouble. Since it was manifestly impossible to establish any insight in a patient with such strong resistance and so much organic fixation, it was felt that the best method of procedure would be to have the patient return to combat and to ask his Flight Surgeon to observe him carefully for signs of anxiety and to work out the anxiety with him on the spot. The patient was therefore returned to duty with a letter of instruction to his Flight Surgeon. After this, the patient made one more mission. On this occasion, he carried out his duties efficiently over a very rough target. He did not faint but returned from the mission completely exhausted and covered with perspiration. The Flight Surgeon again became alarmed in case the exhaustion might be due to organic pulmonary injury and referred the patient to a hospital. In the hospital a physical examination was negative, but an electrocardiogram showed a slight deviation from "normal." This was interpreted by the chief of the medical section as significant and abnormal, representing recent posterior wall damage of the heart. The patient was told that he had suffered a contusion of the heart and should not be returned to flying duty until six months from the date of the injury, because he needed rest. The patient was then discharged and referred back for medical disposition. He greeted the therapist on his return with the statement that he guessed there was something wrong with him after all, because the doctor in the hospital had found it. He was more cheerful than ever, although somewhat more calm and less talkative than when first seen. Because there was now so much organic fixation, psychotherapy did not appear likely to be successful and it was determined to return the patient to the United States for further observation and treatment.

On his return to the United States this bombardier underwent an interesting change in symptoms. When he arrived home he felt nervous and increasingly depressed, in startling contrast with the good spirits he showed on leaving the theater of operations. He enjoyed being with his wife and 7 month old boy, but not to the extent that he had anticipated. Since his nervousness increased during his leave at home, he was referred from the Redistribution Station in Atlantic City to the Don Cesar Convalescent Hospital for treatment. On admission he appeared to be pale, tense, restless and depressed. His manner was still somewhat aggressive and he complained of anxiety dreams of falling in an airplane. He stated at once that he had not realized that he was nervous overseas, but that the doctor had seen it and he was certainly right about it. Neither his anxiety nor his depression had a definite content. He did not know why he felt nervous, and in relation to his depression he could state only that he did not feel that he had done his job overseas. Because of the change in the clinical picture, it was decided to give a pentothal treatment immediately. The patient agreed to this, saying that he wanted to know whether his symptoms were due to his heart injury or to a "mental condition," and that he wanted to get to feel like he did before he went overseas.

After 4 cc. of pentothal had been injected, he was told that he was on a mission and he began to talk. "Going up to North Italy . . . have to take evasive action—flak and fighters around —plenty of evasive action—got to have it. Well, the plane suddenly shook, pulled up back of three other ships, rolled over on its back, . . . falling down . . . down . . . down . . . down . . . down we fell, falling down . . . falling down, fast, faster . . . faster . . . faster. I didn't expect it. We came out of it, but I was hurt—my chest hurt bad—my head was hurting—I was scared. Me scared! I didn't think I'd ever be scared—didn't think any man could scare me. I felt our cause was much bigger. Pilot wanted to go back, but I wouldn't let him. We had a job to do. Boys . . . our boys were having trouble on the ground— our boys, our infantry—we had to go. Every bomb had to count. If we turned back, they wouldn't count. We dropped them—hit the target—smackeroo! Banzai!! Chest was hurting, spitting blood—didn't like the sight of blood."

At this point the patient opened his eyes and looked about in a confused, dazed manner. He rapidly oriented himself, however, and asked how long ago he had been given the injection. He was then asked to talk about his next mission. He said that he was tense and afraid he would mess up, not do his job right. The poor guys on the ground were taking a beating. "When you go over, you've got to hit them. I knew too much about my work—studied hard—knew too much about it to let it go to waste. Army spent a lot of money on me. I do not feel I have given my all. I ought to be in the air either doing a job or teaching a job. I feel guilty; with the training I have received, I have an obligation. Always have a foolish idea in my head, if you want something you have to work for it. Dad liked the easy way out. I was disappointed in him. He was weak. When he had a problem, he would drink instead of solving the problem intelligently. Grandfather always told me anything worth while you have got to work for it,—you have to suffer a while. Grandfather was a doctor, finest in the world. He didn't like dad. We have a problem, family and responsibility . . . instead, he would drink. I had to accept responsibility of being a father to my 15 year old brother. I knew he was at the age where he needed a father's companionship. That's the way I felt when I was his age. He wants me to come home. My other brother is like me. He accepts responsibility. We take care of our mother. I wanted a father to talk to when I was young. My father is a good man— just drinks too much. When I married, I borrowed money . . . started off in a hole. I thought that would stimulate me to get ahead. Married two years and have a happy family. I've paid off all my debts, . . . couple thousand in the bank. Frankly, I'm disappointed in myself. In school they told me I couldn't work at night and keep up my grades, but I did it. I earned money and got through school. Why is it the others completed fifty missions and I could only do eleven missions? I want to fly. You ought to see the citations I have from various officers overseas. Why, I'm not as good as they really say I am. Before I went over they wanted me to stay home as an instructor, but I wanted to go overseas. Guess I should have stayed. You have to fly to teach a bombardier, . . . can't teach it on the ground. Doc, I feel a lot better talking to you—hope it will help to get me to feel my old self again."

It can be seen that considerable material of great importance was elicited during this interview in contrast with the scarcity of material in the first pentothal test, performed overseas. The patient's anxiety and feelings connected with his fall in the plane were dramatically brought out with great emotional effect. In addition, pertinent psychological factors relating to his feelings toward his father were disclosed. In the next interview the material brought out was reviewed with the patient. He had no memory of describing the actual mission and his fall in the plane, and in his customary fashion half-way denied having a fear of falling. He stated that he might feel uneasy in a plane and that this might be connected with falling, but that he couldn't really say that he was afraid. However, we went on to elaborate on the material concerning his father. He stated that he had always been lonesome for a father when he was young. He had, in addition, been in adolescence a "spoiled brat" with no sense of responsibility. He had always tried to get what he wanted the easiest way. Then one day his grandfather had had a serious talk with him. His grandfather told him that he was growing up to be just like his father and that he would have to change and learn how to take responsibility. His grandfather was a very well known and successful doctor, who had never liked the father. The grandfather had suggested that the patient earn his own living and learn how to be independent of his family, saying that the only way really to achieve what he wanted was to work hard for it. After this conversation the patient, according to his own account, had actually undergone a change in personality. He was in high school at the time and he obtained a position working at night and lived on his own income. From that time on, he rejected his father completely and took as his ideal the goal his grandfather had given him.

The patient was then asked if he knew why he felt so depressed. He answered that he felt it was probably because he had failed to complete his job overseas. He was then asked if possibly he did not also feel bad because his behavior had been evasive and he had escaped facing his responsibilities in the same way as his father escaped similar responsibilities. He said, "No, I don't drink." He was told that his way of escaping was not through drinking but through failing to face his real feelings. He was then reminded that overseas he had failed to face up to his own anxiety and fear of flying. He answered that he did not know at that time that he was afraid. He was asked if he knew it now, and he said that he was not sure.

At the next interview, the patient stated that he had made up his mind that he was going to make an attempt to return to flying and that he felt much less depressed. He was asked if he had thought about the comparison between his own behavior and his father's. He admitted that perhaps there was something in it and that he was now trying to recognize what was wrong with him. He asked whether the therapist thought he should return to flying and was told that no definite answer could be given at the present time.

During the next few interviews the patient showed a progressive improvement. He became less tense and the depression disappeared altogether. He continued, however, to have difficulty in regard to his anxiety about flying and constantly vacillated between a desire to get away from planes and his feeling of obligation to the Air Forces. It was still only with the greatest difficulty that he could be brought to describe his reactions to planes and for a long time he remained markedly evasive. He kept saying, for instance, that he thought he would get over his uneasiness in planes by repeatedly exposing himself to flights, and denied that he actually had any definite fear. Because of his continued difficulty in clearly recognizing the source of his anxiety, it was determined to give him another pentothal treatment.

After 5 cc. of pentothal had been injected intravenously, he was asked if he would accompany the interviewer on a flight. He said, "No, I won't go—I won't fly—I don't have to go—I've been grounded." His attitude in this conversation was petulant, like that of a naughty boy. When he was told that he would have to fly, he said, "I can't—planes aren't safe . . . they kill you— they get into prop-wash, then they fall down—down—down. It tears at your face, it throws your head back and twists your neck—it hurts you. I can't do it," and with this he began to tremble and to move about with considerable anxiety and tension. He was then not stimulated for several minutes, at the end of which time he began to talk spontaneously. He was apparently talking to his 7 month old son. "Tommy, don't worry—I won't leave you—I'll be back—I won't go fly—you don't need to worry—I'll be back." A few minutes later he awoke spontaneously and looked about the room in a dazed fashion. He had no recollection whatsoever of what he had been saying while asleep, and, when the material was reviewed with him, he began to express astonishment that he had spoken of falling with so much anxiety. He could not account for his statement in regard to his son Tommy.

When seen next, the patient admitted, with a degree of frankness and realism which he had never before exhibited, that he guessed he must really be very scared of flying. He said, "I know it now, but I didn't know it before. I know I'm scared of falling in an airplane. I guess I have been trying to fool myself about a lot of things. I am really worried about a lot of things and I don't like to admit it." He went on to say that he was very much concerned about his future work in the army and after he got out of service, and that he didn't have the confidence in himself that he once had. He was then told that his confidence and general feeling of security had been shattered by his flying experiences when he had the fall and injury, and that this was only natural, but that he would get over it. He was told that he could never really get better as long as he would not recognize how he really felt, but that, now that he knew what was the matter with him, he would start on the road to recovery. He then asked again whether he should try to return to flying and said that he hoped he would be allowed to conquer his fear.

The answer to this question is intricately involved with an evaluation of the total problem in this case. It can at once be seen that this is a problem of marked anxiety, at first physically bound in an immature and somewhat dependent individual. The patient's maturity, achieved through identification with his grandfather and based on a rejection of his own father, was at best tenuous. It did not appear to represent an actual maturity but rather an imitation of maturity. The attempt to achieve an ego-ideal by imitation, rather than through a real identification, was characteristic of this man. It was the essence of his behavior as a combat crew member, which was characterized by evasive aggressiveness, jocularity and sangfroid. These reactions, actually felt by some combat crew members, were only imitated by the patient while in combat to cover up his actual fright—the whistling in the dark technique. After he had received an overwhelming fright during his fall in the plane, he was able to ignore his actual anxiety by virtue of a conversion symptom based upon the original organic injury; in this he was much supported by medical personnel. As long as he could feel that his difficulties were due to an organic injury, he did not have to accept his anxiety or take responsibility for his failure; thus he experienced no anxiety and no depression while overseas. On his return, however, he lost the protection of an organic illness. He had been told that any injury his heart might have received would clear up after several months. It was no longer possible for him to hide his difficulties under the guise of heart trouble. He therefore was brought directly face to face with the possibility of a return to flying after a period of rest at home, and, now that he had lost the protection of his organic illness, the anxiety emerged. With the appearance of anxiety came depression, based on the realization of the true situation and the loss of face entailed by his failure both to carry out his job and to live up to his ideals. When, under treatment, he began actually to deal with his anxiety and to think of returning to flying, he was able to recover from his depression. In this he was aided by the therapist, who constantly encouraged him to face his anxiety and to deal realistically with the problem. From the therapeutic point of view, however, it was necessary to decide whether it was possible for this individual to return to flying duty. In view of his fragile maturity, his long-standing insecurity and the actual psychological trauma incurred during his fall, it was considered that a return to a flying assignment at this time would not be wise. When this decision was announced to the patient, he immediately reacted with considerable protest. Although he had previously shown considerable indecision on this matter, he now stated that he should be allowed to return to flying and attempt to lick his fear. He was told that this would be a good long range aim, but that for the present he had to go back to ground duties. Thus, responsibility for the decision not to fly was assumed by the therapist rather than by the patient, and in this way the patient's pride was not damaged and the resentment which he formerly felt toward himself because of his weakness was now projected to the therapist. This resentment, however, was only superficial. Actually the patient felt greatly relieved and grateful, and at the time of his discharge to ground duty had recovered from all his symptoms.

.   .   .   .   .   .

The dynamic basis of this patient's difficulties is clearly outlined in the case material. Herein lies an interesting phenomenon, and one by which we were forcibly struck when observing the difference between war neuroses seen overseas and the same conditions seen after a patient's return to the United States. *After his return to the United States, the pattern of behavior resulting from stress becomes definitely linked to the soldier's precombat personality and his previous habitual manner of solving other conflicts. The connecting links are exposed.* The links obviously, are present while the patient is overseas, but they can only rarely be exposed and clearly seen either by the psychotherapist or by the patient. Both are forced to deal too intimately with the derivative but grim present situation. For example, this patient's evasiveness toward his anxiety was the chief object of psychotherapy overseas, and, during the time that he had to cling to it so desperately, its origin in his father's and his own early conduct could not be brought out. Only on his return home, when the pressure was off and a different set of forces began to operate, could these links be established. In the material which will be presented in the following chapters, this phenomenon will be elaborated and an attempt will be made to segregate the underlying patterns of behavior into various groupings.

CHAPTER 9

The Syndrome of "Operational Fatigue" (War Neuroses) in Returnees

OPERATIONAL FATIGUE is the euphemism by which war neuroses are designated in the Army Air Forces. This term was not invented by psychiatrists but is a combat edition of the old diagnosis, "flying fatigue," used in peacetime aviation medicine. Both terms are temporary expedients to hide the neurotic nature of the illness to which they are usually applied—temporary because they are abandoned when the condition necessitates separation from the service. Unlike the diagnosis of neurosis, which is prejudicial, this diagnosis permits the grounding of a man and his subsequent return to flying status.

Murray (45) attempts to differentiate "operational fatigue" from psychoneurosis on the basis that the latter denotes symptoms which are derived from unconscious conflicts arising in early childhood. On the other hand, he believes that "operational fatigue," at least in the early stages, is basically dependent on recent situations and has not yet become irreversibly bound to earlier unresolved conflicts. As we shall see later, this theoretical difference is not substantiated by careful analysis of patients who have returned to this country, and is only apparently applicable to the syndromes observed overseas (25).

Strictly speaking, there are fatigue states as a result both of long-continued nonoperational flying and of combat. Physical and psychological factors contribute to their etiology by constricting the ego's span and reducing its capacity to deal with anxiety. These syndromes are manifested by irritability, sleeplessness, loss of energy, loss of weight, mild gastrointestinal symptoms, headaches and mild subjective anxiety. Just as physical and emotional factors contribute to the production of fatigue states, so the resultant syndromes include both physical and emotional disturbances. They are reversible in the early stages by means of rest, diversion, good food, favorable living conditions, and relief from physical and emotional stress and monotony. For this purpose, rest camps are effective institutions. However, if a few days of such treatment result in little improvement, the condition has been erroneously diagnosed or has passed beyond the stage of spontaneous reversibility. The general use of the term "exhaustion" as a substitute for neurosis is clinically erroneous and facilitates fixation to neurasthenic-like symptoms.

"Operational fatigue" and other terms have been loosely used to cover a wide variety of reactions occurring in men engaged in combat flying, including the neuroses. They place the etiological emphasis on occupation and environment, thus having an advantage for officers who would much rather hear that their men have "operational fatigue" than that they have anxiety states. All the conditions described under the term of "operational fatigue" can best be defined as showing definite physical, mental and emotional symptoms, which develop in normal and predisposed subjects undergoing the stress of operational flying. In the previously normal individual it may be considered as an occupational disturbance, whereas in the predisposed or neurotic individual operational flying acts as a trigger mechanism in activating a previously dormant neurosis. This situation is entirely analogous to the precipitating incidents of traumatic neuroses in civilian life.

There is no question in the minds of those suffering from "operational fatigue" that they have nervous states, nor are the doctors and administrative personnel who are in contact with the afflicted in doubt as to the nature of the problem. But the euphemism has resulted in semantic confusion, because the word "fatigue" implies that rest is obviously the treatment of choice, when, as a matter of fact, rest is only suitable for true fatigue. Overseas and in this country it has required considerable time to overcome this semantic error, but gradually convalescent hospitals have supplanted rest camps. Emotional exhaustion certainly plays an important part in the development of many war neuroses overseas by virtue of its effect in depleting the powers of the ego to master anxiety. Its treatment is prophylactic, but, once anxiety has gained the ascendancy, neurosis is indeed present and must be treated not by rest but by activity and rational psychotherapy.

States of "operational fatigue" overseas were variably classified into syndromes on the basis of stages in the development of anxiety or according to the techniques by which the individual protected himself from consciousness of this emotion. In investigating this syndrome in returnees, there has been a temptation to attempt a classification into syndromes similar to clinical categories of civilian peacetime neuroses. The great variety of symptoms and their possible permutations and the multiple dynamic trends existing in a single patient soon made it apparent that syndromes were impossible to delineate if we were to view the clinical facts with any degree of accuracy. The following are the most frequent symptoms with which our patients enter the hospital, in the order of frequency:

    Restlessness
    Irritability and aggressive behavior
    Fatigue on arising and lethargy
    Difficulty in falling asleep
    Subjective anxiety
    Easy fatigue
    Startle reaction
    Feeling of tension
    Depression
    Personality changes and memory disturbances
    Tremor and evidences of sympathetic overactivity
    Difficulty in concentrating and mental confusion
    Increased alcoholism
    Preoccupation with combat experiences
    Decreased appetite
    Nightmares and battle dreams
    Psychosomatic symptoms
    Irrational fears (phobias)
    Suspiciousness

This list contains the most frequent symptoms but is not all-inclusive. These symptoms are present in every possible combination and to every quantitative degree. It may be noticed at once that they are both subjective and objective, and that among the latter type are, for the most part, evidences of excessive or deficient sympathetic activity.

In our subsequent discussions, we shall make it clear that there is rarely a single psychological trend manifested in any large group of patients, but rather there are mixtures of several trends. All the disturbances are regressive in a psychological sense, in that the individual no longer has a mature and adult capacity to discriminate reality and adapt to his environment, but uses infantile reactions or "lower-level" visceral techniques, which bring him into new conflicts causing anxiety or produce crippling physical symptoms. Nevertheless, for the purpose of description and clarification of the psychodynamics, we may divide the patients into the following groups, each of which is described in a subsequent chapter:

1. Passive-dependent states (chapter 10).
2. Psychosomatic states (chapter 11).
3. Guilt and depression (chapter 12).
4. Aggressive and hostile reactions (chapter 13).
5. Psychotic-like states (chapter 14).

When the medical examinations for returnees, mentioned in chapter 8, were first developed at redistribution stations and convalescent hospitals, division of patients into several categories according to the severity of their difficulties was considered feasible and wise. It was decided that certain minimal symptoms, as evidenced by mild degrees of the various complaints and symptoms listed above, could be considered as normal. The effects of combat and overseas life are universal in producing mild manifestations of anxiety in almost everybody. The majority of those symptoms decrease and gradually disappear with time. Such terms as uncoiling, unwinding, decompression and cooling off are generally applicable and are indicative of the natural and universal course toward recovery. Men suffering from such minimal symptoms are referred to duty and are expected to function normally after the several weeks' interval necessary for integration into their new organizations, although many relapse or become worse on meeting new frustrations.

The second category originally established was labeled "mild," because the above symptoms were all of mild severity, although they did not rapidly resolve, as would be expected if they were the usual or average reactions. Many of these men were sent to convalescent centers for physical activities and to partake in a health-building program coincident with retraining, but with no provision for special psychiatric therapy. After a time it was recognized that this treatment did not suffice for all and that some of these individuals needed care of a more specialized and medical nature.

The third category included those with severe symptoms who showed no evidences of getting better, often becoming worse, and whose clinical disturbance was such that they could not be expected to be made fit for duty or to be improved by physical measures alone. These severe cases were considered to be in need of definitive psychiatric treatment. Remaining the same, becoming worse or even first becoming ill after return to the United States, these patients demonstrate that relief from combat is not the cure for war neuroses, since these neuroses are not transient reactions but may even crystallize into permanent neurotic patterns if not adequately treated.

It became the responsibility of the medical officers in the processing lines of the redistribution stations to sort out the returned combat soldiers with nervous reactions into three categories of severity: minimal, mild and severe. At the Don Cesar Convalescent Hospital, designated to receive cases of "operational fatigue," it was soon discovered that it was impossible in a cursory examination to detect with any degree of accuracy the quantitative differences in reaction implied in these various categories. Many who came to the hospital with a diagnosis of "mild" turned out to be among the sickest patients. Others, who at first glance seemed to be very sick, recovered quickly and could be sent back to duty within a short time. From our experiences it became obvious that only two classifications can be made: (1) the normal and expected reaction, which recedes without therapy, and (2) the pathological state, requiring more or less definitive psychiatric treatment.

The frequency with which states of "operational fatigue" occur overseas is difficult to ascertain. A profusion of diagnostic terms and various confused interpretations as to which neurotic reactions are caused by war and which are due to old psychoneuroses make each psychiatrist's classification individual and not comparable. Everyone seems to be struggling with terminology and classification, which indicates a nondynamic approach to the problem. The question is never: Is this patient suffering from a psychoneurosis or a war neurosis? It is: How much did his previous personality and how much did the stress he experienced contribute to his reaction?

The number of cases of "operational fatigue" sufficiently severe to necessitate grounding overseas is not large. A much higher rate would be indicated if the diagnoses of all severities were included, especially those of patients who continue to function in combat and receive treatment only on returning home after completing their tour of duty. The low rate of grounding as compared with that of other diseases is, of course, due to the fact that mild somatic disease incapacitates men from flying, whereas mild neuroses do not. There is a definite relationship between "operational fatigue" and the type of plane, but none between it and the number of sorties or the number of casualties in the group.

Our figures indicate a higher percentage of neurotic reactions in fliers as compared with ground crews, and also the fact that the syndrome is three times as frequent in enlisted men as in officers. The small percentage ultimately sent to a hospital indicates the large number of patients suffering from mild neurotic states that recede spontaneously.

Among enlisted and officer flying personnel, those who have the least amount of continuous work to do throughout the mission and hence less opportunity to release tension, are the most susceptible to accumulations of anxiety. Fighter pilots are least frequently affected. The frequency with which "operational fatigue" occurs is, according to occupation in the combat crew, in the order listed below:

1. Radio gunner ⎫
2. Gunner ⎪ Enlisted men
3. Engineer gunner ⎬
4. Bombardier navigator ⎭
5. Bombardier ⎫
6. Navigator ⎪ Officers
7. Pilot (bomber) ⎬
8. Pilot (fighter) ⎭

With the help of Willerman, Barrell and Zucker we subjected patients, approximately 300 officers and 200 enlisted men, to detailed psychological interviews and questionnaires. We were interested in the relationship between predisposition and stress and the correlation of these factors with the severity of the neurotic illness. The information elicited contained considerable detail as to what the soldier was like psychologically before combat, what experiences he went through in combat and what symptoms he developed as a result of combat. The specific questions need not be repeated here.

Our studies demonstrated that no correlation could be determined at this distance between the apparent severity of a soldier's missions and the severity of his symptoms, since the sick soldier subjectively interpreted his combat experiences as severe and harrowing and no objective observations were available to us. On the other hand, the sickest patients remembered their past psychological illness and emotional disturbances because their attention was more forcibly directed to these events. Another common fallacy is to interpret the symptoms exposed by the illness as its cause; they are the result.

There was a clear-cut correlation between previous personality trends and the *type* of neurosis. A soldier who before combat had compulsive thinking and rituals showed, after combat, compulsive preoccupation with his battle experiences. Men subject to blue spells or depressive moods reacted with depression to the loss of friends. Predisposition to severe neuroses was indicated more often than not by a low precombat threshold of anxiety. Among the enlisted men, those of the older age group had more severe neurotic reactions. The degree of severity was not correlated with the number of missions, their severity, the theater of operations (men from the Southwest Pacific had more physical symptoms), the gun position, the military occupation, length of time in the army or overseas or in combat, the living conditions, the recreational facilities or homesickness. Men who had had precombat night terrors, sleepwalking, bedwetting, fainting, nail biting, stammering or worrisome matters were no more seriously ill than those without these so-called predispositions (38). On the other hand, there was a significantly greater proportion of severely ill soldiers who had been afraid of the dark in childhood, or who had been disturbed by minor frustrations in civilian life. There were more who had had a lenient family discipline among the mild cases than among those who were more seriously ill.

Of the cases admitted to the hospital 90.1 per cent were not casualties but casuals, recognized as needing hospital care *after* they returned to the United States from a full tour of combat duty. Further evidence of this is gathered from the sources of our patients. This fact, discussed further in chapter 15, is of far reaching significance, indicating the number of men who will require treatment for neuroses precipitated by war long after they have left the scene of battle.

SOURCE OF PATIENTS

	Officers per cent	Enlisted Men per cent
Redistribution stations	81.7	84.8
Continental commands	11.6	11.4
General hospitals	3.8	2.9
Port of debarkation	2.9	0.9

A large number of patients who are processed medically at redistribution stations have the capacity to keep themselves under control while being examined. Unwilling to be diagnosed as cases of "operational fatigue" and fearing hospitalization, they make a valiant effort to hide their symptoms from the medical officer. Often they are successful and are only discovered after being sent back to duty. They are eventually referred to the hospital when the Flight Surgeon of a Continental command discovers the unsuppressed signs of neuroses. The medical officers at the redistribution stations are not easily fooled, so that many soldiers are sent to the hospital still well in control of their symptoms, and it becomes our problem to establish the correct diagnosis. In some patients time alone reduces their control and after a few days they expose their suppressed symptomatology. Others are exposed after psychiatric interviews or a session with pentothal. Some turn out to be normal and not in need of therapy. The following case demonstrates a patient who was sent to us unnecessarily because he was thought to be holding his symptoms under control. It was found that he was not in need of prolonged treatment.

CASE 20: *Diagnostic pentothal interview, revealing a normal reaction not requiring therapy.*

An aerial gunner completed his tour of duty in the Indian Theater of Operations. He stated that he did not want to fly any more unless he could get in a crew with his old pilot, because he had no confidence in these "new cheap guys." He was a mechanic and requested work on the line. On his twenty-fifth mission two of the planes in his squadron crashed on the take-off and burned, killing all the occupants. From that time on he had always been frightened on take-off, but completely confident while in the air. Under pentothal no new data were elicited except that he clearly stated that he knew accidents could happen and people would get killed, although he had felt that this could never happen to him. After witnessing these crashes he felt: "Yes, it can happen to me." Thus, one of his protective devices against anxiety was lost and for the first time he experienced the strange and new sensations of anxiety.

.   .   .   .   .   .

Actually this man did not have a neurosis. There was no lasting nor crippling alteration of his ego, which had lost its feeling of magical omnipotence and only then developed one defensive and successful maneuver—to stay away from airplanes. There had been no spreading of the phobia.

In contrast, the following pentothal interview was elicited from a patient who was rather uncommunicative, stating that there was nothing wrong with him and that he just wanted to get out of the army and go home to be with his wife.

CASE 21: *Dependence and hostility exposed by a pentothal interview.*

After the induction of pentothal and the initial somnolent period, the patient promptly started to talk spontaneously as follows:

"I want out—the army is no good—let me out of this cage; they keep me barred up—I want to be with my wife and to go home to her every night and make a living for her. I want to stop shaking, the public don't like it and I'm ashamed before people—I want to be out—I want to be alone. I don't like officers, I'm scared of them—I don't want rigid rules—I don't like officers, they scare me—they think of nothing but keeping shoes shined and your bed made—I don't want officers—just men like me.

"Don't jab me with that needle—I'm scared of needles— Oh! oh! my head, it just goes around and around—why won't it stop?

"The army ruined me, never did me any good—just like a jail—let me out, I want out. I want to go away, I want to go where people know me. I want to go somewhere where people do things. I want to be with my mother and father. I love them so much—they have done so much for me—I can't repay them while in the army. I want my wife. I'm no good here—she gives me advice and tells me when I'm right and when I'm wrong. The army's just second fiddle. I want to go home and have children. This is not living—this is just murder. They send you to die, for what? So somebody can make money. What good is the insurance without me?—it won't buy her happiness. She's got to have me. The army is no good. Nothing but a bunch of skunks in the army. . . .

"Oh, oh, oh! that pain, oh!" (great emotion)—"fighters at 6 o'clock, they are coming in—no, they can't hurt me, I've got to get back to my wife—I have got to shoot them down—got to get back to my wife—I promised her" (calm). . . .

"My buddy wants to fly—he's crazy, it's death. To die is all right naturally, but to be sent out to die is murder. Those all-night practice missions with bombs—they don't care, we're just suckers. These officers are not worth their weight in gold. I'm scared, I'm scared of them—take them away—take them away.

"Where am I? I want my wife—don't let them take her away from me—she's all I live for, she consoles me when I'm hurt. She encourages me when officers are mean. Take them away. These bars are shiney, they hurt my eyes. Take those skunks away—I'm only a little fellow, take them away, just me and my wife. I want to be happy. I can't be happy in the army. I'm always worried, I'm worried to death, I'm getting old in the army—please let me out."

.   .   .   .   .   .

Under pentothal this surly, aggressive soldier exposed his extreme regression to a dependent and childish state. The diagnostic value of the drug was also demonstrated by the disclosure that the soldier was still sensitive to the traumatic memories of his combat experiences and that his evoked hostilities were still displaced to the army authorities.

Patients who enter the hospital are admitted to a special ward, where they remain for three days and are studied carefully. A complete history is taken and a physical examination is made, including a survey for tropical and exotic diseases. Dental examinations and laboratory studies are performed. Psychological studies are routinely made, with special tests when necessary. The patient is also thoroughly indoctrinated into the hospital program and assigned to classroom and physical activities in the Convalescent Services Division. His military and civilian legal papers are put in order.

After all the preliminary work has been completed, the final step is a brief psychiatric interview, which is summarized on his record. The patient is transferred to a particular ward and assigned to one of the ward officers, who is a general medical officer specially trained by us in methods of treating war neuroses. If the patient presents a more difficult problem and needs special care, he is assigned to the psychiatric specialist on the ward. This psychiatrist sees all the patients, in consultation with ward officers, controlling and supervising their work.

The regular wards are only used as dormitories, since the patients are busy the whole day with physical and mental activities and various aspects of occupational therapy. Therefore a special ward is reserved for the very ill. Here the care is almost entirely psychiatric, with specially trained nurses and experienced psychiatrists in attendance. Finally, we have a complete hospital ward for the treatment of medical and surgical complications, such as malaria or dysentery, necessitating bed care and nonpsychiatric therapy. This ward is under the charge of internists and surgeons.

For the treatment of war neuroses, our principal method has been described as an "uncovering technique" in contradistinction to the therapy most successful close to the front lines, which we have called the "covering-up" method. Reassurance, persuasion, forcing and various stimulating processes are important and valuable for military purposes, since they are successful in returning many men to combat in spite of their anxiety states, if they receive such treatment in the early phases of their difficulties. However, these forms of therapy, used alone, are not rational, once a man has been evacuated to the rear or has been returned to the United States. Efforts to increase the strength of repressing forces may be necessary even then, when no other methods are available because of lack of time or personnel, and are excusable from the standpoint of expediency only.

We have demonstrated that the symptomatology of war neuroses is monotonously repetitive, the identical symptoms occurring in various permutations in almost all cases. Yet the underlying causes vary greatly and are as different as the personalities and experiences of the individuals. It is our task to uncover the dynamic basis of the neurosis, not simply in order to make a diagnosis as to its type and severity but also for the purpose of treatment, because one "cannot fight an unseen enemy." In most cases we find either an older conflict originating in combat, or a new one stimulated by the return home. In each category the ancient and buried conflicts of the individual's early life will somehow be related to the current situation.

Sometimes thorough psychiatric interviews and pentothal probing will reveal no conflict, no repressed anxiety nor memories relating to a living problem. Even if an emotional problem is discovered in these patients, it does not correlate well with the intensity of the physical symptoms, which may persist after their emotional recovery.There does not seem to be an adequate emotional basis, either conscious or unconscious, for often severe subjective and objective symptoms. Furthermore, although no organic disease can be discovered medically, yet these patients suffer from considerable somatic dysfunction.

In one category are patients who seem to suffer from a chronic stimulation of the sympathetic nervous system. They perspire freely, are tremulous, restless and irritable, sleep poorly and look very sick. At times these symptoms suddenly increase, especially in response to mild auditory or verbal stimuli, and the patients react as if they had received an injection of adrenalin. They pose problems concerning which we may only theorize, because as yet we have insufficient clinical or laboratory data from which to draw final conclusions.

Most of these patients have been through monotonously repetitive, almost daily exposures to death and destruction, sometimes with more harrowing specific experiences. Day after day they have been called upon to work at high speed and to respond at a superhuman pitch of performance. Emergency psychological reactions of anxiety and physiological preparedness, with accelerated heart rate, sweating, breathlessness, muscle tenseness and the accompanying metabolic alterations, have overlapped and become not episodic, but almost continuous. Eventually the soldier is removed from the environment of stress and after a time his subjective anxiety recedes. But the physiological phenomena persist and now are maladaptive to a life of safety and security, and they become disagreeable symptoms which reverberate psychologically to cause distress to the patient. They persist longer than the common "after discharge" of anxiety occurring after the danger has passed. It is as if the heightened physiological setting of the neuroendocrine system had become jelled and irreversible, activating peripheral and central nervous structures and smooth muscles continuously or excessively in response to minor stimuli (43).

It is probable that this new setting is an expression of a metabolic and/or an endocrine activity. Although we can determine the frequency of this syndrome and its quantitative extent by objective methods, we do not have available or utilizable means of determining the specific glandular origin. Blood pressure and pulse rates are elevated and sometimes fluctuating. There is no albuminuria. Basal metabolism, cholesterol, glucose tolerance tests, are normal. The thyroid glands are usually firmer and larger than normal. There is a great need for research in finer clinical methods of objectively demonstrating such hypothetical functional endocrine changes and for discovery of methods of treatment, since at present our only therapy is rest, sedation and the passage of time.

Another very small group of patients demonstrates an easy fatigability. They have no ability for continuous mental concentration or sustained physical activity. They are tired all the time and cannot get enough sleep; and these patients do not regain their weight on a high caloric diet. Many have a slow pulse, but there are few other abnormalities. These patients seem to show the reverse of the previously described clinical picture. It is as if they were physiologically exhausted; in fact they look "washed out," often appearing ten years older than their chronological ages. Is this a central, metabolic or endocrine process? We have no answer but simply indicate our clinical observations of a puzzling situation that requires elucidation by research of physiologists and biochemists. The following patient demonstrates this exhausted state.

CASE 22: *Profound physiological and psychological depression.*

A B-25 engineer gunner served in the Southwest Pacific from a base in New Guinea for about eighteen months. On his thirtieth mission he was shot down in enemy territory and experienced great difficulties in returning to his base through jungle and swamp and across rivers, while at the same time he and his crew were forced to evade the Japs and spend considerable time in hiding. During the many days it took him to make his way back to base after his evasion of the Japs, he suffered no particular symptoms. However, on arriving safely at his airfield, he became shaky, sleepless, tired and depressed, and had many bad dreams of being caught and overpowered by the Japs. There was a consistent decline in his appetite, so that he lost over 25 pounds in weight.

In sessions of group psychotherapy with four other evadees, the patient was uncommunicative but not particularly upset by the narratives of the other soldiers. When it was his turn to recount his experiences, he did so in an almost inaudible voice with no great show of emotional reaction. He was therefore seen privately and given a pentothal interview, during which he recounted in detail his harrowing experiences but without particular emotional reaction. Although his external appearance and attitude were depressed, he had lost no close friend and had no guilty feelings.

Physical examination indicated no evidence of endocrine disturbance. His appearance, however, was that of a completely exhausted person, although he had been out of combat for several months. His pulse rate at rest was normal. A blood glucose tolerance test showed a normal fasting blood sugar and a normal curve. Since there seemed to be no evidence of hyperinsulinism, he was given 10 units of insulin twenty minutes before each meal; 50 mg. of thiamine hydrochloride hypodermically daily; a high caloric diet and feedings of 8 per cent Karo syrup and fruit juice between meals. During this regime he gained about 5 pounds, but as soon as it was interrupted he returned to his preceding weight. Gastrointestinal x-ray studies revealed no organic nor functional disturbance. Blood smears showed no evidence of active malaria.

This patient gave no evidence of having a prolongation of a conflict originating in combat. He had no obvious signs of fear or displaced anxiety and no evidence of a new conflict in relation to his return to the United States. He still had some dreams of combat, in which he flew over the target, but these did not awaken him. He was restless, had difficulty in sleeping and in addition to a marked loss of weight (25 pounds) there was considerable ease of fatiguability. During his stay in the hospital, which lasted approximately three months, no improvement in his condition was discernible.

. . . . .

This soldier apparently suffered from a metabolic disturbance which was initiated by his combat experiences and the attendant strain of prolonged anxiety. The source of this metabolic disturbance could not be attributed to a special organ with any degree of certainty.

The patient had a stable personality and reacted normally under the stress of combat. His especially harrowing experiences caused him no great difficulties *until they were past*, when he became anxious and sleepless. This is a frequent reaction to traumatic situations in military and civilian life. The emergency evokes powerful reactions within the entire organism, especially in the vital sympathetic-endocrine system. Metabolic activities are speeded and the ego's sensitivity to external stimuli reaches the point of alertness. The rapidity with which emergency vital mechanisms are set into action is well known, but the slowness of their decrement is not appreciated. Sympathetic hyperactivity seems to persist for long periods after the stimulus has passed. The weary ego, which has borne the brunt of excitation from the external stimulus to the point of near-exhaustion, must continue to master stimuli arising from within the organism as an "after-discharge." Furthermore, during the crisis it functioned rapidly, with automatic discrimination and precision. It now perceives the dangerous meaning of the trauma, its recent catastrophic proximity to dissolution, and reacts with subjective anxiety in retrospect.

Long-continued activation of the emergency mechanisms, manifested by stimulation of the sympathetic nervous system and endocrine glands, may produce a lowered, irreversible physiological setting and even morphological alterations. In the type of case just described, the ego also seems to have been functionally depressed. Continually battered by external stimuli and internal reactions, which it must master or succumb to, the ego develops a state of numbness. The soldier goes through his functions like an automaton with little feeling. Even subsequent catastrophic experiences hardly impinge on his consciousness. He walks through dangers impervious to their significance. This dull and depressed behavior is not an active psychological defense of the ego against experiences that might hurt. While such active defenses occur in the patients under consideration, the ego is more like an inactivated zone or a dead air space which transmits nothing in either direction. These are the bleary-eyed soldiers with blank faces stumbling along the road back from the front. Most of them recover rapidly with physiological rest, but some, like our patient, seem incapable of renewed interest in or reactivity to their environments. Psychologically and physiologically all their functions are depressed to a lower level of activity.

Further diagnostic information is elicited as the therapeutic process proceeds. Psychiatric diagnosis and psychotherapy proceed hand in hand and are not separated stages. Therefore, the physician who treats the patient is also responsible for obtaining all the data with which he has to work, at the same time establishing a transference relationship. Social workers or psychologists are not used as separate "history takers." Rather, histories are obtained by free association with a minimum of interrogation, although recorded according to chronological form. The following material, among other data, is always obtained from the patient during the course of the doctor's work with him:

1. The presenting symptoms and their immediate precipitating causes.

2. The predisposing factors in the patient's previous personality and past experiences; his familial, social and economic background.

3. The quantity of stress on missions: flak, fighter attacks, accidents, crack-ups, bailing-out, evasion in enemy territory, etc.

4. The psychological reactions to combat in various missions during the operational tour; changes with time and stress.

5. Disturbances in interpersonal relationships within the group, including loss of officers, friends and buddies.

6. The morale of the organization and that of the patient.

7. The non-flying stress: living conditions, food, home worries, etc.

8. The disturbances in interpersonal relationships on return to the United States; the disturbing experiences at home or on return to duty in a Continental command.

9. The dynamic factors involved in the total clinical picture.

10. The response to special forms of therapy.

Many of the details in the above categories have been elicited for purposes of statistical studies by special psychological questionnaires. Many of the data concerning each patient are entered in a summary and are available for research studies. The relationship of these factors to the development of various psychological trends will be discussed in subsequent chapters.

CHAPTER 10

Passive-Dependent States

Extremely passive and dependent trends are often found underlying the many symptoms described in chapter 9. These qualities are easily detected in interviews through observation of the patient's behavior, or are uncovered during abreactions under pentothal. The neurotic symptoms themselves are not specific and are only an indication of a state of anxiety caused not by the basic trends but by the fact that they are in conflict with other forces. The need to be loved, emotionally supported and cared for creates strong drives for satisfaction, which are usually frustrated because such great quantities of passive gratification are rarely attainable by an adult in real life. Hence conflict rages between intense desire and frustrating reality. On the other hand, portions of the patient's self-respecting ego may not permit direct or sufficient gratification of his childlike need for love and care, in which case an intrapsychic conflict is developed. The symptoms are thus indicative of conflict but do not specify its nature or the forces involved.

It is easy to dismiss these particular conflicts lightly with the simple explanation that the patient has always been an immature person and is therefore suffering from a psychoneurosis unrelated to the army or combat experiences. Many psychiatrists have been misled into making such interpretations, even concerning men who have finished a full tour of combat duty. Historical data regarding the individual's previous personality and his patterns of reaction, the stresses to which he has been subjected and how these have affected him must be ascertained before such conclusions may be drawn. We have found that the stress of combat is responsible for considerable regression in previously mature men as well as in immature boys (cf. chapter 1).

However, some were far more emotionally dependent than their chronological ages justified, to the degree that they were abnormally attached to home, mother, father or their substitutes. It is to these boys that we may attach with justification the appellation of passive-dependent characters prior to combat, and we could have predicted that many would in some degree react adversely to the stress of combat. It must be clearly understood, however, that it is not dependence *per se*, but its quantity and dynamic relationship to other, more mature and independent ego forces, that determine predisposition to disturbances under stress.

The words "passivity" and "dependence" are too widely applied as derogatory terms indicating maladaptation. It is implied too often that the vague and mythical state of normality predicates a complete and stalwart independence and maturity. Psychiatrists know that there are very few such independent characters. Everyone carries a large quantity of dependence within him into adult life, long after the establishment of an independent social, economic and family existence. It may well be disguised, sublimated or overcompensated. There are many ways in which the normal adult gratifies his dependence, in secret, even without his own knowledge. He may lean heavily on a superior or on an older man, to whom he turns for advice, or he may marry a disguised substitute for his mother. He may become an altruistic supporting figure for others, doing unto them as he would wish for himself, thereby obtaining gratification by identification with the recipient. On the other hand, he may overcompensate against his dependent needs by becoming an aggressive, sometimes hostile, figure in his community (cf. cases 48 and 52), or may indulge his unconscious trends through the use of alcohol. Some individuals express their dependent needs on a lower visceral level in gastric language, as discussed under the heading of Psychosomatic States (cf. chapter 11).

With these facts in mind, let us examine the clinical material to determine how an interaction between past personality and stress produces regression to varying states of dependence and how these manifest themselves clinically in war neuroses (25).

The first case demonstrates the process of regression in a boy who had always remained strongly attached to his mother.

CASE 23: *Immature personality, showing evidences of marked regression to an infantile state after relatively mild experiences in combat.*

A 20 year old Sergeant was a tail gunner on a B-17 and completed forty-nine combat missions. He was a physically small individual with an immature but appealing manner, and the capacity of stimulating protective and almost maternal attitudes in his associates. He had relatively few friends in his combat outfit, but was very close to his own crew, who in turn took very good care of him. He had never been too eager for combat. On the other hand, he was willing to do his share, whatever that was said to be, and to follow his crew into what fate had in store for him. This turned out to be worse than he had ever anticipated. All his combat missions were extremely difficult and toward the end were nightmare adventures for him. Although he could never become accustomed to the atmosphere of danger, during his first twenty missions he was able to control his anxiety and tension sufficiently to give the outward appearance of calm. At the take-off for his twenty-first mission, his plane had just become airborne when a motor failed, resulting in a crash at the far end of the runway. Through unbelievable good fortune, no one on his crew was seriously injured. After this, however, he had no confidence in his pilot or in the plane and felt that every mission would be his last. Although he encountered no particularly hazardous experiences thereafter, and no one in his crew was ever hurt, he felt so threatened by a host of concrete and nameless horrors that he was in a constant state of severe anxiety. In the plane he could not control the tremors caused by his fear of flak or a crash, and at night he was so scared by the weird figures he imagined to be inhabiting the darkness that he could scarcely go to sleep. He knew these were only a product of his imagination but this was small comfort. Yet, if he went to sleep, it was only to dream of crashes in burning planes. In spite of the increasing nightmare quality of his waking and sleeping life, he never asked to be removed from combat. Aware of his growing shakiness, his crewmates attempted continually to comfort and support him, while his Flight Surgeon fed him sedatives. Because of a severe shortage of combat crew replacements, every effort was made to maintain him in combat. From the point of view of maintaining him as a passenger on a combat aircraft, these efforts were successful, although he was not able to contribute much as a combat crew member. At one point he became so excited and confused when under attack by enemy aircraft that he accidentally shot himself in the foot. The injury was not serious. After his forty-ninth mission he appeared to be so close to outright panic that he was relieved from the obligation of making his final mission by his commanding officer and was returned home.

On admission to the hospital after his overseas furlough, he presented a pitiful figure. Tremulous, agitated and depressed, he paced the hospital floors day and night, unable to relieve himself of his constant anxiety or to find any rest. In the interviews with his doctors, he told of his difficulties with the lump-in-the-throat effect of a small, completely defeated, completely lost child. "I can't stand it here," he complained. "I can't stay in this hospital any more. I can't eat the food. My stomach won't take anything but milk. If I didn't drink milk, I'd die here. And I can't get any rest anywhere because I'm scared all the time. I'm scared of everything. I'm afraid of people. Maybe I'm a coward, I don't know. If there's a loud noise or someone claps me on the back, I get so scared I shake for hours. I'm afraid I may hit one of these loud-mouthed G.I.'s when they scare me like that. I'm afraid of water. I used to be able to swim, but now I can't go near it. And why am I so scared of windows?—I guess I may jump out of one some day. I don't know what to do. I can't help myself—I just don't know what's the matter with me. I try, I try to do what you tell me, to pull myself together. I don't want to be like this. I try to get better, but I just keep on getting worse."

During his stay in the hospital, this patient actually became progressively more disturbed, until finally his phobic response to practically everything in the environment reached an almost psychotic intensity. He was unable to tolerate any group activities. Although he was always polite, cooperative, even submissively respectful, individual psychotherapy was limited by his uncontrollable dependent need. With the utmost earnestness, he begged to be returned to his home. "I've got to go home," he repeatedly stated, "before I go crazy here. Please let me go home. My mother is the only doctor who can do me any good. She's the only one who knows how to take care of me. If I don't eat, she makes me eat. She knows what to do for me because she understands me. She won't let me get away with anything either. She'll make me go to bed and stay by me until I go to sleep. She'll keep a light on in the room so I won't be scared by the dark. This morning the nurse scolded me because I didn't want to get up. How could I get up when I didn't get to sleep until after it began to get light outside? What makes her be like that? I'll take a scolding from my mother, but I won't take it from any damn G.I. nurse. I can't stand to look at anything G.I. any more. That's why I'll never get better here. I did my best in combat. I did what they asked me to do. Why can't I go home now before I go completely nuts. I've got to go home, honestly I do."

This unashamed longing to return to his mother was the intensification of a trend which could be seen in his past history. The patient had always remained a little boy emotionally, never really severing himself from his mother. His pre-army school and work record indicated that he had tried hard but had never been able to achieve independence. His father had been killed by a hit-and-run driver when the patient was 13. The mother had remarried soon thereafter, but he never got along with his stepfather, who was a chronic alcoholic and bullied him a great deal. In school he managed to finish the eighth grade in spite of feeling uncomfortable because of his inability to mix socially with the other students. He always wanted to be home with his mother. Nevertheless, after his graduation, he attended a technical high school for four months and then a commercial school for three months. He then joined a CCC camp for a six months' period, after which he did odd jobs, including one year of working on a farm driving a truck. In his own opinion, he never adapted himself successfully to any of these jobs.

At the age of 18 years, with no success behind him, this emotionally immature and dependent boy started the hard life of the army. Notwithstanding his anxiety and panic, he honorably completed a full tour of combat duty, truly a remarkable achievement and obviously a product not of his own but of the group's strength. Although the combat stress was not especially severe, it led to a marked psychological regression to an even lower level of maturity. In his infantile state, the whole world seemed threatening and hostile; his speech and eating proclivities also corresponded to those of a small child. His only wish was to be with his mother. During his hospital stay, there was no remnant of a self-respecting ego to enforce an attempt at maturity or to be approached by the psychiatrist's therapeutic efforts. The patient's symptoms were directly due, not to his combat experiences, but to frustration of his dependent needs by reality. These needs were intensified by combat and could be expected to continue until he was back in his mother's arms. By some miracle, he had escaped a psychosis; perhaps because in reality there still remained the hope of reunion with mother. It was possible that she might be able to nurse him back to his previous state by tenderness and direct gratification and gradual reestablishment of his ego's confidence. For this reason, he was discharged from the army; at home he might be able to resume his previously slow and difficult development toward maturity.

CASE 24: *Immature personality who regressed markedly under the stress of combat.*

A 24 year old gunner was admitted to the hospital with complaints of tenseness and loss of appetite. He had been aware of the former symptom from the time he entered combat, approximately twenty-two months previously. The latter complaint was of more recent origin, beginning some time during his twenty-one day overseas furlough, while he was at home with his family.

It was noted that this individual was quite tense; when answering questions he exhibited marked nervousness by increase in tremor and purposeless psychomotor activity. The initial interview was spent in trying to uncover the general background of the patient's combat experiences. The following facts of importance were elicited: (a) He felt keenly his responsibility as a radio-operator and his value to the well-being of the crew. (b) On his third mission, he saw a ship in his formation explode and disintegrate in midair, thus destroying one of his cherished psychological protections, the magical belief that airmen always managed to escape from a plane when it was hit. (c) He was shot down over enemy-occupied territory and spent six months as an evadee. During these six months, the patient's well-being was constantly jeopardized, and he experienced intense anxiety. At the time of his landing in occupied territory, he was markedly upset by the fact that a waist gunner who had been killed in action was buried in a foreign country in an unmarked grave, probably to be desecrated by machines of war.

The patient's past history showed that he had come from a small, well knit family group. He had led a cloistered existence until he was 21 years of age. During childhood and early youth, he was strongly attached to his brother, older by ten years, who babied him greatly. When his brother left home, the patient resought emotional gratification from his parents, which he had previously (through childhood and early youth) received from his brother. When he reached the age of 21, the patient searched for employment away from his own home. At first he held short time jobs, always returning home when one was finished. This persisted until the patient fell in love and experienced a gratification of his needs from his fiancée. After several interviews, it became apparent that this patient had always been dependent on other people—particularly those close to him.

His initial reaction to the change in environment provided by army life was buffered by a fascination with various aspects of the new existence. He became dependent on close buddies wherever he happened to be. He soon entered combat and began facing larger problems. Further evidence of his immature personality was the fact that his responsibility as a radio operator caused him much anxiety; he disliked it intensely. His immaturity was also reflected in his unrealistic thinking, whereby he believed that airmen always escaped from the plane. It was also evident that he identified himself with the waist gunner who was buried in an unloving environment. When the patient thought this might happen to him, a great deal of anxiety was stimulated. Throughout his experiences as an evadee, the patient was completely dependent on the underground. His isolation and inability to communicate with his surroundings owing to language difficulties emphasized his personal needs.

During psychotherapeutic interviews, this material was reviewed with the patient and his emotional reactions explained. He developed some insight and seemed to improve. The improvement was related not only to this new insight, but also to gratification of his needs by the interest and sympathy of the doctors. The patient obtained a furlough to go home because of an intense desire to visit his mother. Upon leaving for his furlough, he was childlike in his excitement and enthusiasm. He continued to improve and eventually was discharged to duty.

.   .   .   .   .   .

Like the previous patient, this soldier was an immature, dependent person, who had been spoiled and pampered as a child and throughout life had sought relationship with people who could provide him with his customary gratifications. He too could endure severe hardships and stress in combat by using substitutes for mother figures; yet the end result was not greater strength and confidence in his abilities, but severe regression to a more childish attitude. Responsibility caused him great anxiety, made worse when his magical illusions were destroyed. This patient's ego had considerable capacity to endure frustrations and he was able to gratify his needs by a relationship with the therapist and to gather strength through the process of identification.

Combat experiences caused an intensification of this boy's dependent needs. His gastric symptoms were indicative of reaction to separation from the mother whom he needed more than ever before. Because he had the capacity of using other people to substitute for his mother, this patient should be able to continue to adapt as long as he is supported by external human figures. He had, however, no remaining internal strength through which to subsist alone. In this respect he showed the syndrome of ego depletion, which will be discussed later.

CASE 25: *Severe infantile regression secondary to harrowing combat experiences—anxiety state due to frustrations on return home.*

A 24 year old enlisted bombardier had entered the army after graduation from college, where he had maintained average scholastic standing. He was the third oldest of six siblings. There was no history of neurosis in the family or in the patient's personal life; he had made normal social adaptations. He had gone into gunnery training because he wanted to fly, even though he had been washed out of cadet training because of color blindness. He was eager to go overseas but anticipated his first missions with much nervousness. However, he completed fifty-two missions, many of which were severe. His apprehension continued throughout his tour of duty and was always much worse on the way back from the target. What kept him going was the contemplation of returning home after fifty missions. He was considerably upset when two of his best friends were shot down. Because his ship was always in the worst flak, the boys called him the "flak magnet" and some refused to fly with him. His last mission was exceptionally severe and his ship had to turn back because of the flak.

The anxiety and tension he felt in combat persisted on his return to the United States. On his overseas furlough at home, he felt irritable, anxious and restless and had difficulty in sleeping at night. His father and brothers annoyed him intensely. He became disturbed when asked to talk to friends and neighbors and refused to speak before local organizations that were interested in his experiences. He became so disturbed at home that he withdrew from all possible contacts and remained in bed as much as possible. Severe dyspeptic symptoms forced him to adopt a milk diet.

On admission, he had marked coarse tremor of both hands, extreme anxiety, severe insomnia, restlessness, irritability and startle reactions. With psychotherapy, narcosynthesis and the release of much anxiety in relation to the battle situation, the patient improved considerably after a hospitalization of three weeks. About the sixth week, when the problem of his return to duty arose, he became depressed, his tremor reappeared and he developed crying spells. Therapeutic interviews were resumed and considerable improvement occurred, until he was ready for discharge.

He then stated that he did not feel that he could continue in the army. He showed a marked amount of resentment against anything military and stated that, when he was around among soldiers or crowds of any type, in movies or restaurants, he developed a coarse tremor which embarrassed him. Yet he did not want to be discharged to his home. Although he had good insight into the psychogenesis of his difficulty, he did not want to accept help, feeling that he could conquer his troubles himself; nevertheless he had many spontaneous attacks of weeping. Nowhere, either at home or in the army, could he envisage gratification of his dependent needs. He vacillated between a whining, weeping cry for help and a bitter, sneering hostility toward all those in authority who did not cater to him but made demands on him. He had a sort of pseudoaggressiveness which was an effort to overcome his feeling of inferiority. Even after ten weeks of intensive psychotherapy, the patient had regained little independence, but he was returned for a trial at duty.

. . . .

This case typifies the reaction of an initially fairly stable and independent character, whose dependence was largely regressive, forced by the stress of combat. He was sustained by the contemplation of returning home but on reaching there at long last he could not be gratified. The little demands made on him created intense anxiety and hostility. In the hospital he improved only as long as he was safe and secure and not faced with the necessity of returning to duty. Discharge was a threat because nowhere in the outside world could he attain his ends. Thus he alternately whined and snapped, and was completely unhappy. His verbal associations revealed that a close identification with lost comrades had caused a powerful wound to his ego, which then retreated from all adult attitudes. The whole world was hostile because it did not give to him, and the resulting frustrations stimulated his own aggressions. Therapeutic sessions of an hour's duration, held daily for several months, effected little change, but he was sent back to duty for a trial.

CASE 26: *The breakdown of an attempted solution of dependence by assumption of responsibilities, which became too great, causing regression.*

A 23 year old First Lieutenant, pilot of a B-24, who had been overseas for twelve months, entered the hospital appearing chronically ill and depressed but with no complaints. He was raised in a small town, completed high school and one year of college and then worked for a pipeline construction company. His parents had separated when he was 2 years old. On his return home, he married a girl whom he had known for some time. In combat his ship was badly shot up on six occasions, necessitating crash landings. Heavy flak and bad weather forced him to turn back on numerous occasions. After sixty-five missions he was grounded to await return to the United States. Several days later, because of a shortage of pilots, he was asked to take his crew on a mission but refused and the operations officer went in his place. His plane was shot up and crashed in the sea with the loss of all but one of the occupants. The patient then felt badly because his crew looked up to him. They had often written and told their folks they were in good hands as long as they were flying with him. He was a great friend of all his enlisted men, going out of his way to help them. He was their first pilot in combat and would cheer them up and allay their fears. He felt that, if he had gone on the fatal mission, he would have brought them back. Since then he frequently slipped into depressed moods, in which he was overpowered by feelings of guilt over the loss of his crew. During a pentothal interview, this supposedly strong, giving and supporting person had a dramatic abreaction in which he expressed his own great fears of combat and guilt in regard to the crew (cf. chapter 12). He felt that the mothers of the lost crew members probably held him responsible for their deaths.

He then divulged the information that, since the time his father had separated from his mother nineteen years ago, the mother had worked as a housekeeper for a very strong and domineering man, who treated her badly. For some reason she remained in this house for many years. The patient was also mistreated by this man and fantasied that he would some day get his mother out of this situation. At the age of 16 he tried to get a job but had no social security number because of being under age. At the age of 17 he entered the army, and later his mother left her position but not because the patient was able to save her.

Psychotherapy was devoted to making him aware of the dependent trends underlying his real and fantasied attempts at maturity. It was pointed out to him that he had identified himself with his enlisted men and thereby received a vicarious gratification of his dependent needs. His conflict over responsibility for the men was identical with his conflict in regard to his responsibility for his mother. In fact, as he stated, his feelings toward his crew and toward his mother were the same. He felt frustrated about what he had not been able to do for his mother and for his crew. When the "giving role" as a solution of his own dependent needs was destroyed by his desertion of his crew in their moment of need, he regressed and reacted with depression to his own frustrations. As the patient became conscious of his pattern of reaction and the unreality of his guilt feelings and depression, his symptoms rapidly disappeared and he made a very thorough recovery.

. . . . . .

This officer was successful in solving his dependent needs by turning them into the opposite—giving to others. He also received gratification by identification with the recipients. But when this broke down because of his own failure to take his ship out on its last and fateful mission, his defense cracked and again he was in conflict over his relation to his mother. "To be cared for by her or to care for her," that was the question. The uncovering of his conflict enabled his not too badly regressed ego to resume its customary technique of dealing with reality and his inner drives. He left the hospital with plans for making a home for his mother at his next station and thus gratifying his needs while he also helped her. This case again illustrates how ego depletion can result not from lack of outside gratification, but from loss of self esteem owing to the patient's retreat from responsibility. Failure to live up to his ego-ideals and the subsequent state of being on bad terms with himself cost his ego its narcissistic gratification. The patient felt he could no longer be loved by others or by himself.

CASE 27: *Dependent, insecure soldier, who regressed further because of combat experiences—strong aggressive overcompensation.*

This patient, a Sergeant, was admitted to the hospital because of loss of appetite, insomnia, nausea and vomiting, restlessness and lack of self control, which had developed in a theater of operations. Not much information was volunteered about his background and early development. His mother had died of cancer while he was on his way to visit her. His father was not well, and there were two sisters and one brother, but the patient had little to say about them. The patient had been married for several years but had no children. Since his return to the United States, he had been able to relax slightly while with his wife and to sleep somewhat better.

In his initial interview, the patient, a red-haired young man, asthenic in build, was rather tense, restless, resentful and somewhat belligerent. He had very little to say on his own initiative and as little under direct questioning. However, he was quite spontaneous in saying that he was through with the army, that he wanted to be out of it and to return to his civilian work. He stated that his father, who was a contractor, was now too sick to do much himself, and that he, the patient, was anxious to step in and take over. He talked in a loud manner, tried to prove that he was afraid of nothing and discussed superficially some of his experiences overseas as a ground crew member of a heavy bombardment squadron. During three other interviews, he continued to behave in about the same manner, complaining of his sleeplessness and lack of appetite and vague battle dreams. At times he would say that, no matter what happened, he would never return to duty.

After a few days, the patient was given sodium pentothal, to which, surprisingly, he offered little objection, although emphasizing that he was always afraid of needles. The patient began immediately to talk about his experiences overseas. He was extremely restless, turning from side to side, covering his face, crying intermittently. He talked at great length of the landing for the invasion of enemy territory and of the many casualties. While in the desert, he was exposed to daily raids—about half a dozen each day—all emphasizing the helplessness of his group. There were no heavy defense weapons, no ack-ack, no good shelters—not even good leadership. During one raid, he was afraid to run toward his own foxhole. He jumped into another. Another man immediately behind him fell on top of the patient in the same foxhole, thus acting as a shield. When it was over, the man above him was dead. The patient made sure that he got out of the foxhole quickly, since it was not his own and this was a breach of procedure which could result in his being killed by his own men. He continued to relate that a plane which he usually loaded, and which was manned by a crew from his home town, exploded just after the take-off. When he came on the scene, there was nothing left of the plane or of the crew—just a few remnants and part of an ankle, to which clung an engraved gold chain. The patient had it cleaned and sent it to the wife of the dead man. In the accompanying letter he stated that the bracelet was given to him *before* the man took off on his mission. At this point the patient could not contain himself, cried even more and could hardly talk, repeating that he had lied to her but that he could not do otherwise. The same day he had asked this friend, in the event of his death, to send his ring and bracelet to his wife with the statement that he died for her— nothing more. He wrote the same thing to the dead man's wife. He saw the woman when he returned but he could not tell her much. The friend, Stan, was mentioned frequently by the patient during the pentothal interview—"Only a 'Polack,' but with a heart of gold."

Without any stimulation, the patient went on to say that he always liked to fight. When only a kid, he fought his own best friend and nearly killed him. When he went to high school, he asked to be taught how to fight. While fighting, he frequently lost his self control completely and had to be separated from his opponent. He was told by one doctor that on such occasions he goes temporarily insane. Because of such lack of control, he didn't want to fight. But on arriving overseas, he insisted that he should land first in order that he might be in the thick of it. "I love to fight—fight!" In addition to this frank admission under pentothal, he had a number of hostile outbursts while in the hospital but no attacks of overt aggression. His tirades were violent verbalizations of obscenities, directed against a racial group that was responsible for all the bad things in the world and all his own personal difficulties. He used vague generalities, and, when pinned down to facts, was unable to support any of his accusations.

The next two interviews were devoted to a discussion of the possible meaning of constantly wanting to fight. He was told that generally such a tendency really indicates feelings of inferiority and insecurity. The patient smiled and related that he wet the bed until he was 10. Further, he usually tried to overdo everything. He was anxious to make lots of money, and always drove his car extremely fast, but he became easily discouraged and considered himself a failure. When he was about 12, he tried to sell magazines from house to house. He soon became discouraged and felt he was a failure. His mother then told him that he did not need to sell anything, because he brought luck to the family. He spontaneously related how his mother told him at that time that, while she was pregnant with him, he was not wanted. She was extremely dejected during the pregnancy, considering his coming as a stark tragedy. When she told him that, the patient was much hurt but said nothing. While it had not been said directly, he had apparently sensed this all along. Then spontaneously he became quite agitated and stated that his father never cared for him. He would do anything for total strangers but not for his own family. In fact, he hardly knew his father until he was about 11 years old. His father worked in a large city, while his mother taught in a town 100 miles away. She would visit him occasionally, but the patient always remained behind. Then the patient began to curse his paternal grandmother—a greedy and vengeful old person, who apparently had been antagonistic toward his mother and had considerable influence over his father. She should have died instead of his mother or his grandfather. He'd be happy if she died now—adding that he was aware it was wrong to have such wishes.

At the end of the interview, the patient hesitatingly remarked that there was one more thing on his mind, very painful to him, which he had never talked about to anybody. At the next interview, he related that, more than two years before, his wife was pregnant. She knew that he didn't want any children. Both she and her parents made him make the final decision, which he did —his wife should have an abortion. He spontaneously remarked that he could have been a father now.

After the patient's return to the United States, he bought a home for his wife, and he remarked on different occasions that, no matter what happened to him, he wanted to be sure his wife had a home. She had had little early in life and he'd make sure that she would not suffer now. When questioned about any relationship to his mother, he said that his wife had some features of his mother.

. . . . . .

This boy, rejected by father and mother, had always felt unwanted, weak and inferior. Enuresis was a symptom of his early passive trends. He overcompensated with violent aggressiveness and in combat came close to the heroic. Yet he was extremely frightened and sensitive. He had rejected parenthood as too dangerous for his dependent relations with his wife, whom he identified with and gave to as he wished for himself. Overseas he attached himself to inferior men in order to feel superior. Combat broke up his overcompensation especially when, to save his life, the rightful owner of a foxhole had to die. The patient then developed psychosomatic and psychological symptoms of anxiety which did not decrease on his return home. As he became more aware of his underlying weakness overseas, he developed more aggressive and hostile attitudes toward officers and others, with resultant guilt and anxiety. Ventilating these attitudes with insight re-established the patient's equilibrium at the cost of his overcompensations and he left the hospital planning to start a family. The patient, although a Sergeant, can easily be compared to a certain infamous Corporal, and described as a "little Hitler." Domination of or attack on weaker people enabled this insecure, latently homosexual and frightened boy to maintain his self esteem. He and those whom he typifies are potential dangers to the American democracy.

CASE 28: *Anxiety due to rejection on return home—frustration of dependent needs stimulated by combat experiences.*

A 25 year old First Lieutenant, who was a B-17 pilot, completed fifty missions in a period of eleven months. At about the time of his forty-second mission, the patient became aware of nervousness, anxiety, sleeplessness and battle dreams. He was sent to a rest home but could not relax. He returned to combat to finish his missions and was then sent home. While at home, the patient noticed that his symptoms had increased considerably in intensity. He did not enjoy himself and was anxious to get on the move again.

The patient's father was a navy man so that, as a child, the patient could only see him on week ends. His recollections of his father were good ones—a kind man who was good to the patient's mother and who could be relied upon to help solve the patient's problems. The patient's mother was gentle and considerate and showed a normal amount of love for and interest in her elder son. There was one other child in the family, a brother, who was born when the patient was 7 years old. The patient stated that there were always older people in the home. He remembered his grandfather as a nice old man who could tell interesting stories. But the grandfather had worked at night and slept during the day, and the children had been constantly urged to be quiet so that he could sleep. The patient stated without resentment, "We were not given a chance to be children." He also had been restricted by having to take care of the younger brother. His grandmother he remembered as a fussy old woman with whom he was able to get along by doing what she asked. The patient received a high school education. His favorite sport was football and he also played in a band. His first sexual experience came at the age of 18, to which he had a normal response. Three years ago the patient had married, and he stated that his sex life was normal.

In discussing his overseas experiences, the patient stated that during a mission, when he could "let off steam," he felt fine. It was while on the ground with the ground officers that his symptoms became marked. He revealed severe hostility to the army and particularly to ground officers, whom he thought to be incompetent and inefficient. Between missions, in order to steady his nerves, he would take a plane into the air and teach a bombardier or navigator how to fly. The patient had a particular dislike for one of his Colonels, who, he thought, was responsible for many lost lives. He stated that he made no close friends because he did not want to feel their loss too keenly.

During a pentothal abreaction, the patient indicated marked aggressiveness and hostility toward the army, the Colonel and the ground officers, and spoke of some of the hazardous missions. The patient talked of how he would make his home different from the way his parents had theirs. He would have no older person around to be a wet blanket on his mood. Here the patient made an interesting analogy: "You know, doctor, it's like being in combat. When I was on the ground with the ground officers, it was like being at home with the old people. I felt that they were wet blankets on my mood. When I got up in air combat, it was like being and playing with children when I went out of the house. They got me all excited and I felt free and I liked the feeling."

The patient then stated that he had something to tell the examiner—something he had told no one. "When I lived at home, I had a room that was all mine. I played and slept in this room and kept all my trophies there. Well, when I was gone, my father rented this room, and, when I came back, I had no home to go to—I resent this." The patient then went on, "I resented having people around who were wet blankets on my life. I resented my brother because I could not be a kid. I had to be a father to him."

In another pentothal interview, the patient spoke of his father who, like a sailor, would give commands instead of making requests. He told of how he respected his father, and would obey him, and discovered that his father was always right. He spoke of how his mother had aged and how he felt like crying when he returned home and saw this.

He spoke of old people again. He told of how they tried to be nice but they would always forget the little important things like letting him eat food that he wanted, even though it would probably make him sick. It was like the army, he stated,—they gave you a million dollar plane and then didn't give you enough experience. "I don't mind fighting for something I believe in. I don't believe in the army." He continued, "Folks back home meant well, just like the army, but they do little things that tee you off. As soon as I went to the army, they figured, 'Well, he is gone now.' As soon as I got married, they thought I was apart. The whole thing is depressing. Don't have enough confusion in the army—get home and find the same darned thing there. I didn't go home. I was a misfit. No place for me to stay at my home, unless I wanted to sleep on the floor. They treated me like I was something that wasn't supposed to be around. I got home and they asked me if I liked my room and I felt like throwing all the furniture out of the window. My family—they are just as counterfeit as all the rest of them."

At this point, the patient was well out of the pentothal. An explanation was offered to the patient on the relationship of figures in authority. It was explained that the first authority, his father, had never let him down. It had protected him and he had found comfort in its protection. It was then explained how the second authority, the army, had failed him miserably. It was explained that this authority had exposed him to severe dangers and made him afraid—how this authority had even neglected the small things that would have helped him protect himself. The effect of combat was explained: how, because we are afraid, there is a tendency for us to go back to an earlier stage of life, when we were protected and our fears were allayed by our parents. So having reverted to that stage and dreaming of the protection and never failing authority at home, he returned home to find that his mother had aged and his father, "the old rock," his last support, had also failed him completely. He had rented his room to another person, and the patient saw that he could not seek protection where he had always found it in the past. All the old resentments which he had felt in the past were added to his present disappointments. It was explained that it was not his parents' fault; they could not know that combat, instead of making soldiers hardened heroes and men, has a tendency to make them like children coming to their parents for comfort. It was explained that, as time went on and combat fears were further and further away, he would gradually build up to the point where he had been before combat. It was stressed that he would have to react to all this on a grown-up level and begin to assume an independent attitude. The patient then asked, "How would you react to it, doc?" The therapist explained that this was the patient's problem and that he must solve it himself.

The patient stated, "Oh, I see now. I'm looking on you as an authority to lead me and I shouldn't do it."

The next day the patient stated that he had slept well the previous night, that he had been thinking of the problem and that it sounded reasonable. He had sent for his wife to come. He began to eat and sleep well and lost his restlessness.

A week later the patient was smiling and happy. His wife had arrived and noticed the change. He spoke rather laughingly about his attitude toward the army. "I knew there were some good places in the army but I had just heard of them—I hadn't been in any of them until now."

In another pentothal interview, an attempt was made to see just how far treatment had gone. His attitude toward his family seemed to be realistic. He stated, "I realize my folks are getting older. They didn't mean to do anything and besides I have to get out on my own now. If I get a good field, I'll work hard and do my best."

. . . . . .

The dynamics of this case are clearly indicated in the preceding abstract and insight by the patient is shown by his responses. With subsequent good handling in duty, he should do well. He returned home like a child attempting to sleep again in his baby crib. The inevitable frustration revived the old resentments of previous rejections. His wish to be taken care of again like the boy he had been when he left home was a regressive symptom caused by his stress. Two points brought out in this patient's story are discussed elsewhere: the unwillingness to make close friends for fear of reaction on losing them (cf. chapter 12); and the feeling of exuberant independence while in the air (cf. chapter 1).

CASE 29: *A dependent person, who matured psychologically in combat but who was drawn back toward his previous state on return home.*

A 32 year old radio-operator and gunner had stuttered since the age of 10 years, when he had met with an accident in which his nose was broken, leaving him with a flattened bridge. His chief symptoms on admission were apprehension, marked tension and depression, as well as an increase in stuttering. He was extremely hostile toward the army, rationalizing on the basis that he should have had a commission and that there was no chance for his advancement.

The patient came from a well-to-do family, living in a city of moderate size. He had strong inferiority feelings, based on his short stature and a deformed, broken nose. He was the youngest of four children and the baby of the family, receiving a great deal of attention. His schooling was rather desultory and he made many changes. He finally matriculated at a state university, where he stayed for four years but did not take his final degree. He worked in the family business, which was diversified in that they had a large garbage contract, a construction concern and a road-building company. The patient spoke as if he had an important role in the organization and was badly needed because one brother was in the army, another was about to be drafted and the father was too old. Actually, he had a minor position as a sort of straw boss for a construction gang. He did not work steadily but every few months would take off for New York, where he indulged in a quiet, prolonged alcoholic debauch. Several years ago, he met a girl and planned to marry her. He bought a house and furnished it completely, but at the last moment became afraid and retreated from the marriage.

He complained that he had no further purpose in the army, that there was no outlook for his future and that he should go home. His squadron commanding officer mistreated him by court-martialing him for minor aggressive remarks to British soldiers. The court-martial verdict was demotion to a private, a severe fine and limitation to the post for three months. The patient kept on fighting in his missions, and took the punishment so well that the Group Commander completely remitted the sentence of the court-martial. He successfully finished his missions overseas. He noticed some of his symptoms slightly toward the end of his tour of duty but the acute symptoms of tenseness and anxiety did not develop until he returned home.

At home he was much worse and was quite disturbed on being asked many questions, so that after only one week of his three weeks of overseas furlough he took off and reported to Atlantic City. During his stay at the hospital, he met a married woman, with a child, who was awaiting final divorce papers, and fell in love with her. He wanted to marry her, much to his own surprise. He stated that his father also married a divorced woman (his mother) with a child, so that his family would approve. He was somewhat worried about the fact that the marriage would also entail responsibility, which he had never taken before.

The patient reported a single dream while under therapy.

Dream: "I apparently had been a fighter pilot but now I was a pilot on a B-17. My pilot overseas was my copilot, a big fellow, 6 feet 5 inches tall. I was taxying down the strip on the left side. The boys told me I should go over to the right side. Behind the B-17 was a cable which seemed to be dragging along on the ground. I made a left turn at the intersection and got out of the plane to put the cable up on a post like a telephone lineman. The boys kidded me about it and I was ashamed that I didn't know that Operations would have done that and that I needn't have." Associations were lacking.

Interpretation: Being a fighter pilot was being a "lone wolf," as his past life indicated. Now he was to settle down and take responsibilities and be captain of his ship, that is, to become a husband and father. He was attempting to overcome his feelings of inferiority by showing that he, the little fellow, could be the pilot and the big fellow would have to be the copilot. Taxying on the left side of the strip indicated that he was still on the wrong side and wasn't quite sure whether he wanted to take off. The electric cable was his attachment or communication with mother earth—in other words, the old umbilical cord to which childhood was attached. The shame at not knowing how to deal with this cord (Operations—the therapist—would have done that) was his feeling of inferiority, which he attributed to his nose and size, but which was really based on his feelings of dependence. The therapist pointed out to him that the dream indicated the conflict between his childish dependence and his desire to be mature and grown up. It was pointed out that the decision as to the solution of this conflict had been reached some time before. Prior to going into combat, his ego had had no successes, but, when he went into combat and stuck it out, he had become a man, and now his self-respecting ego could not permit him to regress again to a childhood level. Nevertheless, there was that tendency which existed in everyone, since all men somehow or other maintain an attachment to a dependent relationship but in a displaced manner. His dependent needs could be gratified by the praise and adoration of the hero and by the care and affection a good motherly wife could give him.

To be sure, there would be relapses, but he could never go back again.

This man was a strongly passive and dependent character, as his periodic alcoholism confirms. In his successful tour of duty in combat, he had for the first time obtained some confidence in his ability. Returning home, he began to feel the drag toward the old dependent relationship with his family. Only during his period in the hospital had he demonstrated a trend toward continued maturity. This was seen in his planning marriage, which was partially an identification with his father and partially an attempt to acquire a mother figure, and in his forcing the family to acknowledge him as a partner in their business. Nevertheless, there was the conflict between these two opposing tendencies. Psychotherapy was directed, therefore, toward strengthening confidence in himself and encouraging his self-respecting ego. No pentothal was necessary.

. . . . . .

The dynamic explanation of this patient's symptoms, indicative of conflict, gives another side of the picture illustrated by the previous cases. This patient had matured by virtue of his success in combat, an achievement that he accomplished for the first time in his life. On returning home to his old environment, he was tempted to resume his old outlook on life. He and probably many others are even seduced by their mothers, who urge their boys to stay at home, to try every possible method of getting out of the army. "You have done enough; stay home with mama now. I've missed you so much!" No matter which way they tend to go, conflict develops. Some of our patients have miraculously lost anxiety when they have been told, "You *will* stay in the army, no matter if you do have symptoms." The therapist thus takes the decision from the boy and assumes the responsibility for pulling him away from mother. No guilt need thus be attached to the boy's remaining away from home.

The following letter was received from this last patient several months after his return to duty:

"I received the answer to my letter that you sent me and I was glad to hear from you. I felt as though I had to write again as some of the things you told me have happened and others that I said would happen have come true.

"As I told you, I was going to get married. Well, I did, on the thirty-first of August, to the girl whose picture I showed to you. She is a wonderful girl and I am pretty lucky to get someone like her. We had a few troubles at first, like finding an apartment, etc., but we have everything under control now and are very happy. We have a beautiful little house and three weeks ago I bought a car, so we are getting along swell. I have never been so happy as during the past six weeks and the responsibility has made everything else seem small. As you know, she has a little girl of five, so I am a daddy too and I think I am doing pretty good at that, because I always did like children.

"On my side is the work I am doing at the field. I have a pleasant job but it doesn't seem very important to me and I keep thinking about how much more I could be doing outside the army. I am grounded due to my ears, so I am working on the line preflighting radio equipment on C-47 (transport) planes and I am on the night shift, working every other night. Somebody has to do this though, so maybe I am exaggerating things a bit.

"As a whole, we are treated pretty well here and about the only time they are a little strict is for inspection we have every Saturday. Living off the post does have its advantages though, so I guess I can 'take it.' To be honest about it, I am glad I never got a medical discharge as I couldn't be as happy as I am now, even as a civilian."

. . . . . .

The cases presented have been chosen with a view to demonstrating reactions in boys who have had various degrees of predisposition to regression, ranging from the immature child (case 23) to the relatively mature officer (case 28). It will be noted at once that it is not the fact but the degree of regression which is dependent on the precombat fundamental immaturity of the personality. The degree of success of brief psychotherapy also correlates well with the previous maturity attained by the patient before the trauma of combat had exerted its forces toward regression.

It is likewise demonstrated that the predisposition to regressive neuroses and the failures of psychotherapy are related to early home situations. Both spoiling and deprivation in childhood are serious factors in fixing dependent attitudes, which cause so much difficulty when the bearer experiences severe stress. A certain happy combination of gratification and frustration prepares a boy to endure successfully later stress and deprivation. The setting of broken homes, caused by divorce, separation, quarreling of the parents or death of one parent in the patient's childhood, seems to be closely related to subsequent lack of normal development of maturity in the child. It is as if a gratified, happy childhood with biparental influences contributes a reserve strength on which a man may draw in time of danger. He can fall back on the memory of a gratified past, which is the basis of hope for a similar future. In the presence of stress, lack of any degree of past gratification is catastrophic. This observation has also been made in a study of refugee children. The past seems to build up confidence and create resources within the structure of the personality.

The pattern of reaction in the phase of regression is similar to or identical with the past. Previous stutterers, nail biters and enuretics have a revival of their old symptoms giving confirmation to the regressive nature of the syndrome. There are those, like case 23, who express their needs openly without concealment, shame or attempts to strive for a more adult attitude. Others are unconscious of their trends and cry for attention in their gastric language (cf. chapter 11). Some fly to marriage, displacing their desires in seeking a wife capable of substituting for a mother; others search for gratification in alcoholism. Several patients had such indecision regarding their simultaneous dependence and independence that they developed "sleep paralysis" (to be reported by Van der Heide and Weinberg). Some vigorously overcompensate by a false masculinity expressed as aggressiveness and overt hostility, as the patient described in case 27. A few attempt to live out their needs in giving, and by great solicitude for others, especially mothers and wives, to whom they must return because "they need me so much." They fantasy, as many children do, of playing a leading role in the myth of "The return of the hero." We hear over and over again, "Father is no good—I have to go home and take care of mother." The most devastating of all reactions is a psychotic-like withdrawal from reality, as described in case 59 (cf. chapter 14).

Combat and other stress overseas give rise to the stimulus toward regression by reason of the complete absence of safety anywhere in the external world of reality. The universal reaction is a retreat into fantasy and a dream of a magical home, as we have described in chapter 8. This normal system of delusions conflicts with reality when home is finally reached, forcing a reorientation and adaptation of the personality to actuality. In all returnees this requires time for reality testing, during which anxiety is inevitable, but adjustment, although difficult, is eventually accomplished

Other individuals, whose difficulties eventually require treatment, regress further and retreat more from reality, and this produces a functional change in the ego, which loses its discriminatory power, while its control over infantile trends is further weakened. This change is a true ego deformation, irreversible without therapy or without a considerable time being allowed for spontaneous re-education through favorable processes of subsequent life experiences. But why does the stress of combat cause such disastrous regression? Actually it is the less drastic of two evils. Caught between unendurable anxiety and unmodifiable hardships, the soldier is confronted with the catastrophic possibility of denying the presence of the horrible reality by severing all contact with it—by blacking out all perception of it and retreating into a psychosis. His only alternative is to be carried along by the group's strength, as its child, and to exist in the past of safe and secure childhood memories. The soldier becomes a little boy, but this fact is not recognized as long as he is in the group. Only when he is sloughed off, and returns home as an individual, does his infantile regression become obvious. Even during his journey home, he may be supported by hopes of an early gratification of his dependent needs. But on arrival, his frustrations begin, conflict is stimulated, engendering anxiety, and symptoms appear.

The process of regression is an attempt to revert to an earlier mode of behavior that once was successful, since the reality of combat calls for adaptive powers incapable of being produced. The tired, war-weary soldier becomes a boy again. He searches for present gratification by means of old techniques that once were so successful. Unfortunately these regressive patterns are rarely compatible with other self-respecting and persistent ego forces; and they are frowned on by the environment for they are incompatible with the person's stage of development.

In the stage of regression the patient behaves like a child, afraid of strange people and sounds, afraid of heights, and he is only comfortable when at home with mother and the family. This explains his anxiety about reassignment to strange bases among people he doesn't know, and his search for old buddies. This is the reason the patient wants at all costs to get out of the army. He demands attention from everyone, going to any lengths, such as exhibitionism, or even attracting punitive attention by misbehaving. The patient is envious of and hostile to his brother patients who share his doctor's attentions. He reacts with weeping, depression (cf. case 44) or vomiting if his slightest wishes are not gratified. Overt hostility is shown, not to the regulations keeping him from mother, but to the officers who enforce them.

With dependence, most people develop a feeling of inferiority, since they are children compared with their contemporaries. Inferiority feelings incite an aggressive overcompensating attitude, which, if it creates guilt, leads to a further increment in passive attitudes, a further regression. Some of our soldiers become aggressive toward weaker persons in an effort to create a delusion of masculine importance in themselves (11). Their hates stem from their own insecurities. Others become aggressive in the false virility of alcoholism while they secretly gratify their passive needs.

In this chapter, we have cited a few cases typifying some patterns of regression to passive-dependent states. The possible expressions of this reaction are legion. The regression, although it is economical in combat and protective against a psychosis, only results in difficulties on the return home, for it brings the soldier into conflict with his environment, which frustrates him, or it is unacceptable to other forces of his own personality. In either case, he is thrown into anxiety, which is the stimulus for an attempt at new adaptive maneuvers that result in overtly neurotic behavior.

CHAPTER 11

Psychosomatic States

For a long time men have realized that emotional abnormalities caused disturbances in their bodily functions. Common knowledge linked blushing with shame; paleness, increased heart rate and diarrhea with fear; headache and rise in blood pressure with anger. Physicians knew that diabetics spilled out more sugar when emotionally disturbed, that patients with peptic ulcer became worse under severe stress and that asthma, skin lesions and arthritis were increased in severity under certain psychological conditions. But such correlations between emotions and bodily changes were not given serious consideration in the *causation* of disease until very recently. Medicine was under the influence of a separation, a dichotomy, of mind and body. Internists diagnosed and treated a disease, usually of a specific organ or system of organs. Psychiatrists treated emotional or mental disturbances without reference to their effect on the body. No one seemed to deal with the whole person until modern dynamic psychiatry proved satisfactorily that disturbances in emotions may cause disturbances in bodily functions and ultimately disease of an organ.

The aim of psychosomatic medicine is to encourage and bring together studies which make a contribution to the understanding of the organism as a whole in its somatic and psychic aspects. The field to which psychosomatic medicine is devoted is rapidly assuming importance in medicine and the related sciences. It is now realized that the major problem is to develop practical methods for dealing clinically and scientifically with the organism as a whole. Although the organism is a unit, fundamentally different methods have been developed for the observation and management of the psychic and somatic functions. This fact is the real reason for the use of the term "psychosomatic," not any difference of opinion about the essential nature of the organism. Psychosomatic medicine is not a medical specialty, parallel with internal medicine or psychiatry, but an approach which might be applicable to almost any medical, psychological or physiological problem. This approach requires a battery of techniques, including the psychiatric, to determine the relationship between the causative factors of emotional disturbances producing disorders of the body and the effects of a physical disease on the working of the mind. Mind and body are one, simply viewed from several points of reference. When these several aspects are fused, the result is a picture more nearly representative of the total organism.

The war has hastened the development of psychosomatic medicine because the severe stresses which it has imposed on fighting men have brought into the clinical symptomatology of war neuroses thousands of emotionally induced physical disturbances. Hundreds of doctors have witnessed this phenomenon at first hand and have learned of the relationship between psychological causes and physical effects. They are eager to learn further details of etiology and methods of treatment, for they know that therein lies the future of medicine.

It has been common knowledge that organic diseases of the body are accompanied by alterations in feeling and thinking, but it was not so well known that all subjective emotional and mental states are accompanied by visceral and somatic processes. All psychological phenomena, normal or pathological, are associated with physiological alterations, although many are invisible or measurable with great difficulty. Since the body must be involved in order to express feeling, there are no pure psychological or "feeling" syndromes; hence all psychoneuroses and war neuroses are psychosomatic problems. This was clearly stated in the discussion of the symptoms of war neuroses (cf. chapter 9), which include not only the subjective sensations of anxiety but also the physiological concomitants of overactivity of the sympathetic nervous system. Since anxiety is part of a preparation for an interpreted danger or a reaction to it, which stimulates the body for action by alerting almost every organ, the resulting energy, if not adequately discharged, accumulates and then its manifestations take the form of symptoms of illness (cf. case 22).

However, when we speak of psychosomatic disturbances, it is usually with reference to conditions in which persistent or recurrent emotion is only recognized through those physical activities that normally accompany that emotion, consciousness of the emotion in the form of subjective feeling being absent. It is a state of affairs in which nervous energy is in part or wholly expressed through the vegetative nervous system, because some psychological barrier prevents the person from expressing the feeling at the conscious or behavioral level. The emotion is repressed and only the lower-level visceral concomitants are expressed. Since emotion is a stimulus to visceral, smooth muscle activities mediated by the sympathetic nervous system, these phenomena are represented by such symptoms as sweating, tremor, increased heart rate, vomiting and diarrhea.

Because these symptoms are often the sole manifestation of an unconscious trend, they have been likened to the conversion symptoms of hysteria. But there is a very definite difference in that conversion symptoms are an attempted solution for relief of a well defined conflict through the voluntary nervous system, producing paralyses, anesthesias, convulsions, etc. The symptom represents an attempted solution of the conflict, and, since it is solved, the emotion which it aroused can subside. A psychosomatic disorder does not express a solution of a conflict but represents the exaggerated physiological concomitant of the emotion blocked by the unsolved conflict. The symptom does not solve the conflict but is merely its end result, because the conflict prevents the expression of feeling at a higher level of consciousness or behavior and only permits its discharge at a lower visceral level.

With normal acute emotional reactions, there are always somatic expressions. Pathological reactions are either chronic or repetitively recurrent, since full or adequate discharge does not occur, because of conflict with other internal or external forces. This chronicity and repetitiveness is of importance because of the consequences of such long-continued activity. The fundamental thesis regarding *psychosomatic disease* is that long-continued functional alterations of smooth muscles eventuate in morphological changes (12, 13). For example, chronic dyspepsia with hyperacidity, hypersecretion and hypermotility of the upper gastrointestinal tract may eventually result in a peptic ulcer. Actually the dynamic emotional cause of the syndrome of gastric dysfunction in the stage of dyspepsia is identical with that in the stage of ulcer. Thus, the psychiatrist can ascertain the emotional origin of a syndrome, but cannot negate the possibility that organic changes have already occurred. This must be determined by medical and laboratory examinations and appropriate treatment must then be given (13, 60).

When intrapsychic or external blocks are overcome and the patient becomes conscious of the emotion which heretofore he has only expressed vegetatively, psychosomatic symptoms disappear. It has been demonstrated that there is a specific relationship between certain emotions and certain localized visceral symptoms. This has been proved by detailed psychoanalytic work on a few patients and confirmed by statistical analyses of many others through more superficial studies of psychological "profiles." Enough data have already been obtained to establish the specific dynamic etiology of several psychosomatic syndromes. On the other hand, the generalized somatic changes described in chapter 9 are the result, not of specific emotions, but of free anxiety of long standing.

In war neuroses psychosomatic troubles are frequent. The normal visceral concomitants of intense emotion are universal. Men are afraid and can't eat; they vomit, or suffer from diarrhea, rapid heart rate or breathlessness, or from all of these symptoms at the same time. It is when these are prolonged and intensified without full conscious expression of the basic feeling that the pathological psychosomatic syndromes develop. In contrast with civilian cases, the emotion is rarely excluded entirely from consciousness and anxiety is not concerned only with the resulting symptoms. The patient's emotion forces its way into consciousness in some degree, resulting in anxiety, depression or other feelings *and* in lower level symptoms as well (26).

Many patients with psychosomatic complaints are discovered in our routine physical examinations. Others are so ill that they are studied in our special medical wards. The table at the top of page 255 is an analysis of 330 cases, directly referred to the internist of our hospital for differential diagnosis, and indicates the frequency of various psychosomatic conditions.

It can be seen that the most frequent disturbances are centered in the gastrointestinal tract as opposed to the frequent cardiac syndromes observed in the last war. Suggested reasons for this difference will be given later (cf. case 37). The great

330 Psychosomatic Cases

Type	Percentage
Gastrointestinal	46.6
Cardiac	14.4
Dermatological	12.1
Joint and muscle	11.5
Urological	6.3
Headaches and vertigo	5.7
Hypertensive	2.3
Chest	1.1

variety of psychosomatic syndromes makes it impossible for us to present more than representative cases of the most frequent problems. We shall first consider the gastrointestinal disorders.

CASE 30: *Vomiting developed after severe combat experiences as the sole expression of resentment in a previously stable personality—recovery through narcosynthesis.*

The patient was a 25 year old B-26 Sergeant gunner, who flew sixty-six combat missions before being rotated to the United States with his crew. The patient entered the hospital complaining of nervousness and gastrointestinal troubles. He usually vomited his morning meal and then either the noon or the night meal. Between times he was ravenously hungry but on reaching the dinner table a few bites would give his stomach a sense of fullness and he would be unable to eat more. There was no regularity of pattern and no pain connected with vomiting, although at times he was nauseated all day and would have the "dry heaves." He had lost 20 pounds before returning to the United States and there was little change in his symptoms from the time he left combat until he arrived at the hospital.

He had entered combat in a carefree mood and during his first missions he enjoyed seeing the flak bursting around him, and even his own ships going down did not upset him too much. However, as time wore on, he began to realize that the Germans were playing "for keeps" and he began to have some anxiety. On his forty-seventh mission, two wing ships were lost and their crews were killed. This greatly increased his anxiety and he began to have battle dreams, insomnia, loss of appetite, weight loss, headaches, irritability, forgetfulness and vomiting. The vomiting regime started soon after the forty-seventh mission, and, as it became established, some of the conscious anxiety seemed to recede.

During his early treatment, the patient attempted to give the impression that he was self-sufficient and at first was somewhat antagonistic; he resented the fact that he was in a hospital. Among the things to which he objected was the presence of soldiers everywhere he went in town. He had especially disliked them since his return from combat. However, he soon became friendly with the therapist and throughout his stay was pleasant and cooperative. In fact, he seemed to need someone upon whom he could lean. Nevertheless, he often related how independent he was and how he always got along without assistance. During the first interview, he told readily of the onset of his illness. He could not understand why the vomiting had started nor why it continued, and he had become quite disturbed about it and really wished he could get rid of it.

He spoke enthusiastically about his crew and how they were the best anywhere. They got along splendidly and there was seldom any bickering, even on the ground. He seemed to be especially fond of his pilot and said he was the best of pilots but was beginning to go stale just before they returned.

The patient denied any nervous or psychological disturbances prior to combat. He had completed two and a half years of college with the purpose of studying medicine but quit in order to work in a hospital when it appeared that he would have to go into the army. He was rejected from aviation cadet training because of an old fracture of the nose and then was made a gunner against his wishes. His father and mother were living and well and one brother was in the army. He denied that there was any family friction, although he had been semi-independent since the age of 12, making his own way as much as possible. The patient had been married two years and got along well with his wife.

Since thorough physical examination revealed no organic pathology and since the vomiting seemed to be a visceral expression of an unconscious emotion, the patient was given 0.4 Gm. of pentothal intravenously, the aim being to effect a liberation of the emotion. He was started in his verbalizations by the question, "Why do you vomit?" He continued to talk for about thirty minutes as follows: "At Atlantic City, they said I was

nervous. I'm not—I can do two hundred and fifty missions,"
. . . (pause) . . . "I think." ("Why?") "I'm a g— d— good
tail gunner. They haven't hit me, have they? They blasted at
me but we just picked up a few holes. My g— d— head hurts
. . . Hey, you know what? I'm getting drunk. Like more
combat? No! We got a rotten deal" (with much emotion).
"Damn armchair Generals think you can fly forever—too much
flak. See that flak?—you can take a bath in it—too much flak—
here comes one. Hey!" (sits up in bed). ("Did it hit you?")
"No, it got Smith—he was in it. Smith was in that plane spinning
down there. He's a fine b—. How many we lost now? Only
three, but no parachutes come out. Armchair Generals! I'm
sick—don't know what of. I'm sick. I'm telling you, I didn't want
to fly this one, you s— o— b—. Take it easy" (to pilot)—"let's
get the hell out of here—this is too much flak. What's the use, in
five years you look like you're an old man. Those damn armchair
Generals. I'm sick. I feel sick. Let's do something, even if it's
wrong. I'm sick. I'm sick. I never got sick in an airplane before—
O.K.? Watch that fighter, coming in—get him for Christ's sake"
(jumps in bed). "You shoot like a bunch of g— d— rookies.
Hey!" (to pilot) "you're a good Joe—I called to find if everything is O.K. I've never puked in a g— d— airplane but I think
I'm going to. We got all kinds of flak up here. You can get killed
by that s—. Just like Smith and Jones a minute ago. Where's
the smoke coming from? It's awfully dark" (he jumps as if hit).
"Get me out of here. What the hell, I feel like I'm drunk but
I don't get drunk; I can drink any ten of you under the table.
Fifty g— d— missions is too g— d— many. I'm sick just like I
always feel" (rises up and looks around—lies down). "Hey,
Dick, hey! look at my right arm—it's gone. Did it get hit?
I don't want to look. If I haven't got a right arm, pitch me out.
Purple heart—phooey! I'm going to throw up. Get your helmet.
We on the ground?" ("Almost.") "Easy, Dick—easy, old boy—
boy, we made it. You can't kill me. I feel drunk, I don't fly
drunk" (weaves around in bed and breathes very deeply).
"I'm sick. I'm going to quit this racket, Dick—my damn stomach
won't let me fly." (Almost vomits and belches.) ("Would you
vomit if you didn't have to fly any more?") "Damn if I know.
Somebody do something quick, even if it's wrong" (writhes
around in bed). "Those g— d— bicycle Generals—there goes
that fighter. I think I got him. Why they send me to the hospital?

—I'll be O.K. and fly tomorrow. *I'll fly, but I know better—they will get me sooner or later.* I'm sick. Don't touch me, I'll be O.K. I feel something on my arm. What is it? It's awful hot down there though. Did my leg get hit?—feels like my knee" (therapist touches it). "Not that one—see, it's the other" (he touches the left). "Hey, take it easy—am I ever sick to my stomach!" (jumps suddenly). "I'll be O.K. in a few minutes" (noise in the corridor outside the room)—"must be someone running the crew chief's stand. No use me lying here any more—I'm afraid of being an invalid. This is so stupid—flying day after day after day." ("Where do you want to go?") "Back to States." ("Back to your wife?") "Oh, boy!" (smiles). "She's a good kid—the best." ("Would you vomit if you could stay there?") "How do I know?—that's a silly question. I'll tell you something—something's wrong with me. I can't eat or sleep—but don't tell Dick, he'll stop my flying. How long do I have to stay here? Everywhere I go there are g__ d__ G.I.'s, the s__ o__ b__'s." (Every time the curtain blew out and let a shaft of light fall on his face, he would start and duck, saying: "See that flak!")

At this point he was awakening from the pentothal. He was able to recall little of the material without help. He was greatly surprised to find out how he had thought flak was bursting near him every time a shaft of light from a fluttering curtain hit his eyes.

The next day the patient looked much better and he stated his wife had been pleased when he came in last night. She had said he looked less anxious than usual, and he had eaten a whole meal without vomiting. His spirits were higher than at any previous interview. The improvement continued for several days. Although the vomiting had ceased, no increase in anxiety was seen. The patient was playing softball and attending his classes, and he was much more satisfied with the hospital.

Another pentothal treatment was given him a few days later. Much the same type of material was obtained, although the emotion accompanying it was considerably less. The patient seemed to be more aware that he was back in the United States. He continued to be free of anxiety and vomiting for a week, when he met a friend just back from overseas. The friend told him that several of his friends in the old squadron had been killed. He reacted to this with one episode of vomiting, mild anxiety and a return of some tremor of the hands. However, the last symptom disappeared spontaneously in forty-eight hours, which was a therapeutic indication that he was becoming much better and that future incidents like this would become less meaningful to him.

The patient entered the hospital a pale, wan individual, decidedly underweight. During his three weeks' stay, he recovered from the vomiting and latterly was eating five meals per day. His weight increased 8 pounds. Psychologically, he also improved a great deal. The only symptoms still remaining were mild irritability, slight forgetfulness and a lingering dislike of enlisted men. He still stated that he did not want any more combat but was much less emotional in his attitude toward it and willingly accepted return to duty.

. . . . . .

This patient had a stable, fairly well adjusted personality and entered combat with high morale and strongly positive feelings toward his officers and crew. He gradually developed anxiety but only on the forty-seventh mission did his ego recognize the true danger. He then developed severe visceral symptoms but persisted in combat with an overcompensatory aggressiveness. In the hospital, he also demonstrated a superficial independence, which covered up a desire for emotional support. Under pentothal, the regressive nature of his illness was manifested as he verbally expressed hostility to the authoritative figures of his leaders, who did not protect him sufficiently, the "armchair Generals," and at the same time was afraid and apprehensive of all stimuli. As he abreacted his resentment, the symptom of gagging, retching and almost vomiting appeared. This material was synthesized within his ego, for his vomiting promptly receded. It was truly a narcosynthesis, since, although the therapist gave the patient a minimum of interpretations, the liberated feelings were kept in consciousness and then worked through. A second pentothal injection resulted in less violent emotion and was followed by a good recovery. Thus, as the patient became conscious of the angers about which he had never permitted verbalization or even conscious thinking, he was able to give up the lower-level visceral egress to the emotional expression.

This patient before combat seemed to be a normal and stable individual. Yet his early dependence and later overcompensatory aggressiveness suggested that there were unconscious ungratified dependent needs. The stress of combat resulted in gastric disturbances, representing an emotional language which could only be translated under pentothal. Then it was revealed that the emotion was rage at being deserted by supporting authoritative figures, represented by the Generals. His response to the desertion was not conscious nor verbal, because he had never permitted his dependent needs such frank expression. On the contrary, he behaved in an overcompensating independent manner. When narcosynthesis overcame his psychological blocking, his emotions could be verbalized and no longer needed a gastric outlet.

CASE 31: *Vomiting as part of a regressive pattern, caused by combat in a previously immature boy.*

This patient was a 21 year old Sergeant, who completed fifty missions as a B-17 gunner. On admission he complained of insomnia, combat dreams, tremor of the hands, easy fatiguability, loss of interest and excessive drinking. He had considerable stomach trouble. Although very hungry, he would vomit as soon as he took a mouthful of food. He was compelled to drink a great quantity of milk and felt he would starve if they took his milk away from him. He had lost interest in everything and did not care what happened to him, whether he lived or died. The patient slept poorly, because he was awakened by fantastic dreams of being dive-bombed by German planes. When he fired on them with a machine gun, the scene changed and the planes were then cardboard toys and he was shooting at them with a child's B-B gun.

His first twenty-five missions overseas were not exceptionally severe, although he was frightened. As the targets were moved farther up into enemy territory, he suddenly awakened to the fact that this was a very serious business. This feeling was accentuated when his crew went down during a mission from which he had been excused in order to do guard duty. He was very much upset then, could not sleep and dreamed all night. He began to hate the Germans and all planes. He felt responsible for the loss of his crew, as if by some miracle he would have saved them, had he been along. "I should have been with them," he said. "I couldn't stomach it." It was pointed out to him that he expressed his guilt and need for punishment by not eating.

Under pentothal he vividly and dramatically described, in the present tense, an attack by fighters on his plane, and, as he groaned in agitation, he placed his hand on his abdomen. He talked about "Al," the pilot, who was the best officer in the army, and then went into a rage against all officers, protesting against being pushed around by grocery clerks who became ninety day wonders. His own application for a commission had been rejected. He wanted to turn the tables on all officers, put them against the wall and shoot them. All the time he cried, "I've got to get home." He did not want to go to classes, and did not like to obey orders. He wanted to be a little boy, from whom nothing was expected, who had no responsibilities and who could do what he wanted.

At his next pentothal interview, he was quite dramatic, vividly relived his experiences in planes and then, in a childish, simpering way, stated his crew were not dead. Then out came the material how he hated the army because it had killed his friends. When it was interpreted to him that he was afraid and would not admit it and that he reacted to his damaged self esteem by hating the army, he became much more childish, crying and feeling ashamed that he was not a man. He reacted violently to any directions given by the nurse and began to drink heavily. This retreat from a grown-up state with responsibilities to that of a little boy was quite obvious, and, when this was pointed out to him, he said that he had often thought of his boyhood, and described an idyllic childhood with wonderful parents. However, when the patient was 15, his brother, who was four years older, was drowned and his mother went to bed for a year, so that he had to do all the cooking. He could only finish the 12th grade of school and then had to work on a farm and later in a factory.

. . . . . .

It is interesting to note the primitive protective device this patient's ego had adopted: that combat was a sort of game and that magical influences would protect him. But when the going became tough and death struck close to him, the play ceased and reality was faced by his ego. This hard-won and terrifying realism was reversed in his combat dreams, where German dive bombers once more became cardboard toys—a comforting thought, only a game after all. This clear view of combat dangers initiated the process of regression, and like a little child he had to subsist on a milk diet. Interest in external realities ceased and self interest dominated his behavior. When his infantile narcissism had been traumatized, his behavior sank to a vegetative level. Anger against cruel fate was expressed only by the technique of a child—by vomiting everything except milk. At the same time, a childish rage was projected to the army in the thought, "*They* are responsible" (cf. chapter 13).

In spite of the patient's statement that his childhood was ideal, his actual history indicated that he had assumed heavy responsibilities early in life and had been compelled to do his mother's work during her illness and had remained strongly attached to her. Within this emotional setting, the stress of combat evoked, not direct expression of fear and rage at frustration, but only the gastric concomitants of these emotions. His early and excessive responsibilities had forced his ego to become overly independent and intolerant of conscious recognition of his dependent needs. Yet these were so great after fifty missions that they could not be gratified in the army and he was discharged to civilian life.

CASE 32: *Previous gastric distress made worse by combat.*

The patient was a 22 year old ball turret gunner, who entered the hospital complaining of anxiety, loss of appetite, nausea and vomiting, tremor, restlessness and excessive perspiration. He had been in combat duty eleven months and finished twenty-five missions. His nervousness was of gradual development, without any particular precipitating cause. After his twentieth mission, everything seemed to affect him greatly and his fears were no longer controllable. He became shaky, restless, sleepless and anxious. His stomach had bothered him all the time he was in combat but it became much worse as his symptoms developed. His missions were all very severe but not more severe after the twentieth. He felt afraid in his ball turret because he was not sure that his crewmates would pull him out if the machinery stuck in a period of stress.

This patient was the youngest of three brothers. The eldest brother and he never got along well together. When the patient was 15, his father became an invalid and he had to assume the responsibilities for his parents' support. He became a farmer. From the time of his father's death and the increase in his responsibilities, he had recurrent stomach trouble every two or three months. An older brother did not help and the patient always resented this. His sex life was minimal, for he felt that sex was dirty and nasty. He had an antagonistic attitude toward women, whom he believed took advantage of their sex. On his return home, he broke his engagement to a girl with whom he had been going for some three years, because he felt so changed. Discussions of his relationship with women revealed that, while he wanted a woman to give him support and strength, he also felt that women were dangerous because they required a great deal from him in the same way that his mother had been dependent on him most of his life. He was tired of the army and would have liked to get out. He had a strong feeling of inferiority from being a "hick farmer."

This patient had had psychogenic stomach trouble since adolescence, when he was called upon to assume responsibility for his parents' support. His behavior and conscious reactions were normally adaptive and apparently adult prior to combat, but the small boy underneath expressed his emotional longings for passive gratification by dyspeptic symptoms, which were his sole means of expressing hunger for love. Demands of combat increased his passive needs, although he behaved well. In view of his family configuration—being the last child—his fear that his brothers in the combat crew would not rescue him from the turret indicated how much he felt unwanted. A deep conflict in regard to his position in relation to his mother was indicated. On return home, the patient found himself in a dilemma regarding his relationship with women, typified by mother and sweetheart. Would they take care of him or must he support them? The latter was impossible at that time because of the loss of his ego's capacity for overcompensations. The continuous drain on his ego's energies had exposed the little boy, who then had to satisfy his ungratified appetite for love and attention in gastric language since the self-respecting component of his ego would not permit a direct expression of his needs.

CASE 33: *Anorexia and vomiting as a regressive reaction to loss of supporting figures in combat.*

This patient entered the hospital with complaints of fear of planes, nervousness, insomnia, loss of appetite except for milk, and battle dreams, coming on gradually during his duties as a tail gunner of a B-26 on sixty-four missions. His symptoms became worse after his return to the United States for a furlough. His physical examination was essentially negative.

The patient left high school at the age of 18 to enlist in the army. Assigned to the Air Forces, he volunteered for aerial gunnery, and, before he felt adequately trained, he was assigned to an outfit of B-26 bombers destined for immediate overseas assignment. Flying appealed to him at that time and he was greatly disappointed when his position in the crew was taken by a nonflying enlisted man for the trip to the combat theater. He flew his first five missions with a Major as pilot, whom he regarded as a "good Joe" and admired because of the officer's regard and consideration for the enlisted men. The missions flown with the Major were without any significant mishap and relatively free of enemy fighters and flak. On his sixth mission, he was assigned to a permanent crew and was flying his first mission with them, when he witnessed the Major go down in flames in another ship. This frightened him and for a long time he could not forget the loss of the admired Major and developed vomiting of most foods except milk. It was not until his sixteenth mission that his crew began to meet with stiff fighter opposition and intense flak over enemy territory. At this time the patient began to lose control over himself under fire and found himself freezing to his guns and shielding himself behind armor plating when in contact with flak and enemy fighters. On one mission, his plane was badly damaged by flak and the patient had not expected to return. As his missions progressed, the patient became more tense and fearful of planes and flak. Although the intensity of flak continually increased, no members of his crew were ever injured in all their missions. A very close friend of the patient, five years older and a member of another crew, was lost on his fifty-first mission. This boy, Pete, he had admired for his worldliness and knowledge of many things about life. He had made many pleasure trips to London and Scotland with this friend and enjoyed them all because of the things he learned from him. Most of his time away from flying duties had been spent in the company of Pete. He had been pleased at being called "Junior" by him.

After the completion of his fiftieth mission, he was threatened with severe punishment if he did not continue to fly more missions. He continued flying missions under great strain and fear, until he had completed his sixty-fourth and was relieved for a furlough home.

The patient had an essentially negative past medical history. His father died when he was one and a half years old and his mother never remarried. He was the youngest of three children, having one sister six years older and one brother two years older. He has been close to his mother and spoke of accompanying her often to visit relatives and to the movies. His mother died of a "stroke" when the patient was 14 years old and he went to live with an aunt, who was nice to him but scolded him frequently for things his mother had permitted

In the discussion of his symptoms, it was pointed out to him that he still looked for the security and attention of his mother and he always formed an attachment to any individual who would offer him any semblance of affection. His attachments to the Major and his friend Pete were used as examples of that wish for dependence on someone. He was given insight into the immature outlook he had on the world when he enlisted in the Air Forces and trained as an aerial gunner, not realizing the hazards of flying and flying in combat warfare.

In a pentothal interview the patient spoke calmly of his combat experiences but responded with sorrowful remarks when his friend Pete was mentioned. "He was a swell guy. He liked me and he used to call me 'Junior.' I admired Pete. We went to London together and he took me to Scotland on a furlough.

"I want my mother. I felt bad when I lost her. She treated me nice. I missed her in the barracks when the boys and I would have fights and I would lay in my bunk and cry."

The patient felt better after the pentothal interview and the next day the entire subject matter of the interview was discussed with him. It was pointed out to him that he always had a great deal of dependence on someone and his feeling of insecurity and immaturity accounted for his symptoms.

The patient showed marked improvement in the hospital. His appetite improved but he still craved a great deal of milk. His sleep became more restful and his dreams decreased. He presented less restlessness at the interviews. In view of his improvement, he was discharged for a trial of duty.

. . . .

This young gunner had hardly known a father and was closely attached to his mother. For a time, close attachments to older persons in his group, whom he looked up to and admired as father figures, supported him through the anxious moments of combat. When they were lost to him, he could not carry on as before. Yet he could not permit complete conscious expression of his needs. These were expressed on a visceral level by stomach symptoms and a craving for milk. When they were made conscious by means of narcosynthesis and psychotherapy, his symptoms improved.

CASE 34: *Abdominal pain and vomiting, expressing fear and hostility, relieved by narcosynthesis.*

A 20 year old Sergeant served forty-five combat missions as a radio gunner on a B-17. His chief complaints were pain in the epigastrium, constant and dull in character, vomiting after meals and occasional headache. There was a moderate startle reaction to sudden loud noises.

The patient exhibited nervousness and a moderate degree of tension in his first interviews. He wrung his hands and cracked his knuckles constantly while talking but was very cooperative. He stated, "I'm a little nervous and irritable. When I was home on my furlough, I flared up at my mother a few times and told her off. I was sorry afterwards—she still seems to think that I'm a little boy and kept telling me what to do." The mother had always been nervous, cried and worried a lot, while at the same time she was strict and kept the patient and his brother "tied to her apron strings." The therapist asked the patient when he first noticed his nervousness. "I've been nervous ever since my first mission. On the take-off we damaged the ship when we left the runway. The pilot took us to 4,000 feet and we all bailed out. I was scared as hell and I broke a bone in my foot when we landed. I was taken to a hospital and a cast was put on my foot. After this I was grounded for six weeks." The patient then began talking again about life back in the United States. "What makes me mad is these damned civilians. When they can't get steaks two or three times a day, they're upset. Hell, we couldn't even get cigarettes overseas. On Christmas Day we ate C rations. When I was home on my furlough, I was in a restaurant one day. A civilian that sat next to me asked how it was over there. I told him to join up and find out for himself. One word led to another and first thing I knew I let him have it."

The patient then talked of his parents. "My mother didn't want me to fly. I was glad to go in the army and be my own boss. She wouldn't sign my papers or I would have been an officer. She always did treat me as a baby and thought my slightest cold was a serious illness. When I was home she wanted me to promise not to go to combat again. I told her I wasn't going to stick my neck out again." He then continued to talk about civilians and his hostility toward them.

In the second interview, the patient was asked to tell about his most severe mission. He began, "My worst raid was over Germany. We had bad luck that day. On the way out about three hundred fighters jumped us. The two waist gunners were wounded. We had two motors shot out and a third one was smoking. We were just about out of ammunition and gas. We reached the target O.K. and started back. We thought we would have to bail out before we reached home but we didn't. When we got back to our base, we had to make a crash landing because our landing gear was shot up. I really was sick after this raid. I vomited soon as I got out of the plane and I had a pain in my stomach. I was pretty sick ever since my friend, a ball turret gunner, was shot down on his twenty-fourth mission. He and I were good pals. He was married and didn't run around either, so we had a good time together." After a short period of time, the patient made a normal recovery from the news of his friend's death.

On entering the room the next day, the therapist saw a picture of the patient's girl friend. He remarked that she was a very pretty girl and then asked how old she was. He answered, "That's the trouble. She's about 11 years older than I am. Her folks don't think we should get married, but my mother thinks we should. She has been married before and has a little boy 10 years old, but that doesn't make any difference to me, and I don't give a damn what other people think." He continued to speak of what good times he and his girl friend had. He remarked several times that his mother approved of the marriage. He insisted that he was going to marry the girl and asked the therapist's opinion on the age difference.

At the next interview, the patient was asked how he was feeling and he replied, "I don't feel a damned bit better. I still can't eat, and, when I try, I vomit." The patient was then given 7.0 cc. of a 5.0 per cent pentothal solution and told that the motors were being warmed up to go on the Augsburg raid. His muscles became very tense and he began moving his hands and legs, showing much anxiety. For about one hour he actually relived this raid and he talked with the pilot and other members of the crew over the interphone. Every detail of the raid was brought out. He described the wounding of both waist gunners and their plane being attacked by fighters, the motors being shot up and the tail of the plane being damaged. He brought out considerable hostility toward the pilot, which had never been mentioned before. The patient was told that he was now back in the United States and that there was no further need for worry or feeling afraid.

The next day the material was reviewed, most of it being remembered by the patient. He related that he had eaten his first good meal last night and that he had eaten three eggs and a pint of milk for breakfast. The pain in the stomach was less marked. Subsequently he continued to eat well and gain weight. He complained of very little pain in the abdomen and he no longer desired to leave the army. He was discharged from the hospital to full military duty.

. . . . . .

This boy entered the army very young in an effort to escape from the restrictions of his mother's attentions. He made a strong effort to be independent to the point of overcompensating, especially on his return home, as evidenced by his anger at his mother and at civilians. His present intentions of marrying a woman older than himself with a 10 year old child indicate that he is still living out a displaced passive attitude toward his mother. It became essential that this boy in combat repress all fear, which he equated with childish or weak attitudes. They were only expressed in gastrointestinal language. Under pentothal he was able to abreact fear of the enemy and anger at the impotent pilot and to synthesize these feelings into consciousness. He lost his symptoms spontaneously.

CASE 35: *Gastrointestinal distress in the form of hysterical conversion symptoms, representing an intrapsychic conflict accentuated by combat experiences.*

The patient was a 32 year old Sergeant gunner, who appeared prematurely old; he entered the hospital because of depression and restlessness. These symptoms began after about thirty missions and he attributed them to the loss of many friends and to poor food. During his second interview, the patient appeared somewhat depressed and stated that he had lost interest in everything and did not care about ground work or flying. "I'd like to go off in the woods by myself for a week. Thinking of combat doesn't bother me much. I talk about it, but it doesn't upset me. I have occasional nightmares, but they aren't necessarily of combat. I began to feel this way about three months ago—after I had flown about thirty-one missions. While I was home, I felt pretty good. My stomach bothers me though. I have a good appetite, but I got to feel a heavy weight across my stomach. It lasts about three days. No pain and I don't feel like vomiting. I've had it for eighteen months, ever since I had an attack of food poisoning here in the United States. It has gotten steadily worse. At first I thought it was cancer, but I'm sure there is something wrong. I don't care about life any more. I can't get interested in anything. I don't know if I'd feel better even if I did get out of the army. I keep thinking of all the boys in my outfit that I lost."

The patient was tremulous, depressed and perspiring. His "stomach trouble" was not localized to any special place in the abdomen; it was now in one place, now in another. It felt like a weight, as if he were too full or had gas, or as if he needed to move his bowels, though this did not bring relief.

Because of his complete lack of emotional insight, he was given a pentothal treatment. He was asked to talk about flak. He briefly spoke in the present tense of flak—"thick enough to walk on." It would be a miracle if he ever got out alive. He did not give a damn what happened—all this in the most unemotional, flat, hopeless way. Then he talked of friends dying. "It's not right for them to die that way. No one should have to die." And then he began to show anxiety. He rolled his head from side to side and *clasped his abdomen with an expression of pain and asked to be allowed to walk.* "It's too full." The therapist urged him to tell more of his combat experiences which he did in detail. His response was: "I've gone through a lot all my life." At 13 years of age, he worked twelve hours a day in a stone quarry. When asked about what made him work so hard, he answered that, when he was 6 years old, his brother was born by cesarean section and his mother was never well from that time, suffering frequent serious attacks of heart trouble. She had much medical care and consultation with the best heart specialists in the country. Always there was the fear of her dying. He remembered staying up nights with her, caring for her, nursing her, doing the house work. She was nervous and worrisome. About four or five years ago, he began to think it might be better for her to die. He immediately assured the therapist that he had never wished her to die—it was just that she suffered so. Overseas very often at night he worried about her dying.

The patient recalled that, when he was 6 years of age, he was with an older brother in a neighbor's house looking out of the window, waiting for the neighbor to return, and hoping she would allow him to return home (from which place he had been put out), where something mysterious was occurring. He could not recall what he was thinking about. Quite likely, he stated, it was about getting food.

The next day the patient felt no better. The therapist told him that his present distress seemed related to his feelings about his mother. He then recalled some resentment that he had felt when he was 18 or 19 years of age because he had to stay home to care for her. He could not go out—could not leave or get the job he wanted to. He was reminded of his thought that his mother would be better off dead. He said that it was because she suffered so and worried so. The therapist told him that he resented the burden imposed on him, and he was asked to try to remember all he could of the sixth year of his life. His prior life at home was very happy, all the family went fishing together, and so on. He recalled his mother getting fat. Then one day she was in bed, tossing her head from side to side, moaning and groaning: "Oh, Lord!"—and clasping her stomach. He was frightened and he and his older brother were sent to the neighbor's house until evening. When they returned, his mother asked for water. He brought her some but then the water was withheld from her. *He then saw the red and ugly baby.* Later he felt resentment because he could not have things done for him as in the past, such as mother putting him to bed. The therapist suggested that combat drove him back to a greater need for his mother and the subsequent frustration induced the same reaction as when he was a child and his mother was taken from him. Instead of a loving, devoted mother, he only got a mother with a stomachache (with whom he now identified).

. . . . . .

This case is presented to demonstrate the basic differences in the psychodynamics of gastrointestinal symptoms produced by regression of emotional patterns into low-level visceral activity and of those produced by hysterical conflict, as in this patient. The patient was stimulated to an increase in his intrapsychic conflict, eventuating in severe symptoms, by the loss of his comrades, which revived the old conflict over the loss of his mother when she faithlessly had another baby, to whom she was more attentive. Through introjection of the mother toward whom he had disagreeable ambivalent feelings, the patient was able to gratify himself by possessing the mother within him, but also had to be punished by suffering in precisely the same way as she did. His fear of his mother's dying was the result of a projection of hostile feelings toward her. These were made conscious under pentothal. The result was an increase of his own deathlike pain and the fear of cancer inside him. Here we see that the symptom represents an idea behind which is a hysterical conflict; it expresses gratification and punishment. Because his psychological defenses against insight were so strong, little beneficial result was obtained and the patient was discharged from the army.

CASE 36: *Psychogenic headaches caused by repressed fear and anger, increased by combat.*

This patient was a 28 year old bombardier who had been in the army for four years. Two years ago, he was washed out of pilot training. He was sent overseas, where he flew four combat missions of moderate severity. After his second mission, he complained to his Flight Surgeon about severe frontal and temporal headaches, which had been intermittent for many years but had become constant since he had been in combat. Thorough examinations in several hospitals disclosed no organic disease. The patient became depressed, lost 30 pounds in weight and slept poorly. He was sent home by the Medical Board after failure of psychiatric treatment overseas.

The patient came from a middle class family, in which he seemed to be the favorite of the mother. His father was good to him but quite strict in many attitudes. Intermittent headaches began in high school and became more frequent; they were not relieved by medication. They reached an intense stage, although still intermittent, while he was flying in this country.

The patient had a stern facial expression and scowled frequently. He seemed not always to hear people talking to him. He recalled that he developed this trait as a child, not hearing his mother when she called so that he wouldn't have to go into the house. He also did not want to hear the boys call him "Fatty." Under pentothal it was disclosed that the patient had great fear of flying because of the danger of falling. He secretly was glad to be washed out of pilot training. He finally came to admit that he was actually terrified of flying, even as a bombardier, but could not quit and maintain his self respect. Furthermore, he had a great abhorrence of killing people, hated war and felt it was futile. Further light on his past was revealed, indicating that early in life he was rebellious to teachers and authority but later he kept his rebellion in check. He would walk away from all arguments and disputes. In reconstructing these episodes he came to realize that his intermittent headaches developed during periods of unexpressed anger. As the patient became conscious of the relationship of unexpressed fear and anger to his headaches and was assured he would not have to fly again, his symptoms disappeared and he became free of headaches.

. . . . . .

Here we see the relationship between a repressed emotion and a disabling symptom, which at first caused great difficulty in differential diagnosis but finally was found to be psychogenic. Ventilation disclosed that the headaches were due to a conflict between rebellious aggression against an authoritative figure in the army and fear of retaliation. Abreaction and conscious knowledge of the problem, with environmental manipulation (grounding), effected a relief of symptoms. By this we do not mean a cure, for we have not touched the primary source of the conflict—we have only made its later causes conscious.

CASE 37: *Palpitation and precordial distress without cardiac disease, due to repressed emotion.*

A 30 year old clerk spent three years overseas under the jurisdiction of officers who were poor leaders, inefficient and hostile to their men. Living conditions were not good and opportunities for diversion infrequent. During this period the patient, who had never before been ill or had cardiac symptoms, became conscious of his heart.

After several interviews he was able to reconstruct the relation of his heart symptoms to external events. When terribly annoyed with his officers or after some particularly unfair treatment, he developed precordial distress. He was unable to retort or complain to his superiors and would walk off to see about something, change the subject or talk to someone else. His subordinates were foreign soldiers whom he had to train but he could not displace any anger to them, since that too brought down punishment from the American officers. During an interview, he seemed about to get angry at the memory of his past difficulties but turned away from the subject and gave vent to no emotional expression.

After several interviews with and without pentothal the patient was able to express his rage and lost his cardiac symptoms. He made a complete recovery.

We have here an example of a cardiac neurosis in a non-combat soldier who suffered from repression of hostile feelings. He had no outlet for his rage except at the cost of more oppression and punishment. He devised methods for "putting the situation out of his mind." After many months he developed cardiac symptoms, which were the sole expression of his reaction. Even when forced to tell the story, he related the events in the first interviews in a coldly intellectual fashion. Recovery resulted when consciousness of the emotion was made possible.

．　　．　　．　　．　　．　　．

We have seen other noncombat soldiers overseas with cardiac neuroses and certainly many cases have been reported from the Continental army. We have not observed these conditions frequently in combat soldiers. Probably they have sufficient outlet for release of their aggressions in combat, so that not all of the emotion is expressed through lower-level visceral outlets. In the last war, with static trench warfare, cardiac neuroses were common. In this war, with its great mobility and activity, especially in the air, outlets for aggression are available for everyone.

CASE 38: *Psychogenic diarrhea.*

The patient was a 30 year old photographer, who spent two years overseas in a relatively safe environment. He had been closely attached to his mother, whose baby he had always remained. His father died while the patient was still an infant, but his mother never remarried because she did not want him to have a stepfather. The patient was a good boy and had an excellent work record. He lived with his mother and on three separate occasions brought home girls he loved, but his mother rejected them each time and "she is always right." He was in love, at the time of this examination, with a girl of whom his mother approved. After marriage, of course, his mother would live with them.

The patient had never had any gastrointestinal distress until four months ago, while still overseas. There he developed a dysentery, which cleared up under treatment, but since then there had been episodic exacerbations of diarrhea. He remembered that the whole thing began when his wonderful and peaceful job as boss of a small unit was disturbed by the assignment of two wise-cracking, smart boys, who ruined the morale of the unit. He remembered that, every time he suffered from diarrhea, he had been angry about something. While home on overseas furlough, he developed diarrhea after an argument with his partner. He stated: "I don't fight—I just eat my own insides out." These were apparently indigestible for him.

. . . . . .

This patient demonstrated the prolongation of diarrhea initiated by dysentery in a psychologically prepared person. It was obviously a visceral expression of anger which could not be expressed consciously. Disturbances of the lower gastrointestinal tract are common in combat soldiers. They are an accompaniment of fear which precedes a mission and infantile rage against having to endanger oneself. These usually disappear on relief from combat. Those that persist are usually found in noncombat soldiers.

Experience with combat soldiers of every type demonstrates that the most frequent symptoms of visceral disturbances are related to the gastrointestinal tract. These are normal concomitants of severe emotional reactions induced by fearful stimuli (cf. chapter 5). Men often vomit and have diarrhea before going on a mission. But these are temporary reactions and last only as long as the source of fear persists. A gunner may be able to eat no food the night before a mission, yet may have a healthy appetite during the day or days between missions. Some soldiers have persistent nausea, vomiting and diarrhea during a large part of their combat duty, especially toward the end, after long-continued exposure to fear, but these symptoms subside on return to a zone of safety. Yet a large number of patients persist in their symptoms long after return to the United States and are referred to a hospital.

Alexander and his coworkers (3), in their pioneer work on gastrointestinal disturbances, have pointed out the relationship between the direction of psychological trends and the activity of the gastrointestinal tract. Three major functions are described: the intake of food, the partial retention of foodstuff for growth and maintenance, and the elimination of waste products. Correlated with stomach activity is the wish to take; correlated with bowel activities are, in diarrhea, the wish to give, and, in constipation, the wish to retain. These workers have found a high correlation between the nature of a psychological trend, inexpressible at a higher level, and the gastrointestinal symptoms. Subsequent investigators, by studying the exposed gastric mucosa, have confirmed the thesis that normal emotional reactions are accompanied by functional changes in gastrointestinal activities. All of us are aware of such phenomena in our daily emotional lives. When we are unable to *feel* the emotion consciously, it is expressed in *exaggerated* smooth muscle activity. *It is this excessive functioning, alone portraying the emotion, that is productive of symptoms.*

How does combat directly or indirectly influence these psychosomatic symptoms? That the situation of battle stress evokes *fear* and *anger* is well known, but it is equally true that it causes exaggerated *needs*. All of these trends are acceptable in conscious expression *to a degree*. We have heard a great deal about the excellent modern attitude of armies in this war, which accept fully the truth that all men are afraid, and encourage men to be conscious of their own fears and to believe that they are acceptably normal. Up to a point, this is excellent mental hygiene. However, recognizing that one is afraid is no help in dealing with this emotion when it assumes a great intensity. Whether one knows about fear or not, when its energy reaches a certain threshold, it transcends the level of visceral activity, and floods consciousness and the ego, causing disastrous flight, panic or paralysis. This knowledge does not abolish the visceral components of the emotion. A soldier may be angry at his officers and the army and indulge in "gripes" and mild verbalization, but he cannot express the real intensity of his feelings, especially over incompetence in the stress of battle, without serious consequences. Hurt in spirit by constant enemy attacks and loss of comrades, a soldier may admit that he would like to be at home with mother, but in his group he cannot cry and sob in the expression of the longing he really feels. Therefore, in all the psychosomatic disturbances precipitated by combat we see, as we do not see in our civilian cases, a considerable amount of free-floating anxiety indicative of a higher level of expression, but the majority of the emotional expression is felt only as symptomatic visceral disturbances.

Certainly the fundamental process is regressive in that the energies of emotional expression act on a biologically lower level, closely resembling the visceral behavior of the infant. Dyspeptic symptoms and ability to ingest only milk, as a psychosomatic symptom, could well have been discussed under the heading of Passive-Dependent States (cf. chapter 10). Cases 23, 24 and 25, described under that heading, also had gastrointestinal symptoms. However, there is a profound difference between the crying, dependent youth and the milk drinker, and between the hostile, aggressive boy and the vomiter. The difference is that in one the expression is conscious, in behavior or verbalizations, and in the other the meaning of the symptom is not known to the patient. He does not permit himself such knowledge or expression because there is another force within him, an ego-syntonic and self-respecting attitude, that prevents such infantile tendencies from rising to consciousness. This psychological block, effected by ego forces at the behest of the ego-ideal, is stronger than the forces of expression. Since the result is an expression only at visceral levels, the ego has won the battle; it is stronger than the tendency. In fact, it may give a semblance of even greater strength by its technique of overcompensation. Thus, a passive-dependent trend, expressed gastrically, may be accompanied by an aggressive and independent attitude. This only serves to deprive the individual further and increase his longings.

The effect of combat in producing gastrointestinal disturbances cannot be classified in simple terms that indicate a relationship between a specific emotion and a specific symptom. Those with hyperacidity, hypermotility and hypersecretion, requiring milk almost as the sole diet, express a great need to be loved and taken care of. Nausea and vomiting often are the sole expressions of hostility to officers and superiors, which correspond to the gagging of the angry infant. Guilt and depression with self condemnation over the death of a close friend are frequently accompanied by loss of appetite and a feeling as of a load in the stomach. Diarrhea is an expression of anger, fear or restitution because of guilt.

Headaches and vertigo are most often associated with unconscious conflicts involving, as a rule, some unexpressed aggression. The same holds true for hypertension, hyperventilation, various bodily pains and skin rashes. The exact relationship between symptom and emotion cannot always be elicited in the time available. Frequently a symptomatic cure is accomplished without clarification of the dynamics.

The people who develop severe psychosomatic symptoms in combat are usually prepared for these troubles. Some have had the identical disturbances in civilian life, but these usually become so ill that they cannot carry on for more than a few missions. Among those who develop the symptoms for the first time are those whose character structure and past life conform to the psychological pattern of patients with similar troubles in civilian life. The great majority have succumbed to an intolerable life situation and recover promptly on removal from stress and insight into the current conflictual problem. The prognosis for recovery is, of course, better when there is less of a habitual pattern of similar reactivity and the new external catastrophic stress has been most important in the etiology. Those with lifelong patterns of psychosomatic reactions and rigid psychological defenses need lengthy treatment to reorient basic attitudes toward early but persistent conflicts, only exaggerated by recent stress (14). Recently developed syndromes may be cured with narcosynthesis alone even without interpretations. Others require interpretations and considerable "working through." Sometimes recovery is rapid, after a few neutral interviews, indicating that the interest of the therapist has alone been sufficient to gratify the ego and establish its control over the symptoms, but recovery here is tenuous and future relapses may be expected even under only light stress.

Our war experiences indicate that early and adequate treatment of most psychosomatic disturbances is effective, and point clearly to an application to civilian medicine. Patients should not be treated medically for years if recovery is desired. On the contrary, symptomatic relief does not stop the process of structural alteration or fixation of psychological patterns. These states of "functional disturbances" must receive early psychiatric treatment.

CHAPTER 12

Guilt and Depression

ONE WOULD EXPECT the soldier, after an arduous and dangerous tour of combat duty, to be overjoyed at receiving orders for relief, and profoundly happy on his arrival back in the United States among his family and friends. Most soldiers do experience this feeling but there are others who become depressed and irritable. It is difficult for those who have not experienced separation from a close group, from men with whom they have endured hardships and experienced hundreds of adventures, from comrades with whom they have lived in great danger and constant intimacy, to consider such depressions as anything but pathological. As a matter of fact, the normal reaction is one in which joy and regret exist side by side, the former usually overshadowing the latter except under pathological circumstances.

Early in the war, Air Forces squadrons, formed in later phases of training, persisted as compact units throughout the vicissitudes of training and combat. Later, replacements—combat crews and individuals—were sent to already existing squadrons, only then forming units which had never been together before. No matter when it is formed, once a group is molded, the majority of its members hope to return home together. The most severe punishment for enlisted men is to be grounded, so that they are separated from their crews and lose out in their number of completed missions. Many men who have finished their tour of duty before others in the group volunteer to stay rather than "desert" them. We do not wish to minimize the bravery of these persons who volunteer to risk their lives longer than required, but actually the pain of separation from the group is often greater than fear of danger from the enemy. They remain not because of any determination to fight longer or harder but because they are held back by an emotional interpersonal tie. This is "good morale," even though we recognize that it is not a derivative of a fighting spirit and that it does not possess a high degree of intellectual motivation.

It has been demonstrated that men who leave combat be cause of overpowering anxiety develop a secondary depression with a sense of failure at not having lived up to their ego's ideal and the group's standards (cf. chapter 5). To some extent this holds true for men who return home ahead of their comrades by right of honorable completion of their tasks. Even they feel like deserters. Anticipation of the last mission fills them with foreboding that it truly will be their end and that they will be shot down. It is clear that contemplating separation from their comrades sets into action a feeling of guilt and minor depression. The anticipated bad luck is the projected fear of punishment.

Correspondingly those who have been grounded for a few missions, because of fatigue, illness or wounds, volunteer for extra missions between their regular runs in an effort to catch up on their total number and go home with the gang. Personal pleasure and anticipation of homecoming notwithstanding, separation from the others is faced with dread.

In the normal course of events, if the returnee travels home by plane, landing at air bases closer and closer to American civilization, he observes more signs of comfort and luxury. The bare table is covered by a cloth which eventually is white and clean. Mess gear is replaced by gleaming silver, and canned rations are replaced by "chewing food." The men exclaim in joy and seem quite happy, but casual remarks indicate another emotion. "Gee, if the boys in the field could get a load of this," or, "God, it's awful to eat like this when they are eating out of cans," or, "Give me another steak—I'll eat one for Joe."

Guilty feelings without conscious depression are often expressed on a lower, visceral level. One pilot on returning home could keep nothing down. He explained, "This food is too rich for me—I've eaten C rations too long." Another returnee, who had usually been constipated, had a bowel movement regularly after each meal. The guilty feeling is expressed by the hurried disposal of the food either by emesis or by diarrhea, yet the individual is not conscious of his emotions.

When the soldier returns home and receives the attention of the family and is entertained by friends and neighbors with parties, food and drink, he may seem somewhat reticent and sad instead of gloriously happy. The more he receives, the guiltier he feels toward those he left behind; the effect is a gloomy reaction. He often turns down invitations just to avoid this note of depression in his feelings. He dismisses his personal exploits from the conversation and is reticent about talking of himself, not because of any inherent modesty, but because "Joe," who died on the very same mission, haunts his memory with reminders that he has not done as much. In many cases guilty feelings reach such an intensity that the returnee thinks of asking to return to combat as soon as his overseas leave is finished. In the normal course of events the guilty feelings subside gradually and he is content to let fate and the army determine the date of his return to combat.

Up to this point we have described the normal guilty feelings and depression. In most cases these wear off gradually. For some time, on receipt of a letter or news of the old squadron, or when the widow or mother of some fallen comrade requests information regarding the dead or missing man, there are recurrences. For this reason these relatives are avoided as much as possible. The returnee hates to write or talk to them, as such experiences only revive the old feelings of guilt.

We now turn to the pathological states of guilt and depression. It will be seen at once that they bring in no new quality either descriptively or dynamically but are only quantitative exaggerations of the same mental processes that each man goes through; only in quantity of emotion and persistence are they pathological.

CASE 39: *Depression because of separation from the group.*

A 28 year old Staff Sergeant, a nonflying armorer, entered the hospital because of depression. The patient came from a neurotic family and his childhood was marred by a stern, punitive mother, so that he had always felt inferior, unappreciated and guilty about trivial misdemeanors. He was also enuretic until the age of 14 years.

In China, the patient experienced fifty-eight bombing and strafing attacks before being wounded. After several surgical operations he was evacuated to the United States. At the time he was wounded, a fellow soldier with him was killed. The patient felt guilty over this tragedy because he kept this man at work on the base although he had asked for the day off. Furthermore, when the Japs came over the field, he ordered the man not to run but to take cover. The patient kept thinking of his dead friend; his face constantly appeared before him. He could not eat at the mess table although hungry. Under pentothal the patient expressed a strong desire to return to China, based on a combination of reasons. He felt guilty about the other soldier's death, and he felt guilty about leaving the squadron with the job unfinished, especially since the Chinese people were the only ones who appreciated his efforts. Americans had no concept of war and didn't care. The guilty feelings about the dead soldier were easily overcome by appropriate psychotherapy. The desire to return to China persisted, largely because for the first time in his life he felt equal, strong, secure and appreciated within his overseas group. As an individual he felt lost, and searched for strength in other groups in this country. He made frequent trips to a nearby town for religious services but nowhere could he find surcease from the longing to be back in the squadron. His physical condition prevented his return overseas.

.   .   .   .   .   .

This man's depression resulted essentially from the loss of support by a strong group, a support which made up for his own lack of confidence. Compulsive and conscientious, he felt equal and strong when protected by its strength and incorporated in the drive of the total group configuration. He felt powerful when appreciated by the weaker Chinese people. Removal of this support caused his fundamentally weak ego to react with depression. The patient himself knew that nowhere in this country could he find a group strong enough to support him. It is only the common threat of death that welds the soldiers into a cohesive unit. On air fields in this country each man has his outside interests and personal affairs; often his family lives nearby. Overseas everyone's business is everyone else's, because isolation from home and the common goals make the family of the group more significant than any other relationship.

CASE 40: *Depression and anxiety of one year's duration due to loss of a buddy in combat.*

This patient was a Captain, 25 years of age, who entered the Convalescent Hospital because of objective symptoms of depression. He presented an expressionless face; his muscles were quite rigid, indicating a great deal of tension. He did not volunteer much information and never smiled, and his speech was retarded. The patient had been a flight leader in a pursuit squadron and had fought successfully until about his twenty-fifth mission, when a friend, who had been flying on his wing, went up in flames. However, he stated that he continued fighting and successfully completed his tour of duty although feeling badly depressed. He refused promotion to command a squadron. He had been reassigned to a job in the United States, which he liked very much and wanted to keep, but his depression continued and was accompanied by severe startle reactions. When anyone came into his room and made a sudden noise or turned on the light, he would jump out of bed with great anxiety. In addition to the depression and its concomitants, there was considerable insomnia, with battle dreams, which repeated some of the very severe traumatic incidents of his combat experiences. However, he maintained fairly good control of himself and continued to fly. He attempted to decrease the anxiety and depression by drinking, but the only result was an increase in anxiety. He stated that he tried hard to forget his experiences but found it impossible.

During the initial interview, it was learned that he was single, and was a university graduate, who studied hard, made excellent grades and was given a fellowship in animal genetics, which he could not complete because he entered the Air Forces. There was no history of any previous depression and no incident that showed that he could not adjust himself to his normal experiences and environment.

That afternoon he was given 0.25 Gm. of pentothal intravenously. He was then told that he was up in the air on a strafing mission and that the man on his wing was aflame, and he was then commanded: "Go ahead and talk." Immediately he went into an emotional reaction shouting to his friend, whose name was Joe, to "pull up and bail out."

"Why doesn't he pull up, why doesn't he bail out? I hope he doesn't think it's my fault. He's such a nice boy. Such a swell fellow. I hope I'm not responsible for his death. We were together all the time. He lived in the same tent with me and would share anything that he had. When we were on low rations, he would give as much as he could to everyone else." Accompanying all this were tears and sobbing and repetitions of, "I hope he doesn't think it's my fault. He wasn't a good flier. Oh, if I had only picked out another spot, a safer target, but that is where they told me to go, right over those trucks. If I had gone in some other place, he wouldn't have got it. Why did he do it? He should have stayed in formation. He didn't stay where he was supposed to. He came up and took the lead position with me. Maybe I should have given a talk before we went about staying in formation. Why didn't I do that?"

Then he talked about the letter they wrote home to Joe's family and how he couldn't bear to read it. That would start it all over again. "I can't get him out of my mind. I couldn't see his family because they had probably forgotten and I didn't want to stir them up." In this fashion he went over and over the traumatic situation, crying and sobbing.

As this reaction subsided, he was allowed to close his eyes and sleep for a few moments. Then he was handed a lighted cigarette and awakened. He looked at his watch and stated, "I must have been asleep. I had a dream about Joe." His pillow was wet with tears. He said, "Gosh, I perspired a lot."

The therapist said, "No, you were only asleep for a few minutes but you talked to me about Joe and you told me all about it. Let's talk about him some more."

Then in a conscious state he went over the situation again, just as he had done when asleep. Then the patient talked about another boy, who crashed in a low level flight, maintaining radio silence according to instructions although he was in need of help. Then he told of feeling badly about killing the Germans. The interview was ended by the therapist telling him that he had assumed responsibility for the death of Joe that did not seem to be based on fact.

The next morning the patient entered the interviewing room and stated, "I feel like a load has been lifted from my mind, like a great relief. I slept well last night, awakened once and went right to sleep again. I had no dreams. This morning I feel good." There was a silence. Then he said, "I guess I blamed myself unnecessarily." The therapist said, "Yes, you did. Now let's try to figure out why you blamed yourself. Tell me something about your background." The patient then told how he lived on a farm of 650 acres. His father was a successful farmer, who made enough to enable four children to go to college. The first child was born dead, the patient was the second and then there were two sisters, each two years apart, the elder two years younger than he. He had one brother, nine years younger. The mother was mild mannered and very religious. The children went to Sunday school and church, though not forced to do so. The father was very kind and gentle but strict in his attitudes. He rarely spanked the patient but he expected him to live up to his responsibilities. If he did not, the father would look pained and disappointed and tell him, "This was your job," and then do it himself, which the patient states was worse than a spanking. He was always on very good terms with his father and would rather work with him than anyone else.

He then began to talk about his commanding officer and told how this man was an exceptionally strong leader; a person who went on the most dangerous missions himself; a man who was fair and expected everyone to do his job.

The therapist said, "Your C.O. was very much like your father." The patient stated, "You know, I often thought he was like my father, doing things he wasn't supposed to do and doing everything to help us, but expecting the best from us. Of course, not in the same way, because he was a fighter." The psychiatrist then said, "Now let us summarize the things for which you blame yourself. Joe's death—you were ordered to hit the target, even though dangerous; you could do nothing else and could not be responsible for his death. Secondly, you blame yourself for not giving implicit formation instruction, but you were all experienced fliers and had been trained in formations for six months and every man knew his position. You blame yourself for killing the Germans, but you know that was to save the lives of our own troops. You blame yourself about the boy who crashed on the low mission, but it was agreed beforehand that radio silence was to be maintained. You blame yourself for not communicating with Joe's family, but you know that it is not good to stir up a sorrowing family again. So you have a lot of disapproving attitudes toward things which are not really your fault. You behave as if you were still reacting to a disapproving attitude that your father might have had toward you. You behave as if your father's image were looking at you with a disappointed expression."

The patient said, "Well, I have always taken responsibilities and duties seriously. I have never been able to feel that I did give my best unless I worked terribly hard."

To this the therapist answered, "And now your behavior, which is depressed and completely unhappy, is just as if you were intent on punishing yourself and never letting yourself have any fun or pleasure."

The patient stated, "That's it. I can't enjoy things. I wonder why I take his death so seriously," and terminated the interview.

The next day the patient began the interview smiling and stated that he felt as if he could carry on. He now realized that he took his responsibility too seriously but always had felt as if he didn't want to let anyone down. He then told about a younger pilot, 21 years of age, whom he had taught to fly in formation. The younger pilot looked up to him as an older man or father. He was asked, "Something like your younger brother?," and he answered, "Yes, he used to think I was a great guy; I taught him how to shoot, how to hold a gun and how to play all sorts of games. Our C.O. always spoke quite frankly about his opinion of the conduct and performance of the boys; he either disapproved or complimented. If a fellow did his work properly and if he asked for a day off, he always got every consideration."

It was explained to the patient that because of guilty feelings he was punishing himself for Joe's death (which had happened one year ago). This feeling had persisted without any cause in reality. Therefore, this sense of guilt and the punishment which he had been giving himself must be due to some inner feeling, which it was not possible to master unless it was unearthed and brought to light.

He was told, "Now you have said nothing but good things about Joe, how attached you were and what a fine fellow he was, but your guilty feelings about him are due to some negative attitudes toward Joe that you have not yet discussed. Perhaps these feelings were unconscious and a source of your sense of guilt."

The patient then said, "Of course, no one is perfect, but Joe was the easiest person to get along with. He drank frequently and had to be taken care of. Once when we were in the desert and got drunk, Joe tore up the tent in the middle of a sandstorm. There was a family quarrel with the four tentmates."

His attention was drawn to the fact that Joe was not made flight leader. Was Joe envious of the patient? He reconstructed the flight: Joe was flying on the left wing of the patient, who was the leader. Joe flew on the left slightly behind but he veered to the right and forward, to accompany the patient in the lead position. The patient was asked whether he interpreted this as if Joe were out to take the lead as a sort of rebellion. He said he didn't think so, but that he didn't give way because he wanted to maintain the proper formation in the flight. Then he said, "Maybe that is why I feel so guilty, because I didn't give way." The result was that Joe was hit by flak and slid over the patient's plane to the right, on fire.

The next morning the patient entered the room, at ease and in good spirits, and said, "I've been thinking a good deal about Joe and some clue you gave me yesterday brought me to some sort of a conclusion. Probably it is silly, you might not think it is important, but I have been thinking about it. I always wanted to do things and get ahead. I was very ambitious. I wanted to be better than just average, and, when I decided on any ambition, I worked very hard to accomplish it. Sometimes I would win and sometimes I would lose, but I would always work for whatever I wanted. When I was in school, there were four of us on a cattle-judging team. I wanted to be top man but there was another fellow on the team who lived with me and he was awfully good. I had to fight it out with him. We fought it back and forth all year round. In my junior year I was able to beat him. The next year he beat me. There were no hard feelings about it. It was competition but we still were friends."

The patient then repeated several other incidents of competitive relationship with other men and it became clear that he took no pleasure in winning over people who gave him no struggle. He always wanted to win out over someone whom he felt to be superior to him. "When I joined my outfit, it was the same way. We had a C.O. who believed that the leadership in the squadron should come from the boys themselves. There were eight places for flight leaders and the men had to win the job. Even after a man became flight leader, he had to work hard to keep it. We were always practicing, practically all the time. Two or three would go up and try to outfly each other. When we finally went overseas, I wasn't able to take a lead position but I became an assistant flight leader. I was disappointed but worked hard just the same. Finally there were eight of us who were flight leaders, including Joe and myself. But we weren't always given the job of leading the flight. Our C.O. wanted to see how we were able to fly under somebody else's orders. We didn't always fly leader, we frequently flew wing. Once I went up with our C.O. to try to outfly him. I fought him hard and I beat him. When we came down, I didn't say a word to anybody that I had beaten the C.O."

The therapist then explained to the patient the nature of unconscious attitudes which were not tempered and modified by civilized realities; that our unconscious aggression, which arose from the instinctual depths within us, was derived from our animal backgrounds. Sportsmanlike competition was a civilized and modified type of aggression but the real hostile competitive spirit is still based, as far as the unconscious is concerned, on the concept "to kill or to be killed." As a result, victory in competition would mean, unconsciously, that the defeated person had been destroyed as the direct result of an unconscious wish to be rid of that person. Hence, when competition was followed by an actual death, the person felt as if he himself had killed that individual.

He grasped this interpretation and in the same interview was given another pentothal injection. He immediately started out by saying, "I *used* to think I was responsible for Joe's death. I *used* to feel as if it were my fault. I know now that it is just one of those things that happen and I couldn't help it. He was a fine fellow. I was scared to go on that mission. He and I went into the mess hall that night for some supper, but we just nibbled, we couldn't eat. I had no cigarettes but Joe had two packages and gave me one of them. I smoked half a package of cigarettes. Joe was generous like that. I was terribly nervous. It was a dangerous target but off we went in a tight formation. There was a terrible amount of flak over the target. The trucks blew up and I felt good when I saw it. I don't know why Joe came over and tried to take the lead from me. I flew under his lead the day before and *I* stayed in formation. I can't understand why he broke formation and came up toward me and then got into a heavy flak position. But I didn't give ground. *I know now we were jealous of each other and we were really fighting against each other for the job.*"

When he awakened he felt a little dizzy and thought he had been sleeping. We summarized the whole material of the interview again, before terminating the session.

The next day he came in and said he felt perfectly well. He had slept soundly all night, had had no dreams and felt that a great load had been lifted from him. He wanted to go back to duty and felt he could carry on. When he had gone home for overseas leave, his people recognized there was something the matter with him and didn't ask him any questions. The result was that he kept all the experiences to himself and deliberately tried to forget, but there was always that load on his stomach. He now understood that the only way one could forget was to suffer the pain of remembering first. He remembered episodes he thought were funny and amusing, incidents that happened in his squadron overseas. He began to talk about little experiences. Prior to this he had not been able to think about these because they always led his mind into situations which became painful. "It is silly for intelligent people to let things bother them the way I did." *His ego now had confidence in its strength and could dwell on the past without anxiety.* Nine months later the patient was still well and functioning as a successful pilot in this country.

·   ·   ·   ·   ·   ·

This case history has been given in some detail to demonstrate the technique of brief dynamic psychotherapy, which successfully relieved a depression of a year's standing in one week. The man's compulsive character, with a stern ego-ideal arising from the father's attitudes, had found it impossible to accept the hostile aspect of his relationship with contemporary rival or father figures. Such deeply repressed negative feelings became mobilized when the unconsciously hated rival was actually destroyed. It was as if the patient had done the terrible deed and must suffer punishment therefor. The patient had identified himself with his father in his attitude toward the younger brother and toward younger pilots whom he helped. Yet he still competed with father figures like the commanding officer but felt guilty when he succeeded, as evidenced by the fact that he told no one of his victory in flying competition. Therapy was directed toward creating insight into the current situation but the ancient patterns of reaction toward the father were left untouched. After a thorough abreaction of guilty feelings, a neutralization of superego pressure, the patient gained insight into his hostile feelings. This in itself should have considerable beneficial effect on the total personality.

CASE 41: *Compulsive character precipitated into depression after injury and death of comrades identified with brothers toward whom the patient had considerable repressed hostility.*

This patient, a 24 year old radio-operator, entered the hospital with the complaints of nervousness, irritability, insomnia, battle dreams and depression. He flew fifty combat missions in a B-25 in thirteen months. He had trained as a radio operator and gunner, after he failed the physical examination for aviation cadet training because of an ocular defect. However, he made a good adjustment, liked to fly and took great pride in his ability as a radio operator. The patient had high patriotic ideals and felt that he really understood what he was fighting for. He felt that he was well adjusted during his combat tour until his twenty-fourth mission, which occurred in support of a landing. His formation approached from the sea through heavy flak. Stukas were diving through the patient's formation to bomb ships and troops below. A piece of flak penetrated the top turret and struck a gunner in the eye. This gunner was a very close friend and crew member of many months' standing. He descended from the turret and said to the patient, "No, no, this can't happen to me." The patient quickly applied a dressing and mounted into the top turret to cover his friend's position. He frantically called to the other crew members to come to assist the wounded gunner. He could look down and see the blood smeared face of his buddy below him. He cursed the enemy planes and hoped for them to come in so he could shoot them. About this time there was engine trouble and his plane left its formation and soon landed on a nearby field. He carried his friend out of the plane and became blood-smeared himself in doing so. He then accompanied him in an ambulance to a hospital where his wounds were cared for. That night he couldn't sleep and was nervous and jittery, but became less tense and "settled down" in two or three days.

After completing his thirtieth mission, his organization was moved and there ensued an operational lull of about three months. During this time he noticed increased nervousness, apprehension, fear of flying, irritability and insomnia. He developed recurrent battle dreams, particularly one in which he was covered with purple blotches, which he attempted to pick.

On resuming combat he "really began to sweat them out." He dreaded each mission. About the time of his forty-second mission a very good friend, not a member of his own crew, was flying with the patient's old copilot. Their plane was hit by flak and exploded. No parachutes were seen to leave the plane and the deaths of all the crew members were later confirmed. The loss of this friend caused the patient great concern and he became even more nervous and irritable.

He finished his fifty missions by forcing himself. He dreaded each of them, but, wanting to get through and get home, he continued to fly. When he received his orders, they read that he was to return for more combat after thirty days' leave. He felt that this was unfair, that he had done his tour and should go back for good. He complained bitterly to his superiors. He returned to the United States, went to his home for thirty days but was very depressed, anxious and upset because he knew he must go back to combat. He had planned to marry his girl but decided against it because of having to return.

The patient was the second child in a closely knit family of four children, with one older and two younger brothers. His father was in the construction business and of moderate means, a hard worker, who had encouraged his children to be morally straight and religious and to prepare themselves for later life by education.

In childhood the patient was a fat, healthy, "serious" youngster. He enjoyed his schooling. His father offered treats to the child who brought home the best report card and would take him to the rodeo, ball game, etc. The patient became a consistent winner of these treats, until finally the father began taking the other boys anyway. His older brother was a source of some conflict. This brother would kid him about being fat and would delight in provoking him and engaging him in arguments. He and this brother bought an automobile in partnership but the patient never drove it much, "to keep the peace." He always tried to run around with his brother's crowd but was unable to keep up with them.

After graduation from high school the patient decided to enter college and was proud of the fact that he could get a scholarship. He had always been ambitious to occupy an important place in society. He received little financial assistance but got moral support from his parents. His older brother kidded him still and referred to him as "Joe College." During this time, the patient began to get the best of the arguments and thereafter his brother ceased chiding him. Because of the imminence of his induction, he did not teach after finishing college but worked in a factory until he entered the army nine months later.

On the twelfth day of hospitalization, narcosis was induced with 0.4 Gm. of pentothal, injected intravenously, and, after being stimulated by the question, "What about Sid?," he spoke with few interruptions always in the past tense.

He said, "No! No! Sid, it can't happen to me. He was hit in the eye." (Marked emotion with tears and squirming about on the couch.) "I prayed and prayed he would be all right and I cried. I asked the navigator to come back and look out for him. He was all blood—bleeding. He said, 'No! No!' I tried to help but I had to go up in the turret." He paused and then went on. "Flak! Flak! Sid was there. I couldn't see him. I called up Jack (navigator) and told him to get to Sid. I didn't know if he was alive or dead.

"I was crying up there. I was cursing those dirty bastards. I was hoping they would come near. He was all covered with blood. He was a good kid. I couldn't help him out. We left the formation. He looked rotten. I looked down from the turret and saw Sid's eye. His whole face was bleeding. I prayed. I carried him out of the plane. I was all covered with blood; he didn't say anything. At the hospital they were so damned slow. There was another fellow there, all full of holes. I told Jack to go tell them to hurry up. Then they finally came and x-rayed him and put him to bed. I told him I would see him again. I told him Mary (his girl) would love him anyway. He went to sleep then.

"At first, I didn't like him. He shot off his mouth too much. He did—he did shoot down a plane." (Pause.) "All over my coveralls was his blood. All those stupid arguments we used to have. I always talked him down and put him in his place." He was then stimulated with, "How about Al?" Whereupon he said, "He was so crazy. He liked his women and his liquor and got both. He was grounded and didn't have to fly. He would trade cigarettes with the natives for eggs and had them for us when we were going on a long mission. He did so much for me; I did nothing for him. His plane exploded. I prayed that night. I was a heel. I would always tell him off. He didn't come back. I told Sid about it. He died for his country" (tears)—"he did so much for the crew; when he would get a package he'd head for me. I was such a dope. Told him he didn't have any sense. And now he is dead. Then Fred, he was put in another squadron. He was so good. He was married to a nice girl. We were on the mission he went down on. There were fighters and flak up there. The plane started to go down and hit the damned mountain." (Pause.) "I knew I couldn't get out." (Pause.) "The whole thing was crazy. My little brother is out there. He is only a kid. He was only 18 when they took him out where those damned animals are. But what the hell does he say when he writes?— nothing. He's so young, so little. He hasn't lived. I used to always argue with him and tell him off. Once I had a fight with him. I was so smart. I was going to be a big shot. They upset my plans, those orders. I was afraid up there. They had no right" (speaking of ordering him on a second tour of combat). "I was through. I couldn't fly any more. I'm just no good. I was going to show them how brave I was" (speaking of his family) "and make them proud of me. I'm not sure they are."

The following day, material concerning his friend Sid was reviewed. In simple terms his ambivalent feelings toward Sid were discussed. He accepted the explanation given him and seemed more cheerful at the close of the interview. Two days later the discussion was continued, this time about his friend Jack. Here again his ambivalent feelings were pointed out as a possible cause of his guilty feelings. He said he could understand but still felt badly about the way he had talked to his friend. He was asked if Jack reminded him of anyone in his family and he answered that he was something like his older brother. It was pointed out that the old rivalry among the children may have caused him to resent his brother in some way. He was quick to grasp insight into this interpretation, whereupon he was told that perhaps his behavior pattern of compulsive and aggressive rivalry with his brother was also to be found in his behavior with his combat crew "family."

He was next seen three days later and immediately began telling about his improvement. He had ceased to refer to himself as a social misfit. He continued to mix with other people of his own volition. His appetite was good. He was more cheerful. Occasionally he felt depressed for a short time but not so profoundly as at the time of admission. Later he was discharged to full duty.

.   .   .   .   .   .

Ambitious and conscientious, this patient had never been able to fuse his positive and negative feelings, toward brother figures, derived from his early sibling rivalry. His ego-ideal was very highly developed and rigid, as shown in social relations, his motivation for combat and his conscientiousness toward his buddies who were injured. He had solved his negative feelings toward his rivals in the family by identifying with them as best he could, emulating his brother by going with his crowd. His identification with the injured friend was evidenced by his battle dreams in which *he* was covered with purple blotches like the gunner hit in the eye. Punishment for his negative feelings mobilized by the actual death of and injury to the brother figures was thus directed toward his own ego identified with these hostile rivals.

In spite of the powerful pull of the group toward cohesion of all its members, some fliers make a desperate attempt to avoid all close identifications and fight against the compulsion to recreate the family setting in combat. They frankly state they were afraid to make friends because of the terrific reaction if one of them were to be killed or hurt. Examples of the powerful compulsion to repetition, against which these boys are almost powerless, are found in case 58 and case 65. In one, the underground boy became a brother; in the other, a victim became a father.

Therapy consisted in a thorough abreaction of the guilty feelings, comparing them with reality and forcing the patient to face his negative or hostile attitudes toward his friends. This was quickly followed by interpretation of similar feelings toward his real brothers. The result was a striking improvement.

In this case is shown the reaction of a man who under normal conditions has been able to handle his aggressive and hostile feelings but who, under the stress of the combat situation and the loss of his friends, has found his ego unable to cope with the quantity of these feelings, which resulted in anxiety and depression.

CASE 42: *Depression after apparent loss of a buddy, to whom the patient had made a promise which he failed to keep.*

A 23 year old Sergeant had symptoms of tension, apprehension and restlessness during his basic training in the United States. He had experienced a crash landing, following which he developed air sickness in flight during subsequent missions. This was moderately intense, but he seldom vomited and was immediately relieved of his symptoms on landing. All his combat missions were quite severe and his heightened tension and marked irritability increased a great deal after his sixth mission. On his fifteenth mission over enemy territory, he was shot down and spent thirty-eight days with partisans. He developed a marked hostility against his Air Force, because they did not send him and his pals any supplies, which he believed they could have done.

On admission to the hospital, this patient was extremely depressed, irritable, restless and tense. He complained of very severe insomnia and combat dreams. Pentothal interview revealed an even more marked hostility toward the army than he had previously expressed, his only desire being to get away from it all. There was also revealed an extremely marked guilt reaction referable to his best pal, who was flying with the patient at the time that his plane was struck. This friend was severely wounded and the patient admitted tremendous guilt, because they had promised each other to remain together regardless of what happened. Associations regarding this promise indicated that the two boys had identified with each other in every respect for a long period, since the early days of training. The patient was disturbed when his friend married. Then he told how he often dreamed of his friend and stated that he would have had plenty of time to throw him out in a parachute had he (the patient) not been ordered out of the plane by the pilot, who was afraid. He stated that the plane flew on for several minutes after everyone had bailed out and that there was no reason why he could not have thrown his pal from the plane.

During his stay in this hospital this guilt reaction and depression, in spite of long psychotherapy, remained unchanged. After several weeks the patient received a message that his friend was in an enemy hospital and his guilt reaction, instead of decreasing, tended to increase markedly. The reason for this was that he then felt that he might have to face his friend, and he stated, "If he saw me right now, I'm sure he'd want to shoot me. I deserted him and I can never forget I failed to keep my promise and I'll never get over it."

The patient was closely attached to his mother, but expressed marked hostility toward his father, who was a chronic drunkard and who used to beat the patient and his mother a great deal over trifling matters. He stated that he believed that the father was mentally unbalanced. His own conduct in life had been exemplary and his life ideals had been excellent. He had no feeling that he would be affected mentally like his father.

His depression remained unabated, and, although he would return to duty, if forced to do so, he stated that he felt he would crack up completely if he were forced to go back into army routine. He stated that at one time, while he was in enemy territory after his crash landing, it became necessary for the other members of his crew to restrain him from self destruction by tying him in a parachute for eight hours, and he felt that a similar state would be precipitated if he returned to duty. However, he was returned for a trial of duty, because it was felt that discharge from the service would only increase his guilty feelings.

．　．　．　．　．　．

This patient exhibited a severe depression, which was an exaggerated mourning process. It was accompanied by a strong suicidal drive. Some of the force of this hostility which the patient expressed toward his own ego was displaced at times toward the army. But these were verbalizations and rather weak. The depression could not be decreased even with the knowledge that the lost comrade was not dead; in fact, it was deepened. The only clue to the depth and persistence of the depression was the fact that the two boys were so closely identified and that the patient actually expressed his hostility toward his buddy by punishing his own ego identified as that buddy. Such hostility had begun with the prior desertion by the comrade when he was married. This disturbed their relationship. The supposedly dead soldier then deserted him finally and the patient expressed his hostility, which only his superego recognized, by neglecting to push him in his helpless state out of the plane. The therapist, working on the assumption that the man was really dead, was blocked completely when it became certain that he still was alive and "perhaps crippled for life." Then the patient's guilt was exposed to the world and his punishment (depression) had to be intensified. Like all other serious depressions, those precipitated by war experiences do not subside when the apparent external sourse is removed. They continue or increase until the intrapsychic punishment has fully atoned for the guilt.

CASE 43: *Depression following accidental shooting of his buddy by the patient.*

A 27 year old unmarried Sergeant engineer gunner entered the hospital complaining of depression, moodiness and insomnia. Definite guilty feelings and depression had developed after an unfortunate incident, when a friend had lost an eye by a shot from the patient's gun.

The patient completed fifty missions in a B-17. His missions were fairly severe but he was not badly affected until the incident of shooting his buddy in the eye. It seems that, when he charged his gun, it ran away owing to a worn part which he should have noticed on careful inspection. He felt that anyone who knew what happened would hate him. Actually the patient was not blamed by his superior officers and he knew he shouldn't feel as he did but he thought of it all the time—so much so that he believed he would go crazy. Moreover, the man who was shot was a good fellow, who had done many nice things for the patient, and the patient liked him. At the first interview the patient's feelings of guilt were faced with the facts of reality— that the shooting was accidental and could happen to anyone and that he was not to blame.

The next day he was hostile to the hospital; there was too much discipline; he couldn't sleep at night. The night before he had been drunk and fighting. The next day under pentothal he was stimulated to talk about his friend, Paul, but with a great deal of resistance. He talked of Paul as "my best buddy" and likened him to his kid brother. He felt that he would never be any good, the army had killed him and he wanted to go home to his mother, who was so good to him. He didn't care to talk and wanted to be alone all the time. Why did the examiner make him talk? He wanted to get killed on a mission in order to punish himself for what he did to Paul.

The patient had always taken a great responsibility for the home, supporting his parents and his brother. He didn't like this responsibility, but the natural resentments had been repressed and only came out for the first time under repeated pressure of pentothal. His brother made him angry by joining the navy. The patient was never one to be angry and never fought, unless it was necessary for his own defense, and then would feel very sorry if he hurt the other fellow even though he were the attacker. During the course of probing into the connection between Paul and his brother, the patient became worse and was much more resentful to the examiner. It was quite apparent that certain thoughts were becoming mobilized which he did not like to face. At this time he had a dream: "The hospital is being bombed and I am trying to find a safe place." When the examiner went over the real situation of the shooting, again and again the patient stated: "I have the idea that you think I am holding something back on you; well, I'm not. I'll tell you anything at all." He began to deny that he felt resentful toward his father, whose illness forced the patient to support the family. The patient stated: "I felt all right, I didn't feel bad toward him, if that's what you mean." The therapist remarked: "I didn't say that—you said it." The patient answered: "Well, it seems to me that's what you had in mind."

The next day during a pentothal interview he began again stating that he was no good and the reason why he was not successful was that he had to take care of his family. "Yes, I love my family, mother, father and kid brother. I want them to have everything they want. I'll fix them up, buy them a home and then I won't have to worry about them any more. They will probably die in a few years. I want them to have everything before they die. I'll fix them up all right." He then admitted he often wished he didn't have to take care of them and felt guilty about this wish. At the same time, his family did not feel that he was as good as he could have been. Then he said that he was no good: "*I hate everybody. I hate Paul.*" When the therapist asked him about it, he immediately denied his statement with vehemence: "No, he is a good kid, too good, a young kid, and now he will suffer all his life." The therapist then said, "Dominic, I know what's the matter with you and you do too." The patient responded, "O.K., then tell me." So he was told about his strong resentment during the many years of taking care of his family and his younger brother and his repression of these feelings and how he had such a struggle with his aggressions, which got so bad at times that he wanted to hurt everyone. This he admitted. He was told that to atone for these feelings he had gone out of his way to be good and would rather hurt himself than others. The therapist explained how he identified Paul with his brother and that was why he had such strong feelings of guilt, and that this reaction was not due to what actually happened but to the old resentment. The patient said, "All right, you know. Now two people know about it. So what? What do you want me to do?"

From that point on there was an amazing change in the patient. He worked through this sibling resentment during the next few days and was permitted by the therapist to express his real feelings. He began to joke and laugh, and lost his depression.

. . . . . .

Characteristic of this material was the patient's strong resistance to insight which was so dangerous for him. In a dream he likened the destructiveness of such insight to bombing of the hospital; he had to find a safe place. The suicidal significance of returning to combat was quite clear in this case. The strong resistance was due to the closeness with which his hostile feelings toward the family lay to consciousness. The patient was almost aware of them and fought them as a great threat. But the therapist knew these feelings and accepted them as natural. He was not fooled by the reaction of tender solicitude toward the family in the patient's promise to buy a home, which only poorly hid a blatant death wish. "They will probably die in a few years." Again it is apparent that Paul's injury caused depression only because Paul was all the hated family, and the patient's conscience fully recognized this fact and reacted accordingly. Only when the patient consciously understood this and the normality of at least his superficial hostility toward the family did he get well.

CASE 44: *Depression as a result of frustration of strong passive-dependent needs.*

The patient was a 22 year old Sergeant gunner, who had been in the army one year and seven months, having been inducted from a small town in the Northwest. He was of Irish descent and came from a large family consisting of nine sisters and five brothers. He had a normal childhood, and finished one year of high school and then a year in agricultural school. He left school because he felt dull and was no longer interested in his studies. He had many odd jobs but was particularly fond of horses and was learning to be a blacksmith's helper. He stated, "I used to ride horses all day and my motorcycle all night." When he entered the army, he asked to be placed in the cavalry but he was sent to the Air Forces, which at first caused him a great deal of resentment. In combat his early missions were somewhat rugged but did not bother him. On his eighth mission, his plane was shot down in a raid over enemy-occupied territory and he bailed out without injury other than a slight shrapnel wound in the left cheek. He evaded the Germans and was able to return to his base in approximately three weeks. For some time afterwards, he was unable to sleep and kept looking around the corner for the Gestapo and occasionally had a spell of shaking. He endured another strain during continuous interviews with Intelligence Officers for two full days. On arrival home, he was disappointed at the small amount of attention he got from his family because of the large number of children at home.

He entered the hospital because of restlessness, depression, tenseness, tremor, battle dreams and startle reactions. For the first week or so, he was extremely cooperative and discussed plans for further duty in the United States. However, he had dreams of being blown out of his plane without a parachute. There was considerable restlessness and disinclination to remain in the hospital and he did not feel capable of ever going back to combat. Gradually, over several weeks' time, he began to inquire about the possibility of a medical discharge and talked about his hatred of the army. He began to drink and with this to expose considerable hostility to his eldest brother, who had married and lived away from the paternal home but in the same town. This brother did not even see his mother on Mother's Day. Interviews in the conscious state and under pentothal gave material concerned with his desire to go home to his mother and his girl and be taken care of. As he expressed it in a fantasy, he wanted to go home and lie in the fields and watch the little colts play with their mothers. He cried a great deal about his desire to return to mama.

Psychotherapy was directed toward ventilating these passive and regressive tendencies, satisfying them to a degree and bolstering up a certain amount of self-respecting ego which was available for contact with the therapist. It was impossible to get an assignment in the Air Forces at a post where horses were available for him. However, he improved considerably and left the hospital in a condition to return to duty and with a determination to try his best at continuing his work.

. . . . . .

Psychologically this boy had never matured, largely because of early frustrations in a large family in which he had to share affection with too many rivals. After the harrowing experiences of combat, regressive forces threw him back to the point of demanding that his dependent needs be gratified. A secondary hostility developed to his chief and unappreciative rival, the older brother, and toward the army, which represented the bad father who would not let him return to his mother. Under psychotherapy directed toward strengthening his ego, these passive trends could be controlled. This was largely done by first permitting a certain amount of gratification of his dependent needs, by daily interviews and considerate attention. At the same time stimuli urging him to adopt a manly attitude were given him.

The content of the patient's battle dreams, although consisting of material derived from combat, signified by the associations that he had been rejected by all supporting mother figures, without even a chance of survival (no parachute). His whole existence was threatened because of the frustration of his dependent needs and his psychological reaction was anxiety and depression. As the therapist's support gave him some gratification, the need for which he at least understood, he could give up drinking. With confidence beginning to revive through identification with the psychiatrist, the patient accepted return to duty on trial.

CASE 45: *Depression due to loss of a supporting officer, with whom the patient had identified himself.*

A 23 year old armorer gunner of a B-25 entered the hospital complaining of nervousness and insomnia, but it was obvious that he was depressed. He was a short but well built, strong boy, clean-cut in appearance, with an independent attitude. He repeatedly demanded, "How long do I have to stay here? I want to go out and do my job." He had completed fifty-two missions as a turret gunner. When questioned about his attitude toward combat, he stated vigorously, "Sure I'll go back for more; someone has to win the war." While at home he had had a good time fishing and hunting with dad. He displayed some intellectual defect and could not remember names of airfields, of the rest camp he had attended or of his Flight Surgeon, overseas. His speech was slow and there was difficulty in concentrating. He gave the general appearance of moderate organic cerebral deterioration. In spite of his attempt to maintain an independent and even truculent attitude, it was clear that the patient was depressed but had little insight.

Pentothal narcosynthesis revealed him to have been confident in his guns and his ability. "Enemy planes don't scare me. They'll get shot down if they come too close. My missions weren't too rough. Only about Lt. Jones. He was copilot. He was shot down over the Balkans. He was a swell guy. I went to the mess hall to offer my regrets—there was no one there to receive them. I don't want any more of this war. I want to go home to my mommy. She loves me. I like to weld. Why can't I get a job as a welder—that's as good for the war as fighting. I want to stay home with mommy and papa and my girl. Lt. Jones was not like an officer; he was my buddy. I must forget him. I don't want to remember. He was like me, but he is inside me and I'll never get him out."

The patient was aroused and told he could not run away from memories that were inside himself. They would always go with him, especially those about Lt. Jones. He appeared astonished, and angrily asked, "Who told you about him?" The therapist said, "You did, and you told me . . . remember?" "Yes, I remember," he finally admitted.

In the first interview after pentothal he showed strong resistance against remembering data about Lt. Jones. He tried to think of other things as the therapist spoke, and looked around the room. Tears came to his eyes. He understood explanations of the processes of forgetting versus the techniques of working through, but wanted nothing of this. His strong dependent needs plus an element of secondary gain were indicated in his expressed attitude. "What if you do help me?—that won't get me out of the army." Behind this query lay the unexpressed idea, "If I don't react as they want, I have a better chance of discharge from the army." The patient had not written or talked to Mrs. Jones. "She has probably forgotten and I don't want to stir up her memories." Lt. Jones called him Jack and urged him to use his first name. He too was small and even looked like the patient. A few days later the patient requested another pentothal treatment, because he felt better after the first treatment. The next afternoon the psychiatrist greeted him and asked questions about his visit home the previous week end. The patient denied feeling badly and repeated he just wanted to get out of the army. When told he needed another treatment, he objected because it did not do good for long. Finally he said, "I might say something I wouldn't want to." At the same time he denied he had any secrets. When told he meant that the therapist might find out something that he himself was scared of knowing—he told the following dream, elicited piecemeal with no associations: "I was fighting with the Chaplain's son (Jones) and I won the fight but then the Chaplain came in and disapproved."

Under pentothal he refused to discuss Jones. It was his privilege to feel as he wanted to and he just wanted to forget. He reacted to the suggestion that he really was angry at Jones for not coming back, by rationalizations—it was not his fault. The patient insisted he would not talk but admitted jittery feelings and deepening depression, which he stated were due to being in the army. If he had to stay, he would run away and, if caught, would go to jail. Army people reminded him too much of Jones. He was afraid to get well because then we would keep him in the army. In spite of his protests, it was felt that he should be given a trial at some type of work, and accordingly he was returned to duty and carried on successfully for about three months. A relapse followed and eventually he was discharged from the army.

. . . . . .

The material from this short abstract clearly indicates the strong regression to a dependent state, which thwarted therapy because of the patient's tenacious hold on the secondary gain of his illness and his intense need for more support and care than could be supplied in the army environment. The dynamics are, however, clear. Jones was identified with the patient—as he said, "he is inside me, I'll never get him out." Yet he also represented the supporting figure for the patient's dependent needs, which were so great in combat. Angry at his desertion, the patient's wrath was expressed, not in hostile outbursts, but in an attack on Jones inside the patient's own ego. The guilt for the initial anger at desertion was evidenced when the patient expressed his regret at Jones' death to the officers' mess—a most unusual procedure for an enlisted man. His dream indicated how he was wrestling with an intrapsychic conflict, attempting to fight the other ego within himself (Jones, the Chaplain's son). He could not win without intense disapproval of his own super-ego (the Chaplain). The nature of the foreign body within his ego was clearly indicated and the impasse forced him to regress to the level of a helpless child.

CASE 46: *Depression in a compulsive personality.*

A 26 year old B-17 navigator flew twenty-six missions in combat. His missions were extremely harrowing and he was very fearful, nervous and tremulous on each of them. In the course of his missions he became progressively more depressed, anxious and sleepless, and developed occasional nightmares. On admission to the hospital, he frankly stated his chief problem: "I don't want to fly any more. I want a ground assignment. It got me down, always wondering whether I was on the course or not. I was always afraid that my navigation was off and I feared that, if the plane was shot up, it would be my fault. I was always afraid that the walls of the plane would collapse and that I would be hit in the face and lose my eyesight. I became afraid of take-offs and landings. I was always terrified at having to fly over water."

In the course of interviews, it became apparent that the patient was a rigid, compulsive personality, who had attempted to routinize everything. He had always been very particular about the cleanliness and orderliness of his environment. He had always been fearful, reticent, retiring and insecure. He had attempted all through his life to deal with his anxiety in an obsessive, compulsive way. In combat, when it was impossible to have things clean and orderly and neatly controlled, this man's compulsive defenses broke down and he had been left at the mercy of his anxiety. His family history revealed a mother who was a religious fanatic, a compulsive personality who beat her child frequently. The parents were separated when the patient was 4 years old and he never could get along well with his stepfather. Psychotherapy gave this patient some insight into his personality but it was felt that this man should not fly again. When he was able to re-establish his orderly and neat habits and to control his life, his symptoms of "operational fatigue" disappeared, and he was returned to duty.

. . . . . .

This patient illustrates the frequent type of breakdown demonstrated by rigid, compulsive personalities, whether they react to combat or only to the poor living conditions overseas. There they cannot live out their rituals and they react most frequently with depressions (cf. cases 4 and 16).

The clinical symptoms of depression in the returnees differ little from those seen in other reactive or neurotic depressions. The physical appearance is one of psychomotor rigidity, as evidenced by a rigid, masklike face, staring eyes that wink infrequently, and a general paucity of movement. These individuals volunteer little information and have no spontaneity in their associations. Most of them suffer from varying degrees of insomnia associated with a considerable quantity of free anxiety. They are tense and restless, unable to sit still in class or in occupational therapy. Some others are lethargic and sleep for greater parts of the day. A great many of our patients with depression are tearful and cry easily, especially when recounting their difficulties. Most of them are self-accusatory and self-depreciating. Outbursts of hostility are common, especially under the influence of alcohol. They are emphatic that they do not care to live any more because there is nothing left in life for them. We have seen no suicidal attempts and only a few gestures. That self-destructive tendencies have been so well controlled is understandable in view of the fact that a socially acceptable outlet for suicidal drives consists in volunteering to return to combat duty, where a less sordid death is sought.

Catastrophic dreams are extremely common in soldiers suffering from depression. These have been interpreted since the work of Freud (21) as an attempt on the part of the ego to master anxiety. Although this may be true in some cases, combat dreams, like all dreams, are individual and serve a particular personal purpose. In the depressed individual, catastrophic battle dreams are punishment dreams with a strong masochistic coloring. The patient attempts to renew his good relations with his ego-ideal by suffering, in order to atone for the guilt attributed to his unconscious hostility. These dreams, in which there is so much suffering, disappear as guilty feelings abate.

At this time, we can delimit two types of personalities most predisposed to depression. The passive-dependent person is most likely to feel depressed on separation from the group and to react with depression at home on frustration of his needs for gratification. On the other hand, the compulsive-obsessive personality reacts most readily to the loss of a buddy in combat, to poor living conditions and to deviations from smooth-running performances. These men show marked repetition compulsions which force them to recreate the family circle with all their tenderness and hostility displaced to the military group. Officers become fathers, comrades are brothers, almost at first sight. Loss of these loved objects, toward whom quantities of unconscious hostility are harbored, disturbs the whole psychological equilibrium of the individual. In these cases the unconscious hostility evokes guilt and self punishment. The superego reacts against the unexpressed wishes, or interprets innocent deeds as the cause of the comrade's death. These thoughts or actions are identical with prohibited thoughts of or behavior to siblings or father, which were not tolerated by the external parental figures of the patient's early environment.

Regardless of the origin of the depression, it represents the ego's conscious or unconscious reaction to the fact that it has been neglected, rejected, betrayed or punished by an impersonal fate, by living figures in reality or by its own ego-ideal. In this statement, we deliberately pass over for the time being the origin of such feelings. We do this because too many psychiatrists plunge into the handling of a case with the bias that the man has a depression, ergo he has repressed hostility. Actually the first step in handling the emotion of depression is to ask the question, "Who or what is hurting this boy?" By doing so, we can get a sharper perspective, not only of the unconscious forces at work, but also of the task, failures and successes of the ego.

The passive-dependent patients who are frustrated or rejected react with depression, because of disappointment and pain. Men separated by death from supporting figures or thrown upon their own individual resources by separation from the group are depressed because of the feeling of loss of love from the outside. Those who are punished because of guilty reactions to their own hostilities feel deserted and unloved by their sadistic and intolerant superegos (cf. case 65).

The dynamic basis of depression is similar to that which we are accustomed to uncovering in the depressions of civilian life. The most severe cases, particularly those that react to the deaths of close friends or comrades or loved officers in the group, give evidence of strong previous ambivalent relationships to brothers or father, when their past personalities are uncovered. In most of these cases the mourned person is one toward whom the patient has had a great deal of repressed hostility. In every case it can be determined that the mourned person was one with whom the patient had identified, or who represented a figure to which he had been ambivalent. Depression, however, is not always based on the actual loss or death of a person. We have seen that the normal reaction of guilt on leaving the group overseas may become quantitatively so great that it becomes pathological. In this case, the patient is still under the influence of the strict military superego and is still identified with his comrades in combat.

The closer to consciousness the hostility lies, the more free anxiety accompanies the depression and the more amenable it is to therapy after abreaction. The silent, deep depressions are poorly treated by brief psychotherapy. Outbursts of displaced hostility, provocative behavior to evoke external punishment (cf. case 51), alcoholism and suicidal drives to return to combat are frequent reactions against the depression itself and are difficult therapeutic problems. Pentothal readily facilitates abreaction of dependent needs and of anxiety in relation to guilt. With little pressure, hostility to lost objects can be brought to the surface. Least successfully and less frequently can one evoke consciousness of the original derivation of ambivalent feelings within the family group since these are often deeply repressed. In general, most pathological depressions respond well to psychotherapy.

CHAPTER 13

Aggressive and Hostile Reactions

Some soldiers of this war have little hatred toward the Germans, although in many instances it may be directed against the ideology of fascism, the Nazi activities or some other abstraction and it often is directed against the Jap soldier. In our culture the most efficient fighting man is not one consumed by a self-destructive emotion like hate. Once the enemy has given up the fight, he is treated like a human being, given food, water and cigarettes and prompt, efficient medical care. Hatred could not be turned off like a tap on surrender, but our soldiers take the respected enemy as prisoners rather than vent revengeful hostility on them.

This is all the more true of our flying personnel, who fight machine against machine, gun against gun. They become greatly disturbed when the pilot of an enemy plane comes close enough for them to see his destruction; they are uneasy when strafing transport vehicles containing personnel, or troops on the road. For the same reason many gunners are not anxious to press their claims to have shot down enemy ships, as if lack of official credit creates less guilt than a recorded positive score. In one squadron a Greek-American gunner strafed a parachuting German pilot and was ostracized by his fellows for two weeks as punishment.

It is true that in battle the enemy is soundly cursed with numerous derogatory adjectives and dire threats of revenge, all made after the death or injury of a comrade. However, psychiatrists overseas who listen to the war-weary soldier speak under pentothal hear little in the way of enemy-directed hostility. Watch and listen to the soldier relieved from battle and you do not observe a tough, fighting, aggressive fellow. In attempting to contrast the normal soldier, unscathed psychologically from his battle experiences, with the psychiatric casualty, we saw no greater quantity of overt expressions of aggression in the former. The happy, high-spirited veteran filled with liquor caroused a bit, broke a few windows and violated a few regulations but only as an expression of a general ebullient spirit.

Why is this? Have we not heard that war creates a new type of superego that permits and condones release of aggression and facilitates abandonment of old repressions? Was not one of the major sociological problems after the war supposed to be concerned with the animal-like warriors whose unleashed hostilities, no longer directed against the enemy, would be directed against society? It has become quite obvious that for the majority of men, removal of external prohibitions against killing and even encouragement of human destruction do not develop a killer. Neither the soldiers of the First World War nor those of the British, Canadian or French armies in this war reacted in this way. Normal men nurtured by American civilization do not care to kill even though external prohibitions embodied in law, regulation and police are removed.

However, the returned soldiers and particularly those suffering from war neuroses show much more aggressiveness and hostility in their verbalizations and behavior than was characteristic of their precombat personalities. They are resentful and openly angry at civilians and toward soldiers who have not been overseas, and are freely and destructively critical of what they see and hear at home. Many get into difficulties with civil and military law. Their favorite word of depreciation is "chicken s—t," which is used to describe the morally soft, selfish attitudes of people who think only of their own interests, and not of those of the soldier. It is our conviction that the apparently normal as well as the sick combat veteran is far more aggressive and hostile on his return to this country than when he was overseas in combat (26, 29). We shall inquire into this phenomenon through the study of a few case histories.

CASE 47: *Hostility toward authority released after loss of confidence in a leader and increased by loss of support from the father.*

The patient was a 21 year old B-24 gunner, who was shot down on his first mission and spent ten months as an evadee in enemy-occupied country. He entered the hospital with complaints of irritability and "rheumatism" of the right knee and ankle. The patient was a red-haired, red-faced, well developed, well nourished white male, who was tense, anxious and depressed, and who sat with his head down, picking at his finger nails. He was of average intelligence, answered questions readily and spoke slowly and quietly.

On his first mission he was shot down over occupied territory. Five members of the crew were injured and the remaining four, including the patient, were ordered to escape by the pilot who had taken charge of the wounded. For ten months the patient lived in a constant state of anxiety and apprehension along with the other three, and endured all the deprivation of a hostile country, namely, lack of food and shelter, fear of capture and death, and utter lack of security.

At the first interview, the patient demonstrated marked hostility to our Allies, whom he accused of not trying to help the evadees; against the Intelligence for telling them it was an easy mission; and, under pentothal, toward the bombardier of his group. After a few weeks' stay in the hospital, a general aggressive attitude toward the whole army was expressed. The patient stated he felt worse on arriving home, when he discovered that his father was 70 years old instead of 67 years of age, as he had thought. He could not explain the meaning of this reaction.

He was the second youngest of a family of eight, all siblings being married except the patient and a young brother. The patient stated he wanted to get married, but could not because he had to take care of his folks. The patient's father was in the last war and was wounded in the right leg and his son always looked up to him as a hero. Apparently there was a stable background with stable parents.

The patient worked for an electrical concern, as did his three older brothers, and he was a shop subforeman before entering the service. Apparently he did his work well and was promised that his old job would be open for him on his return. The psychiatrist was impressed with the fact that the patient had always had a high regard for authority in his relationships at home, at his civilian job and in the army.

Under pentothal the patient let loose a long tirade of hatred against his bombardier, who was the only commissioned officer with him as an evadee, accusing him of being a coward, not a man, and surely not an officer. He scornfully exclaimed, "He (the bombardier) was going to be the leader! He's no officer, he's a yellow s__ o__ b__." He also related how he wanted to shoot this officer and was sorry he didn't. From the story, the bombardier apparently had lost his nerve as an evadee and the patient was afraid this officer was going to surrender to the Germans and so endanger planes and men to come in the future. The patient stated that he wanted to go home, that he was through with the army. Subsequent interviews revealed a strong sense of guilt for only completing one mission, especially after arriving home and being treated as a "hero."

After a thorough abreaction of his feelings of hostility toward the bombardier, which were accepted as justifiable, therapy was directed to giving the patient insight into the basis for the intensity of his hatred for this man and its spilling over to cover all authoritative figures. He soon saw that being let down by one officer had evoked a rage against all father figures, especially when he needed them most. He quickly regained confidence in himself and assumed an independent but not hostile attitude.

.   .   .   .   .   .

This fairly stable individual under the stress and strain of an acute, prolonged and dangerous situation, needed more than the usual amount of protection and security from authority, which he had always previously trusted. Instead, he saw that authority break down and fail to give him support. Later, on arriving home, he realized that his old father, the primary basis of authority, was also unable to give him support and that he had to give support to his father when he needed it so badly himself. All of this resulted in a picture of hostility directed against authority and its representatives. A guilty reaction was secondary to this conflict and the hysterical pain in his right knee symbolized an identification with his father and his father's suffering, as punishment for his own hostility.

CASE 48: *Hostility unleashed after failure of leadership and breakdown in group morale.*

A 20 year old gunner had tremendous hostility to the army, particularly officers, who "get away with everything." He had great hostility toward his parents, his fiancée and all civilians. This boy had enlisted in the army, with much eagerness to fight, and had enjoyed his training and early missions. He displayed much enthusiasm and showed complete disregard of danger to himself as a tail gunner in a B-24. On his twenty-first mission he suffered a severe emotional trauma. On this raid, consisting of sixty ships, some peeled off and returned to the base before reaching the target. This left him as the tail gunner in the tail ship of the remaining formation. As they approached the target they were jumped by twenty-five German fighters and also received tremendous attacks of flak. His ship was badly damaged and he suffered minor flak injuries to the buttocks. How his ship in its damaged state returned to the base is still a mystery. No punishment or censure was ever meted out to the crews that had fallen out of formation, a lack of justice which made the patient intensely angry. He became enraged at the officers in the army. He was profuse in the use of profanity and obscene language and in outbursts against them, and accused them of being yellow. After six days of intense drunkenness and aggressive behavior he returned to flying, but after several weeks had to be grounded because of marked instability, uncontrollable alcoholism and aggression in the form of fist fights and obscene language.

He talked of his own crew as being good and having to protect the weaker crews. He was wounded several times but did not tell his pilot for fear that he would turn back. In spite of this initial zest for combat, his enthusiasm declined so markedly after the traumatic incident that he was able to fly only nine more missions. He complained about the fact that "they give you no credit for what you do." During his stay in the hospital he continued to drink and had relations with a married woman twice his age. He stated that he never used to do such things, that he was brought up to be a decent boy, not a criminal. He felt the army had ruined him and he often cried in self pity.

The end result of this boy's experiences is easily evaluated: from an independent, courageous, aggressive soldier he regressed into a crying child who wanted to go home to mother. He lived out this tendency in sexual relations with a woman twice his age. This regression was suddenly precipitated when his superior officers clearly demonstrated their weakness and he felt deserted and unprotected by the unexpected weak leadership of the group. The support provided by a strong group-ideal disintegrated and the soldier had to seek within himself for strength. This he could not find, for something had happened to his own ego-ideals: "I used to be a decent boy, not a criminal." He had regressed and become more dependent in the process of group assimilation and found it now absolutely necessary to have a strong external authority to hold him in line. Without such pressure he lived out his revived infantile complexes by having intercourse with a mother figure and expressing open hatred of his father. His externalized father could be hated without a sense of guilt because he had lost his internalized superego. This patient's regression had gone so far that he could no longer be retained in the army.

CASE 49: *Hostility toward an unfaithful wife displaced to the army and its officers.*

A 23 year old Sergeant was admitted to the hospital from a Continental base, where he had been assigned after his return from overseas several months previously. He completed twenty-five missions in B-17 planes as armorer gunner. Prior to military service this soldier lived in a small Northeast community, where his basic social adjustment was poor. He found it very difficult to engage in many of the ordinary social amenities and devoted much of his time to working on the farm or to hunting and fishing. Since late adolescence he had used alcoholic intoxicants rather steadily and occasionally to excess. With this personality background he returned from combat with minimal symptoms of "operational fatigue" and was given an assignment as ground armorer. Upon his return he discovered that his wife, to whom he had been married for several months prior to overseas duty, was living with another man. This distressed him and aroused his aggressiveness to a point where he wondered why he didn't kill both of them. However, he regained control of his feelings, but developed tension, irritability and hostility toward the army. When he felt that he was again losing control of his feelings, he reported himself to the Flight Surgeon and arranged to be transferred to the hospital.

From time to time his irritability and tension reached a high point, but for the most part he gradually made a much better adjustment in the hospital. He anticipated return to duty with a great deal of apprehension, inasmuch as he felt himself incapable of adjusting to the petty hostilities and machinations of the permanent party personnel. Therapy, directed toward giving him insight into the fact that his irritability and hostility toward the army were a displacement from his inner frustrations, was accepted but not well synthesized. He was returned for a trial of duty.

.   .   .   .   .   .

Hostility toward the army was displaced from that directed, but unexpressed, toward his wife. The army came to represent the means by which he was separated from and hence lost his wife. In this manner the army officers symbolized the bad father of his childhood, who interfered with his exclusive possession of the mother.

CASE 50: *Mobilization by combat of an old repressed conflict involving hostility.*

The patient was a 20 year old Sergeant, who had completed twenty-five combat missions as a gunner. He entered the hospital complaining of terror dreams, in which he was usually strafed, and of depression and restlessness. He had been addicted to the excessive use of alcohol since going overseas. The patient did not feel excessively nervous during his combat missions except on take-offs and landings, although he had many severe missions and lost several close friends. His terror dreams were usually of dive bombers strafing him while he was alone on a hillside near a pub. If he went into the pub they would wait until he came out, ten to twelve in number, but he was never hit. In another type of dream he would be walking in Germany along a railroad track, trying to find his way home. He could only see German women and every time the RAF came over they would drop their bombs around him. These he heard but never felt or saw. These terror dreams began during a one month period of grounding after his second mission.

The patient was the youngest of six siblings. He finished the tenth grade of school, making average grades, and then went to work. His first sexual relationships were with prostitutes, who disgusted him and caused him to be anxious about venereal disease. He never was well adapted socially but there was a group of three or four boys with whom he associated. After several weeks' stay in the hospital under psychotherapy the patient had numerous dreams relating to his sexual desires toward his brother's wife. The dreams always involved frustrations of his desires, with punishment and a subsequent regression to childhood pleasures of eating. Actually his brother's wife had tried to seduce him and he was sorely tempted; he recounted many instances when this sister-in-law undressed in front of him. He lived in the same room with his brother and his wife, who actually turned out to be a prostitute and whom his brother subsequently divorced. This same older brother since early childhood had eaten the best food and stolen things from the ice box that were intended for the patient, who always came out second best. "I'd go off by myself and cuss him. I'd never run around like he did or have friends like he did."

. . . . . .

This patient's history indicated that his traumatic combat experiences restimulated his old conflicts. The German planes, the bombs which attempted to destroy him and caused him to seek refuge, were his own hostilities projected outward, derived from great envy of his older brother. Fear of retaliation forced him to regress to a state of passive dependence in which subsequent envy and resentment caused him to be increasingly hostile and fearful, thereby creating a vicious circle. Combat mobilized old aggressions toward powerfully hostile external figures, which attempted to destroy him. In his dreams, refuge in a pub, dependence, was his only defense. The attempt to return home to childhood gratifications was disturbed by his own hostile sexual curiosity and he was in danger from noises (his brother's coitus). It is interesting that the battle dreams were readily replaced under psychotherapy by frank sexual dreams ending in punishment and regression.

CASE 51: *Repressed hostility toward a lost comrade, causing anxiety and a state of tension.*

A 24 year old B-25 pilot entered the hospital, complaining of nervousness and a feeling of inner tension, "as if something must come out." Prior to military service, he was a baker and had had no unusual diseases or nervous disturbances. He came from an economically poor family. Overseas he completed fifty missions of low level bombing. He had a feeling of being poorly trained and lacked confidence, so that he was continually apprehensive. After the twenty-fifth mission he had to force himself to continue, for he felt like quitting. He was much concerned about his family while overseas and managed to buy them a house with his savings. He became greatly disturbed when a friend was shot down and worried about how long his own luck would hold out. The commanding officer of the squadron was not a good leader. The patient himself had a very loyal crew, for whom he took a keen responsibility.

Overseas he always imagined the tragic possibilities of each mission, but, when his friend was shot down, he began to feel that his own number was up. He was upset when a cannon shot hit the gunner on his wing ship and he saw the blood flow from the turret. On being returned to the United States, he enjoyed his overseas leave and was sent to a Continental training field, where he developed restlessness due to worry about flying with students.

In the first pentothal interview he described the accident in which his friend Fred was killed and as he cried he stated how he loved Fred. "He was a good, likeable boy, blond like me." He had a great deal of guilt about Fred, who had asked his advice just prior to his first mission. Fred was a very stable person and had looked after the patient, who had depended upon him for instruction. After Fred's death he got along by feeling that Fred's spirit was helping him and this kept him flying. As an instructor in this country he was afraid that his pupils would stall, as Fred did just prior to his fatal accident.

In discussing his past history during psychotherapeutic interviews he brought out the fact that he had always supported his parents, since his father was incapacitated by an injury occurring when the patient was about 8 years of age. He still sent them about a hundred dollars a month. There was a great conflict concerning the family and social conditions at home, since his parents were both foreign-born and communistic. He told how his older brother was the favorite of the family and received better toys, more privileges and more attention.

In the second pentothal interview, he went into further detail about Fred, and how he had helped the patient, even giving him money. He was afraid that his advice to Fred the night before the accident might have had something to do with his death, since he advised flying in very close formation. The irrational nature of the patient's guilt was brought out to him. Since actually he could not in any way have been responsible for his friend's death, it was suggested that perhaps he had some resentment toward Fred. The patient then recounted with considerable feeling that Fred was always telling him to do things and that there was a hate building up in him toward Fred, even though he felt so dependent on him. It was pointed out to him that this guilty feeling was a reaction to the resentment against Fred, who had been so good to him and so loyal; he resented his own dependence on Fred, which probably came from his past pattern of behavior. The patient saw then that his attitude toward Fred was like his attitude toward his older brother, the favorite. It was pointed out to him that he was envious and attempted to identify himself with Fred as he did with his older brother. He admitted that every night before going to-bed he would think about Fred and his good qualities and how helpful he had been, and then a few thoughts about Fred's disagreeable qualities would creep in but would be quickly pushed away.

After these interpretations, he began to think he was as good a pilot as Fred, although Fred thought he was very "hot" and was very critical of others. He then began to think that he could make a good instructor.

The next day he made a social call on a family in the neighborhood and was able to endure the family scene without irritation or disturbance. During the next few weeks he slept well, gained 7 or 8 pounds, and felt that he could go back to duty and continue as an instructor. He worked through the various interpretations and gained a thorough understanding of how his guilt concerning Fred was related to the family situation.

.   .   .   .   .   .

"Inner tension" was the expression of repressed hostility that this patient used. He soon learned that it represented negative feelings toward the mourned comrade. These were a duplication of identical attitudes which he had toward his older brother. It did not take him long to work through this interpretation and recover his equilibrium.

CASE 52: *Hostility engendered as a reaction to loss of security by an insecure, dependent boy.*

A 24 year old Sergeant entered the hospital, stating: "There's nothing wrong with me. I just want to get out of the army. Fed up, moody and can't sleep." His first three missions were uneventful but the fourth was tough. He lost a few friends, and cried and worried about them. The fifth mission was a practice night sortie. The crew were sleeping in the radio room when their ship was riddled by 20 mm. shells from a night fighter. There was a mad scramble for 'chutes as the airplane went into a steep dive. "I've never been so scared in all my life." The plane was landed safely but he "had the shakes for a couple of weeks." He developed malaria at this time and spent thirty days in a hospital, losing a number of missions, so that he was forced to fly with green crews to catch up with his own. He conquered his fears and became immune to any harrowing circumstances.

The patient had left school in the last year of high school because he was fed up with it. He then had worked in the poultry business, helping his father. He had been somewhat "wild" in those days. His mother had died in childbirth at the age of 33; the patient was 3 years old at the time and did not remember her. He was the third child in a family of six. He had not smoked, bitten his nails or drunk since coming home, because of a girl he had met and had fallen in love with.

The patient seemed cooperative, pleasant and free from anxiety, but showed no spontaneity: "Nothing wrong with me. I'm just fed up with the army. I've done my job. I'd have been O.K. if I hadn't come home and found how things were and met this girl." The gist of the interview, by the patient's own admissions, was that he wanted a medical discharge because the girl would not marry him while he was in the army. He produced a letter from his girl and one from his family urging him to bend every effort to getting out of the army.

Under pentothal the patient stated he had never lived until he had gotten in the army. He had never made such good friends. He cried a good deal about the loss of his friends and mentioned that, if he had had a normal family life, this might never have happened to him. "My sister was the only one that pulled me through. I would not quit because of her." At no time was there much emotional display. On coming out of the pentothal state, the patient was surprised at the material uncovered. "I've never told anyone that before." He discussed things more freely and supplemented the history and interview with more information. He had had no family life. He would leave home in the evenings and come in late, and had no interest in the home. His father was an old country farmer, who only worked, ate and slept, and his stepmother paid no attention to him. The only family figure that had any hold on him was his sister. The picture presented seemed to be one of early insecurity, followed by entrance into the army, with a temporary feeling of security previous to combat.

Subsequent interviews were conducted with the idea of getting the patient to become aware of his condition and to analyze his hostility for the army and officers. Acceptance of material was nonexistent at this time. A second pentothal treatment uncovered two apparent guilty reactions, which were concerned with the deaths of two friends, one of whom he had identified with.

At the next interview he asked if the therapist had noticed any tension in him, because he felt as if he would blow up. He wanted to know why he felt that way, and also why he felt so insecure and restless? The first wedge had been driven. His army life was considered first and then, step by step, his early experiences. His lack of and drive for security were explained to him, with insertions of material of his own. He began to understand his needs and then to see a possible solution. As he understood the basis of his hostility, his symptoms subsided.

. . . . . .

This boy, who had had no family life, no mother, no support from his father, no love and no security, developed an aggressive and hostile attitude toward the world and sought a circle in which he might "find" himself—"the gang." His early army experiences made him feel good. He was part of a team. He made friends easily and found friendship necessary. In combat, with the loss of these friends, his insecurity broke through— unfortunate incidents gave him a mild feeling of guilt. He developed a hardened exterior, taking the stand that "when you get it, you get it. It's tough." He tried to impress everyone with this defensive attitude.

His meeting of the girl on his return and subsequent "falling for her" were a manifestation, apparently, of his desire to find someone who would take care of him and give him the love and security for which he had been striving. At the same time he unloosened all his rage against the army and his officer father figures for first promising support and then withdrawing it. The fathers were to blame for not protecting him against the harrowing enemy and not giving him the love and security he desired. In a sense this boy's problem was a new edition of an old repressed hostility originally directed to his own father.

CASE 53: *Hostility in a precombat psychopathic personality, unconsciously directed to evoke punishment.*

A 33 year old Sergeant completed twenty-three very severe combat missions as a gunner on a B-24, in spite of the fact that his right index (trigger) finger had been missing since an accident in 1916. He spent two hundred and eighty-two combat hours in completing these missions, which fact tends to bear out the severity and length of each mission.

Symptoms of apprehension, tension, insomnia and irritability became quite noticeable after his fifth harrowing mission and gradually increased with subsequent missions. He lost numerous close friends while overseas, two of these standing out in his mind very vividly.

He had always been of an irritable temperament and hard-headed, and frequently fought with his brother, who was older, more dependable and "a better guy than me." He stated, "I don't know if it's my disposition; I'm the more excitable type." His brother could lick him until the patient reached 18 years of age. "Then I got the best of him and we didn't fight any more." After high school graduation he left home and during the economic depression held odd jobs. He then worked in a radio-auto store and spoke of it as "our business," though he had no financial interest in the establishment. He stated that he would not return to this work after the war, because "I'm too irritable to meet the public." Once he quit for a month in a dispute with his boss referable to a vacation, but the boss wrote to him and he went back to work. He had an auto accident when he was 20 years of age and was arrested, but his boss "bought him off." He was arrested in 1938 for driving while intoxicated. He had been in twenty, perhaps fifty, fights while intoxicated but seemed to think this not particularly unusual. He stated also that his whole crew used to fight among themselves quite a bit but he did not do more of this than the others. He was engaged once but the engagement was broken on a "fifty-fifty proposition, I guess," and he had few dates for several years afterwards because he was quite depressed about this affair for a long time. His mother committed suicide in 1938, which was a very severe shock to the patient. She was 58 years of age at that time and the patient stated "she wouldn't hurt a fly." The preceding information was obtained after much hesitancy on the patient's part and he refused to discuss his family background further.

On admission to the hospital the patient displayed very marked apprehension, tension, irritability, depression and animosity toward the army. His only desire was to find some means of getting out of the army and he displayed very marked verbal aggression against all officers and authority of any kind. He was seen on several occasions during the two weeks following his admission and each time his symptoms and irritability remained unchanged. He continued to express this hostility toward the army and everyone who suggested a figure of authority to him. Insomnia, tension and combat dreams continued unabated. He expressed great fear that he would commit suicide in the same manner that his mother did. He did not drink very much during the first ten days of hospitalization. His reaction toward anything suggestive of army routine or authority was one of very marked verbal aggression, and he frequently would get up and pace the floor and threaten anyone who tried to give him an order. He stated, "If the C.O. of this hospital should walk in this office and tell me to stand up, I'd tell him to go to hell, and, if he commanded me to stand up, I'd sock him in the nose." It was quite evident that this patient was undergoing considerable strain in order to keep himself under sufficient control even to carry on a conversation. In his interviews he would talk continuously for thirty minutes in an uninterrupted manner, during which he would expend much of his pent-up hostility in the form of verbal aggression and expressions of hatred against the army and the injustices which he claimed had been meted out to him. He admitted that he had continually argued with crewmates in Australia, and further questioning brought the admission that he believed he was to blame for most of this. He did not give vent to his resentment while in the theater of operations because "we were tied down and restricted." Now he threatened to kill the guy who "breaks me." He stated, "I'm fed up with G.I.'s."

Under pentothal he expressed himself as follows: "This damned army! I think about Dave. He was a regular guy and one of the best. I cried when I saw him. His whole forehead and the top of his head torn off. The army shouldn't have done that. If that's the kind of guys that run the damned army, I want no part of it. I can never take an order that I don't see Dave's face. He was a friend to every guy. Those six month boys are the ones who are giving the orders, making three or four runs over the target. I don't think I can take another order. I can't take it and I'm not going to take it. All this b— s— they put out here in the States. I thought we'd get at least a little consideration. I'm just washed up with everything."

On several occasions the patient violated hospital regulations and eventually a firm attitude was adopted toward him. He was placed in detention, brought to trial and given a stiff fine. This had a remarkable effect on him. During the remainder of his hospitalization, he was most cooperative and, so far as could be learned, gave no trouble on the wards, stopped drinking alcoholic beverages entirely and was almost what one might call an ideal patient. He was discharged with the notation: "All symptoms of 'operational fatigue' have completely disappeared. However, these symptoms will probably recur if he is placed back on flying status. In spite of his personality he will make a fairly good readjustment in the army, (1) if he is not allowed to 'get by' with disciplinary infractions and (2) if he is given a fair break and not reduced in grade without good reason." This patient was returned to duty.

The surprising climax to this case history is the fact that several letters from the soldier at his new duty station indicated that he had adjusted well, was happy and enthusiastic about his work, and had maintained his recovery.

. . . . .

There was little doubt in our minds that this patient had been psychopathic in his aggressive drives since early life. His work and social history disclose an aggressive, impulsive, wandering person. Even then he destroyed his chances for advancement. Later, in the army, he did likewise, getting drunk the day he was to receive a promotion. In combat, fate itself took care of the punishing process and gratified his masochistic needs. Back home he again had to search vigorously for people to punish him. As a member of a group his own anxieties could be submerged. As an individual he openly sought for aggressive forces to hurt him. This need had to be gratified before his anxiety disappeared. This was recognized and a firm attitude taken toward him. The improvement was spectacular. Firmness, not kindness, was what he desired. This is one thing he can be sure of obtaining in the army, so that his recovery should be permanent as long as he is a member of a disciplined group.

CASE 54: *Aggressive behavior in an immature boy, somewhat regressed after combat, for the purpose of receiving attention.*

The patient was a 22 year old gunner, who had completed his tour of combat duty overseas without more stress than usual. He entered the hospital with complaints of insomnia, restlessness and nervousness. He soon showed us that he was to be our problem child. He dressed outlandishly and in words and behavior was loud and exhibitionistic at all times. He had a sense of humor and created quite a few laughs but became increasingly disturbing. He stayed up all night and attempted to sleep in the daytime and paid little attention to his appointments. After repeated warnings he was placed in the guardhouse and ignored for a week. He asked to see the therapist and humbly promised to behave. He was then told what his whole behavior meant—it was that of a little boy using every artifice to attract attention to himself, even though it was punitive attention. He grasped the interpretation and subsequent psychotherapy went along well. He was given some gratification of his dependent needs as his cooperation increased. During the first week he presented an exaggerated picture of a severe anxiety state with tremor, restlessness and insomnia. After he understood the meaning of his behavior and its failure in obtaining for him a medical discharge, he lost all his symptoms. He returned to duty as an exemplary soldier and was assigned to traveling to large cities recruiting for the Air Forces.

. . . . . .

This patient represents a large group of youngsters who are either immature or have been pushed back into immaturity by their experiences. They have endured stress well in their group organization and at home have lapped up attention and adoration. Then return to duty looms up as a frustration, for no more are they heroes occupying the nation's thoughts and interest. They anticipate returning to Continental bases as ordinary soldiers to do routine, monotonous and unimportant jobs, including K.P., latrine duty and guard duty. They make a last desperate effort to avoid this fate and seek for a medical discharge. They strive for attention, even though it will be punishing. They reveal the common mechanism observed in children who desire attention at all costs and obtain it by exhibitionistic or naughty behavior. In a sense the aggressive behavior is a flight from anxiety. Consciousness of his motivation started this boy on the road to recovery.

CASE 55: *Hostility reactive to a homosexual conflict accentuated by the symbolic significance of enemy attacks.*

The patient was a 29 year old, single, B-17 engineer gunner. His presenting complaints were inability to sleep, eat or concentrate, headaches, tension, restlessness and preoccupation with battle. The patient had flown twenty-five combat missions.

In the initial interview the patient had difficulty in remembering his tour of duty in any detail and was quite irritable. Nevertheless, he described the loss of many good friends overseas, including his crew, who were shot down while the patient was at a rest home. He was very devoted to the crew and described himself as looking after them like a father. His missions were very severe. The adjustment that he made while overseas was satisfactory but somewhat thin. He was demoted from sergeant to private for insubordination to superior officers. He expressed contempt for officers and figures of authority repeatedly throughout the interviews. The patient came from a lower middle-class family. He had one brother and two sisters, to whom, he stated, he was devoted. The parents were alive but not well. The father was a roustabout when the patient was a boy, but he was injured when the patient was about 18 years old, making it impossible for him thereafter to earn a living. The mother had been ailing for years. The patient stopped school in order to help support the family. This he did with considerable success, eventually purchasing a house for them, sending his brother to college and paying for the confinement of his sister. In the course of the psychotherapeutic interviews it developed that the patient had always been a hostile, aggressive individual, who would fight at the drop of a hat and who in earlier years was an amateur boxer. While he was overseas he got into fights frequently, and upon return to the United States on his furlough he beat a civilian. His dreams were frequently about fighting and on several occasions he dreamed of beating some enlisted man into a bloody pulp. Once in such a dream he struck the wall violently and injured his fist.

Pentothal narcosynthesis resulted in abreaction of emotion in the present tense, the chief conflict being the fact that he was not with his crew when they were shot down and he felt responsible for this. Psychotherapy did not succeed in removing this unreasonable feeling. The patient displayed great rigidity in his attitude during interviews and was usually evasive, vague and skeptical. An outstanding fact in the interviews was his childlike devotion to his mother. There was no question of his resentment toward the entire family, but an effort to make him conscious of this resulted in considerable negative feelings for the therapist. It became progressively clearer that it was virtually impossible to keep him talking about the current transference situation. An attempt to speak with him of the past also resulted in his becoming antagonistic. The patient did not develop any insight into his situation. He continued all through his hospital stay to sleep poorly, to vomit his meals frequently and to suffer from harrowing, aggressive dreams, such as being attacked by a man with a meat cleaver and defending himself by gashing his assailant's throat. His headaches continued unabated. The only insight that the patient reached was that there was a relationship between his physical symptoms and his emotional difficulties. He made up his mind, after he had been at the hospital for some time, that only separation from the service would help him. In view of the intense resistance he displayed to therapy, the violence of his rage and the severity of his symptoms, medical discharge was the only solution.

. . . . . .

Fundamentally, this patient was a dependent individual who all through his life had successfully overcompensated his passive trends by being the supporter and adviser of his family. His childhood attachment to his mother had not evolved into a normal adult attitude. He had strong unconscious resentment toward his family. In combat his passive needs were increased but were compensated by his becoming the father figure to his crew, with whom he could secondarily identify in a receiving role. When the crew were shot down, the patient was at the mercy of the anxiety engendered by frustration of his passive needs. Consequently, a tremendously hostile, aggressive attitude developed toward the army and all authoritative figures. He was an enraged personality, who had not been able to make a new adjustment to the army.

Brief psychotherapy was unsuccessful in breaking through this patient's hostile attitudes toward the army, which were displaced from an intrapsychic conflict. The patient in life had defended himself from a strong unconscious homosexuality, so vividly portrayed in his dreams. In the combat crew he acted out the role of the kindly father figure, which protected him from his unconscious wishes to be the helpless and attacked, the recipient of homosexual attentions. In therapy his defenses were so strong that he refused to enter into any discussion of transference or past feelings.

In many cases, although it is easy to see the homosexual conflicts underlying the symptoms and dreams of patients, such conflicts do not reach as frank an expression as in this patient. Because of the brevity of our therapy and because of the facility with which these conflicts can be handled in the transference by nonsexual interpretations, it serves no purpose to attempt to bring these conflicts into consciousness, even though we know that behind many problems of guilt, depression and hostility lie homosexual patterns.

To enumerate the external causes of the hostile-aggressive attitude to authoritative figures demonstrated in these illustrative cases, we may make the following list:

1. Loss of confidence and trust in leadership (case 47).

2. Loss of group morale (case 48).

3. Hostility displaced to the army from other rejections (case 49).

4. Mobilization of old repressed conflicts (case 50).

5. Mobilization of repressed hostility from a current conflict (case 51).

6. Reaction to loss of dependent gratification (case 52).

7. Hostility of psychopathic personality in order to evoke strict supervision (case 53).

8. Hostility of dependent personality to gain attention (case 54).

9. Defensive reaction against unconscious homosexuality (case 55).

In none of these patients do we find the expression of hostility toward the enemy. Pentothal abreactions frequently elicit crying and sobbing antagonism toward "those bastards," but it is the impotent wail of a child. The really hostile expressions and behavior are directed to the army and the man's own officers and leaders. Although there may be a nucleus of truth in the reasons given and the acts of the officers on which the patient rationalizes may be correctly stated, this hostility is derived from within and is evidence of a neurotic reaction.

When we analyze these seemingly heterogeneous cases closely, we find that basically the hostility is often mobilized by failure or loss of the group morale or organization. This failure may be in leadership or in the total group configuration. It may result from failure of comrades to continue necessary relationships through their death or loss, obviously an uncontrollable failure. The failure may stem from loss of group life by rotation of the patient home, a procedure which he strongly desired without knowledge of its disastrous secondary effect.

The dynamic forces behind the external precipitations of hostile and aggressive reactions will be discussed in chapter 15. The old unsolved neurotic conflicts involving hostilities are obviously often restimulated by the conditions of war. But new aggressions are derived from the special results of stress, when it is severe enough to cause psychological regression. The personality returns to a stage when anger is expressed directly to supporting figures who have rejected or failed to support the individual adequately. Deprivation, loss of love, loss of self esteem, are stimuli to a diffuse attack on any or all parental figures without producing a sense of guilt, since rationalization is adequate and internal checks on aggression have been lost by the very process of regression.

The sullen, antagonistic, disrespectful patient with large quantities of hostility is often a difficult therapeutic problem. He may have no insight into his illness and his negative attitude toward the therapist blocks his treatment. Those that are fearful of their hostilities or feel guilty about them offer better prognoses. Many seem unable to verbalize their aggressions and repetitively liberate them only in action. This group is the most difficult to treat and from it we have the greatest number of failures. In many of these cases chronic symptoms develop early in their clinical course, which resemble those of the intractable cases still suffering since the last war.

CHAPTER 14

Psychotic-like States

THE TERM "PSYCHOSIS" has an ominous connotation, indicating a serious mental disturbance with a bad prognosis for permanent cure. That this is not always the case has been borne out by our experiences with psychotic-like breakdowns in combat soldiers in whom rapid recovery could be effected with little difficulty (26).

By definition a psychosis is a profoundly regressive reaction in which there is a considerable break with reality. The reality-testing functions of the ego are lost or diminished, so that unconscious drives or forces are more or less directly and openly expressed. This differs from the break with reality made in the neuroses in which an incomplete gap is covered up by other synthesizing forces within the ego.

In a sense the neurotic reactions produced by war are efforts on the part of the ego to prevent a break with reality on the larger scale characteristic of the psychoses. They are reactions to negate the external trauma or to isolate the anxiety thereby stimulated. The phobias protect the individual by keeping him away from the trauma. The compulsions dispel the dangerous situation by magical formulae or gestures. The hysterical symptoms completely block out entire perceptual systems to avoid cognizance of the danger. In the traumatic psychoses the ego crumbles and ignores either reality or the great anxieties stimulated by it. Overseas the psychotic reactions seen mostly in ground troops were due to a negation of reality by the process of dissociation, which has been described in chapter 5. In the psychotic-like reactions in returnees the ego loses its integrative capacity from the pressure of anxieties that have been stimulated by traumatic experiences and have been pathologically prolonged.

Nightmares are a most frequent symptom in almost all cases of war neuroses. These awaken the sleeper with profound terror and often it requires several moments for the patient to reorient himself in time or space. He awakens with a start, often in panic, thinking he is back in combat. All the symptoms of profound sympathetic excitation appear, as if there were an acute emergency. These take the form of tachycardia, perspiration, dyspnea, tremor and sometimes diarrhea. Occasionally the patient is paralyzed or converts his panic into action and desperately tries to find his way out of the dangerous environment. At times this action is frenzied and purposeless; at other times there is a slower, deliberate "sleepwalking" in an effort to leave the hospital. Occasionally there is an aggressive attack on the nearest person with the most convenient weapon at hand. The patient's roommate may be hurt or may narrowly escape injury.

These nightmares occur when the ego is asleep and has given up most of its normal discriminatory functions. The unconscious tensions created by combat are held down by the ego as long as it functions successfully. During sleep they are able to press upward with such force that the ego is powerless to distort them into a disguised dream; they are expressed realistically and the weakened ego reacts as if the stimulus were external. Eventually the ego regains mastery of the situation, especially after adequate therapy.

The following case reports represent a similar process occurring in the day time.

CASE 56: *Partial loss of ego discrimination—depression and anxiety due to repressed hostility.*

A Sergeant radio-operator was shot down over enemy-occupied territory on his fifth mission, but evaded capture and returned to his base after a month. He entered the hospital with the complaints of nervousness, sleeplessness, nightmares, depression, loss of appetite and tachycardia. His most disturbing symptom consisted of illusions that he was back in combat. During the day, while busy and interested, he had no trouble. However, when he lay on his bed alone with no one else around, or shut his eyes, or at night in the dark, he was immediately transported back to his dangerous past. This was not in the form of a memory or dream, for he actually felt himself to be in combat or eluding the Germans. It took a few minutes for him to orient himself after opening his eyes.

He was treated with a group for several sessions but after a short time he asked for a personal interview, which revealed that his symptoms had become much worse since his return home. This boy had a good background and his early life was uneventful. He was an adopted child and did not remember his real parents. At home he became depressed because he found that his girl friend had become friendly with another service man. He apparently accepted this in good grace and asked her not to break off with this man, since he was going overseas and the patient didn't want him worried when he got into combat. He arranged to spend the early part of each evening with his girl so that she could be with the other man for the remainder of the time. He entered the hospital uncertain whether the girl was more interested in him or in his rival. It became apparent that a great deal of his depression was related to the repressed hostility which he had toward his rival. However, some of it was displaced toward the army and officers. A more detailed study of his character showed that he had never been able to express any hostile competitive attitudes. The symptoms of his combat neurosis were due to repressed aggressions toward the enemy, a repression that was not completely successful because free anxiety dominated the picture.

Psychotherapy was directed toward helping him to accept the normal nature of his aggressions and permit them to become conscious. The therapy was directed particularly at the current edition of his competitive hostility, namely, that related to his rival. As he began to see the nature of his true feelings and their normality, his anxiety and depression decreased. He was able to verbalize negative feelings toward other men and officers in his squadron. His rigidly masked and depressed face assumed expression and he began to enjoy his stay in the hospital; sleep soon became normal and he recovered completely from the illusion of being in combat. He developed courage to send for his girl and her mother and had them spend two weeks with him. An understanding was reached that after the war they would get married.

. . . . . .

This patient demonstrated the phenomena of lack of spatial or temporal orientation when he closed his eyes. Losing the reality-testing powers relayed to the ego through vision, his weakened ego returned to the frightening experience of combat and flight from the Nazis. The source of the burden which his ego had to bear was uncovered during treatment. This patient could not overcome his compulsive character and express his aggressions against the dictates of his strict superego. He found himself in the same dilemma at home in competition for his girl. His depression and anxiety were a combined reaction to the unexpressed aggressions stimulated by war and home situations. The perpetuation of his hypnogogic hallucinations of catastrophic danger was due to the fact that the danger of his own hostilities was still present, and was in fact increased. They were projected to the enemy and reacted to as toward an external enemy. They could not be mastered until the ego could deal with the real enemy, his own internalized aggressions.

CASE 57: *Paranoid-aggressive state, mobilized by frightening war experiences, producing sleep paralysis.*

The patient was a tall, heavy-set 22 year old gunner radio-operator, who had been overseas twenty-two months. He was tense, hesitant and not very clear in relating his difficulties. For the past few months he had been unable to get along with other people and unable to take orders, and had developed a preference for being by himself. Lately, at night, he had been feeling as if his whole body were paralyzed. The patient felt as if everyone, especially officers, were against him. In public places people looked at him queerly and he could not endure their gaze.

His illness began a year ago while he was overseas, after an episode in which German parachutists attacked his camp but were driven off. He was very much frightened, and afraid he might be killed, and he nearly shot one of his own men with a machine gun. Four or five months ago, while still overseas, he would often feel paralyzed at night as he would think over the unpleasant events of the day. He developed marked insomnia, headaches and preoccupation with unpleasant combat experiences. Hallucinatory visualizations of women and children being killed, of starving children and of bombings were experienced. He found it hard to concentrate, had great difficulty in talking about the war and could not stand hearing others talk about it. He had episodes in which he became enraged, and he had only a thin control over his aggressiveness. Sometimes he became very tearful when aggressive. While stationed at a Continental air base after his return, he could not stand doing duty, developed hatred of army discipline and had strong impulses to strike officers who gave him orders. He felt much better when he was with his wife, who took good care of him. The patient stated that he wanted to go away to some place alone with his wife for six months, and to see no papers and hear no radio.

While overseas he received news of his father's death from tuberculosis. His father had been ill for several years in a sanitorium. The patient was much attached to his father and eulogized him. His mother was a very nervous woman and had hysterical attacks; she had threatened suicide a number of times. The patient was the eldest of seven siblings, five of whom were living. There was a good deal of ambivalence toward a brother who died at the age of 9 of pneumonia. One sister had convulsions frequently. During his school days he had a very quick temper and was in many fights. Prior to enlistment he had various jobs and worked for one year for a firm that made woodwork products.

. . . . . .

This man was struggling with a severe and intense homosexual conflict, symbolized by his experiences overseas. He tended to be somewhat forgetful, and had difficulty with dates, particularly of recent events, but for the most part he was correctly oriented.

The patient presented a pathetic figure; he just wanted to be alone, away from everyone and everything. He had regressed to the level of a frightened and badly dependent child, needing his mother (wife) to take care of him. He had the delusion that everyone was against him, which was a decided break with reality. He had no rationalization for his paranoia and it was not systematized nor related to any particular persons. Actually he became paralyzed when emergency actions should have been stimulated by dangers. He was afraid, yet almost killed one of his own men. His paralysis represented a conflict between homosexual submission and aggressive reaction, neither being victorious. In reaction at home he retreated to a dependent position. His aggressions were expressed in visualization of death and destruction, which represented the end results of his own internal reactive drives. He then feared that others knew about his hostile tendencies and watched him just as his own superego carefully guarded him against aggressive outbreaks. He recovered sufficiently to be discharged to civilian life but he could not be of further use in the service.

CASE 58: *Severe paranoid reaction and mobilized aggression after harrowing combat experiences.*

A 22 year old assistant engineer gunner completed seven missions overseas. On his last mission his plane was shot down over enemy-occupied territory, where he became an evadee. He eventually reached his base after many difficulties and narrow escapes. During the time he hid away from the Gestapo, a young boy, 18 years old, who had no connection with the underground or with the army, brought him food at his place of confinement. This boy was caught by the enemy and tortured in an effort to make him expose the patient's whereabouts. Unable to endure the torture, the boy succumbed, after which the patient developed a tremendous degree of guilt.

The patient had marked loss of weight, depression, guilty reaction and violent dreams in the hospital, but nevertheless stated that he felt fine and did not want to get out of the army. His greatest desire was to return to combat and be killed to atone for his terrible crime of causing the foreign boy's death. Almost every night he dreamed of this event and awakened with the feeling that the boy's uncle was after him with a long knife. This also occurred in fantasies while he was lying in bed, not asleep. He awakened with the feeling that the uncle was in the room and he often searched around under beds and behind doors for him. He felt that people were looking at him as if he were a murderer. The patient stated that he was entirely well and needed no treatment and therefore refused to take a pentothal injection. There was nothing the matter with him that he could not straighten out himself with time. Yet his paranoid projections were so strong that he fought with people who seemed to be accusing him of murder. He could not get along with any other men and wished to be left entirely alone. The men reminded him of German soldiers and he wished to hit them. Under the influence of alcohol he attempted to escape from the hospital, as if he were escaping from the Gestapo.

The patient was the second of four siblings. One older brother was in the army and he had a younger brother about the age of the foreign boy. He stated that, when he first saw this boy, he thought that he was his younger brother. At home the patient had a poor relationship with his father, who treated him as a black sheep and would accuse him unjustifiably of anything that was done in the family and punish him severely. The younger brother was the favorite of the family and toward him the patient always had some resentment.

The patient was treated intensively for several months but all efforts failed to change his paranoid state. The tortured boy was his responsibility and he could not be shaken in his belief that he himself was responsible. No rational consideration of the boy as a soldier fighting for the common cause, just like himself, could lighten his load of guilt. The boy probably represented the patient's brother, against whom he had considerable resentment. His own superego representing his father's attitude was unnaturally strict and was projected into the hallucinatory uncle who came to exact revenge. The patient's severe experiences had produced a regression in his personality, so that the superego had been loosened from its internal position. It became largely external in the form of the uncle and others pointing the finger of accusation at him. The only solution was suicide in the form of return to combat. His return could not be permitted, since the patient was psychotic and needed much therapy.

CASE 59: *Psychotic-like regression in a strongly overcompensated, passive boy after severe emotional trauma.*

This patient was admitted to the hospital one evening and immediately requested a private room. He had a vacant look on his face and refused to face the medical officer. He kept staring out of the window with a terrorized expression in his eyes. He told that he was an evadee from enemy-occupied territory, the only man to escape from his ship when it was shot down. When he reached home in the United States, he learned that his sister had aborted when she heard that he was missing in action, and he felt guilty about the death of her child. He was heavily sedated with amytal. Food and medication taken by mouth were quickly vomited. The general medical officer believed that the patient was a full-blown schizophrenic, who was actively hallucinating the presence of Nazi agents pursuing him. He seemed to feel that the doctors, nurses and other patients were dangerous enemies, and he reacted with fear to their presence.

For the first interview the patient came into the room staggering under the effects of drugs, which had also produced dizziness and profound visual changes. He was permitted to smoke and sat on the chair with his head between his legs, staring at the floor in abstraction. Every once in a while he would shake his head vigorously, as if to remove some cobwebs. He would suddenly rouse himself from his abstraction with a startled look of abject fear on his face. He was put on the couch and sufficient pentothal was given him to produce a deep sleep. As he roused himself two hours later, the therapist simply told him that he was back at home, in a safe place, and that the dangers were over. He then related that his ship blew up over enemy territory, and that he went from house to house, always fearful that he would be captured. He wore a civilian disguise and carried maps and was liable to the death penalty in case he were caught. He told of being surrounded by Germans with machine guns. He went from town to town dressed as a peasant, making short stops and always riding on the train platform. At one point a native kept bothering him with questions, so that there was only one thing to do. He pushed him off the train. As he related this, he expressed great guilt, based on the feeling that maybe the man was trying to help him, for the underground asked him a lot of questions also. He told of a Gestapo agent, disguised as a beggar, who stated that the fliers who escaped would be hounded by the Nazis, who would catch them, no matter where they went. He told how he could not bear to look at a person in uniform because it reminded him of his experiences. The only interpretations given were that he was now home in the United States, in a safe place. He was taken to the ward and sedatives were discontinued.

That evening he was visited and showed a marked startle reaction on being touched. The next morning the therapist again visited him and suggested he eat breakfast and went with him to the kitchen. The therapist sat with him as he ate a few mouthfuls of toast and drank his coffee. It was suggested that he shave and get a hair cut. He said he had no money, so he was given a dollar.

The next day he was brought to the office. He looked more wide awake and in contact with reality, but he would frequently lose himself in abstraction, returning with a sudden start and searching the room for signs of danger. Every effort was made to make him feel that the therapist was his friend. The doctor sat close to him, held his hand and asked him to talk. He stated that he had tried to keep up a brave front at home during furlough, because his mother was worried about him, but that he had not been able to hide his troubles. He asked whether he could go home before being sent to duty. A furlough was promised, which he did not seem to believe. He said that, if he were transferred to some camp, he would have trouble all over again. He seemed shaken by some inner terror every few moments and his hands perspired profusely. His pupils were widely dilated and his whole expression was one of terror.

He was asked to talk about his experiences. He tried to resist this, saying that he must forget. He was told there was only one way to forget and that was to talk it out first. He then told about his crew, so many of whom were married, and he sobbed when he said, "Why couldn't it have been me instead of them? What are their wives going to do, all alone with babies? That poor guy in the ball turret, his wife just had a baby—I saw its picture. Why couldn't it have been me?" They went on their third mission and were hit by a rocket. They tried to get out of the radio compartment but the door jammed. Then suddenly the ship exploded into hundreds of pieces. The patient was blown up. At first his parachute would not open and he had to tear the cover off. Then a Nazi fighter kept diving at him as if he were going to shoot him, apparently just playing cat and mouse. The patient screamed to him, but he kept it up. No one else in his ship got out. He should have seen the wives of his crew when he got back, but he couldn't.

It was felt that enough had been exposed and the patient again was reassured that we would get him well, that the danger and difficulties were over. He agreed and understood the interpretation that part of his mind seemed to be living in France and part of his mind was here. He stated that, when he awakened, it seemed as if people were watching him and he got frightened. It took a long time until he was sure where he was. It was obvious that this boy was not schizophrenic but was suffering from a severe anxiety state with a marked regression of his ego, which was incapable of differentiating present from past reality and considered the whole world a hostile place.

The next day the patient entered the office with a marked difference in his attitude and appearance. He was able to look at the examiner more frequently and steadily and to look out of the window; he did not smoke as much. He stated that he was up most of the night, doing a jigsaw puzzle with the nurse. He went to sleep about 5:30 a.m. He was still unable to retain his meals. He had asked several people around the ward if the therapist kept his promises, which referred to the promise that, after he got well, he would be given a furlough to go home.

The discussion about his last mission was reopened, which evoked some trembling and a few very short periods of abstraction. He said he never was afraid of missions, in fact liked to go on them. The crew was in the radio compartment after the ship was hit and no one was able to open the escape hatch. The patient tried to push open the door against the slip stream and got it half open, when the ship exploded. When he landed, he tore off his parachute and ran for the woods. He saw some children in the field and he persuaded them to take him to their house. He then told of staying in the woods for a few days without anything to eat, gradually making his way toward home, sometimes being accepted by the natives and helped, and at other times being rejected by them because they were too scared. The basic fear reaction to the topic was much less than the day before. He said he would like to go up in an airplane again, any kind. The therapist suggested that they take a walk, so they went out on the beach and sat in the sun. He looked around, observed the boys in bathing suits and the birds, and said, "Gee, it's pretty here." He was taken to the Red Cross and shown where the various recreational rooms were located. The patient felt very tired physically, so he was brought back to his room, where he said he would like a cup of coffee.

Because it was Good Friday, the patient was given permission to call his mother. She promptly told him that his brother had been reported missing in action yesterday. In the afternoon he was found lying on his bed, Bible in hand, looking at his brother's picture. The psychiatrist told him that he felt sorry but that after all he too had been missing and perhaps his brother would return as he had done. There seemed to be more reason than ever for him to get well. He wished he could go home to see his "mom" but not in the condition he was in. He then asked the therapist to get him a sandwich. He was given a tray and he ate heartily for the first time.

The next day he came into the interview smiling and clear-eyed, with upright posture. He said he had just been flirting with a girl on the beach. As he was forced into talking about the mission and escape through enemy territory, he became tremulous and bowed his head and said he only wanted to forget. It was again pointed out that he couldn't forget, that he was always partly living in the danger situation. He could only master this danger by remembering and learning that it was past. Poorly educated as this man was, he had good psychological understanding. He wondered where his brother was. When he looked at his hands, he could only think of the men he had killed. When he ate food, he could only think of the poor peasants he had met who didn't have enough to eat.

He began the next interview with a bright and shiny face, but again became depressed, abstracted and tremulous on discussing war experiences. While escaping from the Germans, he had spied on Germans and noted airports and troop concentrations and even counted planes on fields. He was not afraid. Before reaching home in the United States, he got very drunk, but on arriving home he couldn't drink on account of mother. The family had made him feel that he was responsible for his sister's miscarriage. His brother went into the AAF as a gunner because of the patient's example. He couldn't get the other boys out of mind—their wives and babies. He payed the therapist the dollar loaned him and admitted he felt fine except when thinking of his experiences. He was not afraid but reacted to the sense of guilt. The irrationality of his sense of guilt was stressed.

The next day he was asked about a nurse's note that stated he had awakened with a bad dream. He didn't want to talk about it at first but then said he dreamed: "My brother, who is missing in action, was captured by the Germans, who beat him in an effort to make him talk, but he refused." The patient said, "He would be like that but I don't know why I dream that because they wouldn't beat him." The therapist said, "I think you mean in the dream that I am trying to make you talk and endure the pain in these interviews." He smiled and said, "I never thought of that." Then he said, "What shall we talk about?" He was told that it was up to him—he could choose. "I'd like to talk about home," he said with a smile. "I saw a niece of mine that I had never seen before and she was awfully cute, the little baby." Then he stopped with an expression of pain. He was told, "Now you are thinking about the miscarriage your sister had. Why do you still think that you are to blame. No one accused you of it." He said, "If I could only see my sister, but she didn't come home. She is with her husband in Oklahoma; he is waiting to be shipped overseas." So it developed that the patient had not been accused by the sister; he had not even seen her. He said, "This beach reminds me of S——. I remember being in the mountains looking on one side and seeing the darkness of one country and the lights of the other, with the cars going on the road. He said that he wasn't afraid and told how he had, one night, walked right through a German camp with soldiers every few feet and had never been accosted. He told of being taken into the home of a young married couple and how the wife treated him so kindly, like her child; how, in another place, he dug cabbages all day for the peasant who took him in, and in another place he talked English to a boy, 6 years old, who had been in England. The therapist pointed out to him the discrepancy that, while over there, where every person was a potential enemy, after his initial fears, he walked unafraid and even spied on the Germans, whereas here in this country, where people are glad to see him and everything is safe, he felt frightened of everyone, thought people were spying on him and had a large amount of guilt about his behavior. He understood and said, "I can't understand it. I can't understand why. It seems like I was walking in a trance over there; but I don't feel afraid any more—I feel much better. All last night I thought of what you said yesterday, how the feelings of guilt and fear were due to my own ways of thinking and not due to the real situation."

During the next interview the patient talked about his background, how his father had owned a farm and was a part time brakeman on the railroad. He fell off the train and suffered a back injury which layed him up for three years. This may have had some connection with the patient's guilty reaction to throwing a curious Frenchman off the train. The father died when the patient was 11 years old and the family became impoverished. The mother sold the farm and moved to the outskirts of a city. She supported the nine children and refused to send them to an orphan asylum. The father's favorite child was the younger brother, now a prisoner of war. The patient worked while he went to school, helping support the mother, and left after the third year of high school to work as a helper in an electric furnace. He did well until just before leaving for the army. He was making $18 a day, most of which he gave to his mother, as he did his overseas pay. He told that there was a gang of boys at home, of which he was the leader. This gang would play gangster and army with pistols and shotguns, shooting up the neighboring houses. They didn't smoke or drink or go out with women but were the tough boys of the town.

He was asked, "You never were afraid, were you?" "Oh no," he said, "I never was afraid. I have been shot a couple times," and he showed knife wounds on his hand and over one eyebrow. He used to have fights, in which he would beat up the other kids severely. "I got quite a reputation in my town," he said, "but I only did that when somebody provoked me." He had a girl, 18 years old, now in high school, with whom he had been going steady, but the difficulty was that there were religious differences.

Slowly the patient changed as he began to feel safe and protected and was forced to ventilate his experiences in simple interviews without the aid of pentothal. He seemed to gather strength from the therapist. When he first came to the hospital everyone recognized him as a pathetic, frightened little boy and the nurses mothered him a lot. As he became better, he changed into a tough, rough, inconsiderate person with adolescent cockiness. He broke every regulation at the hospital and in town and got into trouble with the police. He became his usual aggressive self as he got "well." This self was incompatible with army service, so that he was given a medical discharge. He was next heard of as having taken a job in the neighboring city.

. . . . . .

The dynamics of this patient's conflict became quite clear This was a fundamentally passive-dependent boy, who had never had sufficient gratification of his passive needs. With the early death of his father he was forced into premature responsibility. At the same time he developed a very marked overcompensation, becoming the tough boy of the town without ever experiencing the subjective sensations of fear or anxiety. He loved to fight, he liked the bombing raids and he wanted to go back to combat. Suddenly he was thrust into a situation where he was overwhelmed by anxiety and his ego, never having developed any technique for dealing with anxiety, regressed. As an evadee he had considerable gratification of his dependence by the women who took care of him. His regression was manifested by the trancelike state in which he moved around among the enemy. This regression, with the ego's interpretation that there was no discrimination between friend and foe, danger and safety, was obviously not an illness at that time, since the reality corresponded to this interpretation. When he returned home needing a great deal of gratification and was subtly accused of being responsible for his sister's miscarriage, he met another trauma, which was actually rejection. It was then that his ego lost all its discriminatory powers and virtually became paralyzed.

The treatment has been: (1) to gratify his dependent needs, that is, to nurse him along; (2) to substitute the therapist's discriminatory powers for his own, and (3) to help him reestablish his compensatory reactions and bring him back to the state of the tough little boy.

CASE 60: *Psychopathic personality, precipitated into a severely aggressive, homicidal state by the experiences of combat.*

A 25 year old engineer gunner of a B-24 completed twenty-five combat missions. His mother had had repeated "little" illnesses and was quite nervous. The father died, of a ruptured appendix, when he was 7 years of age. There were four married sisters in good health, and one brother, who was serving time in prison for armed robbery. The patient had been a sickly child. After the father's death he and two sisters were sent to an orphanage, owing to the inability of the mother to take care of the entire family. While he was in the institution, his physical condition improved. However, the discipline was extremely strict, the patient often being beaten with a rope and generally made to feel very unhappy and bitter. The superintendent, who was later sent to prison for embezzlement, was very sadistic. The patient ran away from the institution on numerous occasions and returned home, but was always sent back and punished for having run away. He completed only one year of high school and then went to work. During his adolescent years he suffered from injuries, on four occasions becoming unconscious, the longest time being seven hours when he was hit on the head with a baseball bat at the age of 16. He and his brother got along very poorly together. He stated that his brother was no good and was always getting into trouble. On two occasions the brother attempted to kill the patient. The difficulty between them always arose as a result of the brother's treatment of the mother and other women. The patient joined the CCC in order to escape from the orphan asylum. He spent one and a half years in this organization and was finally dishonorably discharged because of his inability to get along with authority. He subsequently had jobs in structural steel, making auto parts and as an auto mechanic. At the age of 15 the patient started going with a girl, whom he married three years ago. His statement in regard to this marriage was that he felt sorry for her, since they had had sexual relations and he was afraid that he had ruined her life. He was never happy in this marriage and, on several occasions, suggested that his wife start getting a divorce. The patient always preferred to be alone and was fearful of what might happen to him. He used to carry a blackjack as protection, particularly against his brother. He told of stealing cars on several occasions, with other boys, for the fun of it, but was nearly sent to prison for this once. He indulged in masturbation between the ages of 13 and 16 but never since then. He recalled sexual relationships with another boy while in the orphanage, but overt homosexuality had not persisted.

The patient had been in the army for twenty-seven months and trained as an engineer gunner. He was in two crashes in the United States before going overseas. During his combat experiences he was very fearful from the first mission. His missions were quite severe. He was in two crashes overseas. He recalled the twelfth mission, when they were shot at by a German battleship, as being "rugged" and described the shells as screaming like wild cats. On the seventeenth mission all four motors cut out at 27,000 feet and the plane came down to 2,000 feet before the motors were started again. On his twenty-third mission his plane was hit. He was knocked out of his turret, and his copilot, bombardier navigator and radioman were all killed.

He wanted to quit after the twelfth mission. He became very restless, and headaches, which had bothered him all his life, increased. He lost his appetite and complained of tension and of being fed up with everything. On admission, the above-named symptoms were still present. He appeared depressed, tired, pale and anxious, and stated that he felt very often as if he wanted to kill someone or himself, that he could stand no more. His treatment during his stay in this hospital consisted of partial analysis, including the use of pentothal, and an attempt was made to show him the mechanism of the development of some of his difficulties. During his stay he was very cooperative and anxious to help himself and the therapist.

The essential dynamics involved in this case largely revolved around the marked feelings of hostility in relation to his mother, his brother and all people representative of authority. Being fundamentally a dependent personality, the early experience of being sent away from his home to an environment of marked severity was largely responsible for the initiation of his feelings. Combat could not be said to have been responsible for his present condition, except to the extent of having greatly mobilized his feelings, to the point where he felt unable to handle them. He developed severe tension, avoiding companionship because of the danger of overt hostility.

This psychopathic personality vacillated between an aggressive hostility, overcompensated independence and a passive drive, which was always frustrated. This vacillating equilibrium was intensified by the great increase of his passive needs, arising out of combat experience. The result was a dangerous character, who was likely to commit either suicide or homicide. It was necessary to discharge him from the service.

．　．　．　．　．　．

The examples of psychotic-like reactions which we have presented indicate gradations in the extent to which the ego breaks with reality. It at once becomes apparent that there is no essential difference between cases designated as neuroses and the psychoses. There is a quantitative difference—no more. Yet quantity may so change the clinical appearance that it seems as if a new quality has been added. The underlying dynamic basis of the aggressive-hostile person may differ in no way from that demonstrated by another, yet the behavior of the latter may be quantitatively so at variance with reality that it assumes the proportions of a psychosis. Both psychoses and neuroses are regressive in that old infantile modes of thinking and behavior are re-established. The neurotic reaction is less regressive because part of the personality adopts a defensive measure against such retreat, or deals with the regressive symptom once it has formed in an attempt to synthesize it into the total personality.

The most severe psychotic-like reactions were observed overseas, particularly in ground troops. Some ground echelons on frequently bombed airfields likewise showed these severe regressive reactions. They were variously mislabeled, from the malignant appellation of schizophrenia to the benign diagnosis of hysteria. They recovered rapidly on removal from combat and with adequate psychiatric care. Unfortunately, many of them have been given shock treatment on the assumption that they were schizophrenics. This has a tragic homeopathic flavor: to treat a man who has regressed, because overpowering hostile external stress has been too much for his ego, by giving him another powerful (electric) shock! By the time the soldier reaches these shores with or without therapy his break with reality has usually diminished, so that we then see only relatively mild disturbances. Loss of ego discrimination *in toto,* severe states of dissociation and complete black-out of a perceptual system are rarely seen.

The types of cases observed in this country are usually those with partial loss of the ego's capacity to discriminate dangerous from safe reality, paranoid reactions and hostile-aggressive behavior. Partial loss of reality-testing functions on the part of the ego is primarily due to a process of regression caused by the stress of combat. As we have seen in chapter 10, return to the infantile state of dependence carries with it the childish uncertainty and insecurity in relation to the whole external world. Viewed through the eyes of a child, the human and natural figures loom large and dangerous. This stimulates apprehension and an irritable preparedness against forces that may destroy the child. The secondary reaction is often a defensive aggressiveness toward everyone.

However, there is another reason for the anticipation that danger lurks in every corner, and that is the ego's conditioning to long-continued experience with strange sounds and sights. There are no safe people or things and so it continues to react violently to minor stimuli. Furthermore, the patient's own hostilities, mobilized by combat, do not cease at once. They persist as internal dangers, which the ego must continue to react against in the same pattern as external dangers. They are projected outward and treated as enemies. Such projected hostilities are responsible for the paranoid trends in so many men. The unconscious statement is: "It is not I who am hostile—it is they." Secondary aggressive reactions and considerable anxiety are evoked.

Psychopathic personalities, among whom we include a heterogeneous group of asocial individuals, are great problems because of their overtly expressed hostilities, alcoholism and aggressive behavior. When we look at their records, we usually find the following sequence of events. Before combat they showed the early signs of severe character abnormalities in civilian life and in training. In the latter period frequent company punishment, A.W.O.L., and often court-martials are written in their service records. Stockade punishment, loss of rank and pay losses had little deterrent effect. Overseas some of these enlisted men and a very few officers were aggressive, fighting and often heroic figures. Here at last their psychopathy was well adapted to their social milieu. Many of them received promotions, decorations and honors. But the return home is a sad sequel, because the aggressive behavior is no longer adaptive and trouble ensues. These psychopaths become worse after combat because they have had aggressions mobilized and approved of by external father figures, and, having corruptible superegos, they have no automatic checks on their asocial behavior. Many of these boys are destined to receive severe punishment, including discharge without honor, in spite of their services in combat. They realize this and beg to be discharged from the army while they still have rank and a clean record. Flying officers must usually be grounded, as they cannot avoid the temptation to fly low or to do acrobatics.

It becomes apparent that the psychotic-like states are benign and due to a reaction to external stress or to forces stimulated by these stresses. There are few previous psychotic patterns and little biological basis for psychosis. Deeply rooted ancient traumata are less important in causing these psychotic regressions than the current powerful forces of reality.

CHAPTER 15

Psychodynamics

To UNDERSTAND the dynamic factors underlying war neuroses observed in this country among returnees, one must be familiar with their genesis overseas. But that is not enough; the effect of combat on soldiers who do not develop overt illness overseas must be known, because many soldiers become emotionally ill only after returning home, although they have been prepared for this turn of events by their experiences abroad and in combat. The combat veteran who succumbs for the first time at home, long after he has left the dangerous atmosphere of combat, is also suffering from the effects of war.

Returnees who have been sent to our hospital may be grouped into several categories, all showing the same clinical syndromes in varying degrees of severity:

1. Those whose regressive reactions originated overseas, but who are now undergoing a successful and spontaneous process of "unwinding," "uncoiling," "cooling off" or "decompression."

2. Those with neuroses which originated overseas, but which persist with unabated severity, sometimes becoming progressively worse.

3. Those who develop new conflicts, due to failure in adaptation to the home environment, because their personalities have been altered by overseas experiences.

4. Those who show a recrudescence of previous anxiety states, or who develop them for the first time owing to apprehension concerning new duty assignment or fear of their future.

Our statistics show that only a few of our officer and enlisted patients are casualties who have been sent home by Medical Disposition Boards. Their number does not correlate well with the frequency of the diagnosis of "operational fatigue" or "anxiety states" made overseas, necessitating return of the patient to the United States. Many of these patients are not referred to the hospital from ports of debarkation. Probably most of them have been re-evaluated and returned to flying, limited to the United States.

How does it happen that these individuals, who were very ill overseas with severe anxiety states, psychosomatic conditions or conversion symptoms, are able to re-establish behavior sufficiently normal to pass the rigid medical examination for flying? Malingering is not in question, since objective as well as subjective symptoms were always present overseas or these patients would not have been sent home. It is this type of case that has given some confirmation to the idea that war reactions are not true neuroses. Goldstein (22) has been the most outspoken of those who contend that, although the symptoms due to war events have many characteristics of reactions to be observed in neurotics, they are not neuroses, since permanent personality changes do not usually develop, no fixation of symptoms takes place and complete recovery is the rule. According to Goldstein, catastrophic conditions evoke uneconomical reactions of anxiety in the organism because of the extent of the external threat, failure to cope with it and the breakdown of the "capacity of abstraction." This breakdown only persists or recurs when insecurity continues or danger threatens again.

Certainly return to a safe and secure environment at home often effects dramatic cures, which can only be attributed to the cessation of dangerous external stimuli, and these otherwise healthy soldiers are not likely to experience similar catastrophic stress at any time in their future lives. However, if Ground or Air Forces personnel are returned to combat duty after a relatively rapid recovery from severe psychological reactions, relapses are the rule. Men who have become psychiatric casualties overseas are less severely ill and show a higher rate of recovery in the United States than those whose psychiatric symptoms became disturbing or obvious to them after their return home. Their stay in the hospital under treatment is shorter and they present fewer signs of illness (cf. group 1). Incapacitating anxiety released them from combat earlier than those who finished their tours of duty, hence the stress that they endured was less and their early breakdowns protected them against later, more devastating regressions.

Other soldiers, sent home because of illness, suffer from severe symptoms of anxiety, based on or attached to inner difficulties that are not uncovered while they were still overseas (cf. group 2). There, the entire interest of soldiers and psychiatrists is centered on the traumatic effects of combat. It is difficult to focus attention on the personal meaning of terrifying, ubiquitous battle stimuli, when the reality is so overpowering and produces anxiety in everyone. In fact, even old neurotic anxieties are satisfactorily rationalized and blamed on the war situation. The clinical picture is often dramatic and related to specific settings of combat and to particularly harrowing experiences. Reactions are monotonously stereotyped, colored more by the impersonal aspects of the external stimuli than by the individual psychological pattern of the soldier's inner life. This fact is illustrated by the case histories of patients observed and treated overseas and again in this country by the same psychiatrist; only the latter observations reveal the personalized reactions to combat (cf. chapter 8). In other patients, anxieties spread and become internalized, to involve and disrupt more and more of the personality. Untreated, the emotional disturbances seem to remain permanent or even to become decidedly worse. Anxiety has the capacity of initiating a vicious circle, which perpetuates itself, increasing the severity of the resulting neurosis (cf. chapter 6).

The contrast between the first group of temporary neurotic reactions and the second group of severe and often progressive neuroses brings us to the difficult but unavoidable discussion of what we really mean by war neuroses. Are they temporary reactions to catastrophic events, are they something different from psychoneuroses and do they justify a special nosological designation? Our concern for a clearer definition is by no means academic, because on it are based the principles which guide medical officers in their treatment and disposition of those nervous states. All gradations of opinion have been met, from the reactionary attitude that anyone who cracks in battle is a "weak sister," a psychoneurotic, to the equally exclusive point of view that neuroses precipitated by battle are "caused" by war.

One's first clinical impressions in a zone of combat are that there are basic differences between war neuroses and psychoneuroses, but these early conclusions are dispelled when the same or similar patients are studied after relief from battle or return to the United States. Basically the war neuroses show the same characteristics as other neuroses and the same imperceptible gradations into psychotic states, since they represent more or less successful defenses against dissolution of the ego characteristic of a psychosis. The patients show the well known phenomena of regression, repression, isolation and dissociation. They deal with their regressive tendencies by the typical mechanisms of projection, introjection and displacement, turning into the opposites, inhibition, overcompensation and sublimation. Sick or well, every combat soldier reacts to the stresses of the harsh realities of war according to how his previous psychological patterns have prepared him, and he reacts only to the proper quantities of specific stimuli to which he is sensitized (10). In other words, in our opinion, the *neuroses of war are psychoneuroses*.

Yet there are some quantitative features common to most war neuroses that give them, as a group, an apparent distinction from all other neuroses. Overseas the fears of battle predominate as the striking, overwhelming emotion. For patients and psychiatrists, all anxieties, all insecurities, pale into nothing compared with the fiery red of the external dangers. All anxieties are rationalized on the basis of the real situation because, as the ego's span constricts, its capacity for discrimination between various dangers and recognition of their source decreases. Furthermore, the stress is so tremendous that no internal emergency response can cope with most situations. No countermeasures can destroy the external hostile forces, which in themselves prevent expression of the inner forces. The result is that the ego is beset by hostilities and aggressive reactions from without and within, and is thereby threatened with dissolution. Its self-preservative drives can only adopt diffuse and uneconomical secondary defenses to avoid the dissolution of a psychosis. For this reason, dissociations, isolations, amnesias and partial negations of the external world are adopted. But this failure of action is only temporary—there is a cushion of resiliency in those who promptly recover, and they are many. Those who continue to be ill, later perceive their experiences as significant in the light of interpretation, in the personal meaning for which they are prepared. *Thus, after the initial blow, the reaction is internalized and repetitive according to the previous patterns of the personality.*

Chronic neuroses suffered since the last war by patients observed in veterans' facilities (34), and the long-standing traumatic neuroses of civilian life, also demonstrate certain clinical phenomena which give them the appearance of being a special type or entity. As we have previously noted (26), the chronicity of these disturbances is not entirely due to neglect or failure of early treatment but is based on certain dynamic factors arising from an interaction of a particularly predisposed personality and special types of stress. Within a few days after the onset of their neuroses, these patients develop symptoms which are firmly stabilized. An explanation cannot be given which applies to all these patients, yet certain common features are observable. Their precombat personalities tend to be of the compulsive type, with much reaction formation and stubborn, rigid character. Many are psychologically incapable of dealing with even moderate quantities of hostility by any other method than repression. Yet they seem to be stimulated by external stress to develop great quantities of aggression, which they cannot tolerate in consciousness. Acting on this type of personality, as in prisoners of war, a stress which mobilizes great aggression but hinders its expression, or a stress which occurs so suddenly that the experience does not reach a conscious level of verbalization, predisposes to the development of an intractable war neurosis. The stimulated response is inhibited from attaining more than internal sympathetic activity; no external expression in words or appropriate behavior can occur. Thus the inhibited action syndrome of Kardiner (34) results. Such patients develop fixed secondary physiological responses and probably morphological changes in the tissues eventually. They suffer from repeated battle dreams, which are true efforts at mastering the trauma through action in fantasy, tend to withdraw from social contacts and show a high degree of continuous irritability. Under pentothal the release of some of their aggressions often shakes them into violent symbolic gestures or even convulsive spasms, but treatment is frequently unsuccessful.

Many psychiatrists insist on using the term "traumatic neurosis," indicating the identity of war neuroses with a type of disturbance seen in civilian life as a result of accidents, especially in industry. But there are several differences. The civilian traumatic neuroses usually occur as a result of a single violent stimulus, the latent period is short, some sort of physical injury is usually concomitant, the secondary gain is huge and socially acceptable, and ego-ideals are hardly ever in conflict with the illness. War neuroses are rarely the result of a single experience but are usually the result of many factors, including monotonously repetitive dangerous stimuli, difficult physical activity, intolerable external environmental conditions, and protracted and repeated evidences of desertion by all supporting and friendly human figures and of violent disruption of close personal ties with dead and wounded comrades. There is a long latent period before the soldier succumbs, physical injury is usually absent and the ego disruption is tremendous, often leading to severe regression and long-persisting disorientation. The illness is the stimulus for a new and serious conflict with the ego-ideal, increasing anxiety, so that removal from combat may become more secondary loss than gain (49). The anxiety associated with the illness is then less tolerable than the fear of battle. Finally, war neuroses develop after the protective factors, such as morale and the "widened ego spans," the so-called "military egos" of men in closely knit groups, have collapsed (56).

Are those who do not promptly recover on return to safety, or who become worse, truly suffering from war-induced neuroses, or are they psychoneurotics who have always been psychologically weak? In the last war 65 per cent of the psychiatric casualties were shown to have had previous neuroses, but 45 per cent of those unaffected had similar histories—only a 20 per cent difference (40). In this war, Canadian psychiatrists reaffirm the concept that neuroses of war are precipitated in men with preceding personality difficulties and maladjustments, whereas the successful combat soldier has had a relatively normal past life. Henderson and Moore (31) also state that war neuroses as seen overseas are "made in America." 30 per cent of their patients had previous head injuries with unconsciousness lasting fifteen minutes or longer, 35 per cent had previous sudden and overwhelming psychic traumata in civilian life, 65 per cent were previous nail biters and 15 per cent had been enuretic. The typical family background consisted of a sadistic, alcoholic father and a nervous, oversolicitous mother. The reader is referred to chapter 9 for a comparison with our own statistics, which do not confirm these findings.

Raines and Kolb (50) in their excellent analysis of combat fatigue and war neurosis in naval men make the following statement.

"For our purposes, then, we have established four arbitrary criteria for the diagnosis of 'war neurosis' or 'combat fatigue':

1. A stable personality prior to appearance of the traumatically determined emotional disturbance.—There should be no objective evidence of maladjustment in childhood or adolescence.

2. A combat experience of sufficient intensity to render it feasible as a precipitating agent.—The mere threat of combat is not enough to produce neurotic symptoms in men other than those specifically predisposed, i.e., the psychoneurotics.

3. Objective evidence of subjective anxiety.—The patient suffering with war neurosis does not discuss his combat experience with equanimity.

4. Recoverability.—It is our belief that all true 'war neuroses' will recover in a comparatively short period of time with even relatively superficial therapy. When symptoms persist in disabling degree beyond two months under treatment, either the treatment is not adequate, or the psychoneurosis is not simply 'combat fatigue' and has its roots in a deep-seated emotional conflict which long antedated the traumatic experience."

These authors insist on four criteria for the diagnosis of war neurosis: combat dreams, startle reaction, subtle personality changes and an irrational sense of guilt. They believe that the psychological mechanism associated with the traumatic neuroses of war are found in all men. It determines the extent of the reaction but not its content.

Braceland and Rome (6), also dealing with navy personnel, indicate that there are four gradations of response in which the psychosomatic reaction to combat may be pictured: simple fatigue and fear states, combat fatigue, psychoneurotic reaction types and psychotic reaction types. The first category is an early stage of reaction in which there is a preponderance of somatic reactions. Combat fatigue is a further stage in the neurotic evolution and is characterized by heightened irritability (including startle reaction and night terrors), overactivity of the sympathetic nervous system, fatigue, personality changes and recoverability. The categories of psychoneurotic and psychotic reactions are colored by combat experiences but are essentially the result of strong predispositions.

On the other hand, Hastings, Wright and Glueck (29) report that fliers who failed psychologically under minimal stress did not have any particular neurotic predisposition, although they were not highly motivated for combat. Studies of 150 men who successfully finished their tours of combat duty revealed that half the men came from families showing considerable degrees of emotional instability, and approximately 50 per cent of the men themselves had a previous life pattern of emotional instability. For these men, their war experiences were simply not the adequate stimuli for neurosis overseas. About half the men were extroverts; the others were introverts or rigid personalities. There was no correlation between the severity of their experiences and the intensity of their symptoms.

These quotations from the literature are sufficient to give the reader the general trend of the current controversial opinions. We believe that the opposing concepts of strong predisposition or lack of predisposition indicate restricted points of view, because they are based on an "either/or" outlook, which has been abandoned in every field of medicine, including psychiatry. Since before the days of Osler, who used the analogy of the "seed and the soil," disease has been considered as a product of activators or stimuli influencing an organism prepared to respond to them. Whether it be the tubercle bacillus or the psychological stress of battle, these stimuli, in varying quantity, can only affect organs or persons susceptible to them at the moment. The reaction to an overwhelming dose of tubercle bacilli or to only a few, or the reaction to a violent-harrowing combat mission or to only a near crack-up, depends on the preparedness of the stimulated individual to respond at the specific threshold level. We have often repeated that anyone, no matter how strong he may be, may succumb to a war neurosis if the stress reaches his threshold. In chapter 4, we have described persons succumbing to minor, less than average, stress; in chapter 5, we have described those who were affected only by severe stress. The resulting clinical symptoms were identical, with some variations in degree independent of the stress. It seemed overseas as if the content of the neurotic reaction was nearly always the same—free anxiety predominating, guilt and depression in the background. Overseas, we also considered the identity of content as an indication of the domination of stress to be the most important factor in the production of war neuroses. But when we studied the same and similar patients after their return to this country, we then realized for the first time that the real content of the neurosis was as individual as the person and his entire life background.

We shall now examine the four criteria for the diagnosis of war neurosis set up by Raines and Kolb. The criteria of a "stable personality" and absence of previous neuroses prior to the emotional disturbance are used for the differentiation between war neuroses and psychoneuroses. This revives the ghost of normality, a myth which we thought had long been buried. Stability and instability, indicating neurotic tendencies, are not innate or acquired quantities applicable to the possessor's every reaction. Stability is a dynamic momentary characteristic dependent on a specific manner in which an individual overcomes specific obstacles to accomplish certain goals. Neuroses are representative of specific failures of adaptation and are usually well circumscribed. Even psychotic reactions do not always permeate the entire personality. Stability is variable in each person's life, from time to time, depending on the quality and quantity of stress and frustrations.

"Combat experiences of sufficient intensity" cannot be measured or averaged because they are not objective, even though they seem so real at the moment. What is traumatic to one may be innocuous to another. One flier may crack up after the death of his buddy and yet be unafraid of enemy planes, while with another the reverse may be the case. The personal meaning of stress is ultimately more important than its superficial appearance and cannot be judged by a medical officer, unless he uncovers this meaning by careful individual studies. In chapter 3, we have indicated how good motivation, training and morale all combine to help to keep a man fighting. Powerful group morale may keep an anxiety-ridden person strong and brave, low morale may undermine a brave and stable person so that he becomes a psychiatric casualty, indicating that neurotic reactions are dependent on other factors in addition to stability and stress.

"Objective evidences of subjective anxiety" in the form of insomnia, restlessness, startle reaction and signs of sympathetic overactivity are usually present, but many phobic defenses are so successful in isolating anxiety that both its subjective and its objective manifestations may be absent when the flier is away from his plane. But even then he is suffering from a war neurosis.

In order to make a differential diagnosis between two conditions, whose limitations and ramifications have not yet been universally accepted, one cannot use "recoverability" as a valid criterion. Certainly the short time of two months for recovery under treatment cannot be utilized as a differentiating factor, especially when it is linked to the term "adequacy." The nonspecificity of psychotherapy and the divergent abilities of therapists are so great that the effects of treatment cannot be a test of a diagnosis.

Our experiences force us to conclude that war neuroses are reactions of persons ripe to respond in an individual manner to a particularly meaningful stress. This way of reacting is discovered, not near the battlefield, but in a safe and secure hospital in this country (cf. cases 17, 18, 19). Returnees may have persistent symptoms or may develop difficulties for the first time, yet are no different from those ill for the first time in a combat zone. To recapitulate: every war neurosis is a psychoneurosis, since the old unsolved conflicts of the past are stimulated by stress to assist in the production of a neurotic reaction and in its persistence, once it is formed.

Attempts have been made to differentiate war neuroses from psychoneuroses on the basis of the source of the instinctual trend which is in conflict with reality or other internal forces. It was suggested that psychoneuroses are due to conflicts involving the sexual instincts and that war neuroses involve man's aggressive instincts. Clinical evidence does not support this differentiation. Libidinal interests return to their early goals and undergo displacements just as do other personality functions in the process of regression. The early integration of a man into the army group, before combat, affects his love relationships because individual sexual tendencies are antagonistic to the group. The cohesive group requires inhibited or displaced tender feelings; the individual is forced to regress to an adolescent state, in which homosexual friendships and "buddy" relationships are temporarily substituted for adult heterosexuality. As regression, which is normal and inevitable in the formation of military groups, occurs, even earlier stages of direction of drives reappear. Food, love and attention are sought as a child searches for oral gratification. The soldier is always hungry and he often expresses his pleasure or displeasure in gastrointestinal language. If the process of incorporation into the group is successful, the soldier's energy is to a considerable extent displaced from his own ego to his brothers-in-arms, his leaders and the group itself. The individual is less concerned about himself and develops more altruism (20). In substitution for self love, he gains the affection and support of his group and his leaders, as well as the gratification of serving an ego-ideal which produces the warm glow of self esteem (19).

In the presence of external danger or because of a breakdown in the group unity, the soldier's interest may return to his own ego, especially when it is wounded by the psychological experiences of battle. Then self love, self interest and preoccupation with self preservation initiate the development of anxiety, which may be so overwhelming that the soldier becomes a psychiatric casualty. This is especially likely to happen if his experiences have been responsible for considerable ego regression and if his individual ego-ideal is not strong enough to substitute for the lost military superego. As if this were not enough, when his regression, which determines a new and more infantile organization of his drives, incites needs which cannot be satisfied, another painful neurotic conflict ensues.

From this discussion it becomes clear that the sexual drives whose energy we term "libido," in the broadest sense of the word, are as significantly involved in the production of war neuroses as in that of any psychoneurosis. Our experiences with war neuroses overseas and in this country have demonstrated that both aggressive and libidinal drives are involved in the conflicts, regressions, anxieties and symptoms produced by the action of stress on the human personality.

The majority of our patients in this country recognize their illness or it is detected by medical officers for the first time after their overseas furloughs or after return to duty (cf. group 3). Some of these men no longer suppress their symptoms, since their purpose of completing a tour of duty and returning home has been achieved. However, most of these neuroses are due to failures of adaptation by personalities altered by combat experiences, reacting to minor frustrations and difficulties at home and separation from their groups. The development of nervous symptoms in anticipation of new and safe assignments in the United States (cf. group 4), and the neuroses originating from difficult redomestication, illustrate the presence of a lasting alteration of the soldiers' personalities. Exposure of the underlying emotional trends by appropriate methods reveals quantities of abnormalities that cannot be considered as passing reactions to external stress. Persistent symptoms originating in combat indicate prolongation of anxiety, but the newly developed disturbances are based on new conflicts originating on return to this country. In the former group, persistence of the neurosis indicates lack of adequate therapy, marked paralysis of ego functions with regressive tendencies due to overwhelming anxieties, continued insecurity, or the mobilization of a serious personal conflict previously well repressed. It may also be due to tenacious hold on the benefits of the illness—the secondary gain. The newly developed disturbances signify the failure of adaptation to a normal environment, to new problems creating insecurity, or to a return to an old conflictual family situation by a personality altered by combat experiences.

The single general diagnosis of "operational fatigue," applied to war neurosis, does not indicate the numerous types of psychological reactions precipitated overseas or in returnees included in this category. Such vagueness has its advantages, because, when diagnoses derived from our current classification of civilian neuroses are applied, they lead to considerable confusion and misunderstanding affecting both therapy and prognosis. This has been most evident when such terms as "hysteria" are used for severe states of regression with amnesia, or when "schizophrenia" is applied to the conditions of personality dissociation. Certainly the terms "neurasthenia" or "psychasthenia" are uninformative. We have found it wisest to indicate the symptoms of the neurotic reactions rather than to label them specifically as special syndromes, maintaining more interest in their dynamic basis than their label. Almost all neuroses, overseas or at home, manifest themselves by identical objective signs and only slightly variable subjective symptoms. Therefore classification is only possible according to dynamic factors. Among returnees, we have discerned several overlapping trends, which we use as rough differentiations according to which is most outstanding, recognizing that all are usually present to some degree in every case. They are the passive-dependent, psychosomatic, guilty-depressive, hostile-aggressive and psychotic-like reactions. They are all manifestations of regressive psychological processes in that the personality has abandoned whatever maturity it had attained and retreated to previously gratifying stages of adolescent or infantile reactions.

In order to understand these regressive processes, the reader should again refer to chapter 2, in which the combat personality is delineated. The initial process of integration within the group consists in abandonment of much of the mature individuality of the civilian in order to become a part of a well organized military team (19). It means the substitution of a superego based on military standards and goals for an individualized superego. This regressive process is not all a loss to the individual because, aside from the gain to the army, the soldier himself obtains a gratification of his dependent needs from a strong father-leader, and he acquires the strength of his group and has an acceptable goal for his hostilities (56).

On this personality the stress of combat acts by increasing the regressive processes. Since there is no escape in reality from the hostility of the enemy and the authoritative pressure of his officers, when combat threatens even the strength of the group, the soldier has recourse to magical thoughts and gestures, religion and fantasy and to hope for the future based on memory of a better past. His inner psychological life is a retreat in fantasy to the safe and secure childhood past.

Some of these youngsters suffer from what we have called the *syndrome of ego depletion*. They have given, in independent and aggressive behavior, far beyond their capacities without replenishment through love and affection by anyone in the hostile world around them or even their own ego-ideals. They have overdrawn on their banks of psychic energy and are in a state of psychological bankruptcy. This also creates a tendency for the ego to break with dangerous reality and retire to fantasy, or to psychoses if predisposed by deep fixations to infantile stages of development. In this state, they attempt to rebuild a reservoir of ego strength through accretion and replenishment from others. In so doing, they resemble children in a stage of development when such an overwhelming intaking process is normal for their chronological ages. They want everything—love and attention. But they themselves love only those who give, and turn with rage on those who deprive. This marks the beginning or increase of a childish sullen attitude toward officers and all figures of authority.

These regressions are masked as long as the soldier is in combat and a part of a group. But support for endurance of the cruel reality of war by fantasies of the future is possible only in the absence of reality testing. Since these fantasies are concerned with the complete dependence remembered from past childhood and are not expected to be gratified until return home, they enter into no conflict with reality overseas. But when confronted with insufficient satisfactions at home, they are destined to involve the soldier in new frustrations and conflicts and to cause severe anxieties.

The psychiatric casualty, whose personal threshold of anxiety has been reached and whose ego has been weakened to the point of incapacity, precipitates out of his group. The soldier who has successfully completed his tour of combat duty and is sent home for a rest from battle is likewise separated from his strong and supporting group, his leader and his brothers-in-arms. Anxieties, which he had suppressed for the sake of finishing his tour of duty and returning home, now appear on the surface with full intensity. Regressive processes become unmasked and make themselves felt as powerful needs which are difficult to satisfy.

The returnee is again an individual but he is like a "lost person." Like a bewildered child in search of a group, he attempts to re-establish his position in the family as the adolescent that he was when he went off to war. But his family cannot receive him in that capacity. Furthermore, nowhere at home or in the army in the United States can he find a cohesive group as strong as that which he left, or the same type of leadership. His military exploits, as evidenced by his decorations, stamp him as a man and often a hero. Instead of returning to the passive-dependent gratification that the family has given him in the past, and this without the price of risking his life at every turn, his family put upon him more responsibilities, in fact a greater burden than he had to endure before he left home. As a result, he develops anxiety and irritability, which produce the clinical symptoms of an anxiety state identical with that of the war neuroses that occur overseas. He has no protection from the dangerous environment because all stimuli impinging upon him as an individual are treated as dangerous. The patient behaves like a child with a phobia, in that his own hostilities are projected to the outside world and frighten him in the disguise of catastrophic dreams and various illusions. He may react to this

by withdrawal into a neurotic state of fatigue and excessive
lethargy. He may react with a state of alertness or apprehension,
producing irritability, aggressiveness, insomnia and dreams of
catastrophic happenings.

He keeps in frequent correspondence with members of his old
group, searching for them at every base, and has contempt for
anyone who does not wear the ribbons indicative of overseas
duty. In groups of other returnees, he resumes a semblance of his
carefree, strong and aggressive spirit, often violating rules and
regulations with indifference, but as an individual he is a weak
and passive child. He is easily led by psychopathic characters as
well as by any others.

Since the dependence caused by regression cannot be gratified, the resultant frustrations produce conflict between the
patient's needs and reality. The result is a neurosis, dominated
by depression due to the feeling of not being loved and by
aggressiveness as a reaction to the depriving environment. This
creates new anxiety, because of fear of retaliation, and further
augments regression. In addition, the childlike position of the
regressed person makes him feel more anxious and uncertain
concerning the world, and he reacts with apprehension to the
mildest stimuli. The process once started initiates a vicious
circle.

But not all patients expose their regression so clearly in this
passive weeping and depressed state. Many show evidences that
parts of their egos refuse to accept this tendency, resulting in
intrapsychic conflicts. Psychosomatic disorders may be the only
means by which regressive tendencies are permitted expression.
Others take flight into marriage or alcoholism; some turn their
needs around and become solicitous over parents and family.
A few react to their needs by overcompensating aggressiveness,
even volunteering to return overseas. By these means, anxiety
is avoided and their needs are repressed or satisfied only by
displacement. Only under pentothal can many of the inner
trends be exposed for the first time.

The regressive reactions depend on the degree to which the
soldier's weakened ego, supported previously by the group and
an external father figure, can function alone at the behest of his
own ego-ideals. These are re-established with difficulty and he
behaves as if he had not reached that stage of maturity when
such ideals have become internalized. He is ambivalent to all.

His wounded ego searches for surcease; each deprivation creates further hostility. The army and officers come to represent the hated father standing as an obstacle in the way of his goal of obtaining mother unshared with anyone. There are no resources within himself—all affection must come from without.

The degree of regression to a state of passive dependence is related to the individual's psychological organization as well as the quantity of stress he has endured. How much is an individual fixed in a dependent attitude by deprivation or spoiling in childhood or as a secondary solution to a conflict involving hostility? In these people, regression and breaking down of displacement and compensations is easier and regression is more extensive. This can never be determined by fragments of past history, such as enuresis or nail biting, alone, but only by knowing the longitudinal pattern of behavior. The degree of regression depends to a great extent on the previous adjustment of the individual, on the quantity of immaturity coexisting in adult life and the severity of the trauma that he experiences in combat, on the disturbance created by separation from the group and on the gratification or frustration that he finds in life after this separation.

An almost universal reaction of returned combat personnel is guilt and depression in varying degrees. Normally this passes away in a relatively short time but the pathological quantities are represented in illness, frequently necessitating hospitalization. The dynamic factors involved in the several types of depression in men who have completed their combat duty include unconscious hostility to a lost comrade, identification with a dead buddy, inability to resubstitute a civilian for the strict military superego and reaction to frustrated dependent needs, which we have previously described.

Many of our patients, returned home from combat, show evidences of depression related to the death of some close companion, friend or crewmate. They blame themselves for some act of commission or omission which they hold responsible for the misfortune. In most of these cases, it is easily discovered that the loved comrade was also the object of negative feelings, which were suppressed or repressed. After the loss, the patient's conscience, interpreting the unconscious negative feelings as death wishes responsible for the tragedy, institutes a punishing attitude toward the ego. The patient must suffer the pangs of conscience for the ubiquitous ambivalence rife in any homosexual society. Self condemnation, feelings of guilt, and depression, with all its characteristic symptoms, result.

Men with strict superegos expressed in obsessive-compulsive characters most frequently react in this manner. However, almost always, studies of returnees reveal that the lost comrade has been identified with a brother or father figure of the patient's past, toward whom he has carried identical ambivalent feelings. Uncovering techniques quickly expose the fact that Joe, who was killed in battle, was only a current edition of a competitive brother, toward whom the patient had much unconscious hostility. Almost invariably the relationship between current and familial figures is the basis for the irrational sense of guilt. Insight quickly lifts the depression.

The soldier may cling to the externalized group superego as he struggles to revive his own. Thus he may still judge his behavior at home in terms of the group standards overseas and react with guilt and depression to his life of luxury, his worthless existence. On reporting for duty again, unattached and unassigned, it is then that he misses his group most, and, as he lives a life of ease and safety, unable to shake off the military ideal of his group, he reacts with guilt, probably because he is violating the standards of conduct to which he has been accustomed. He does not seem to be able to set his own superego into action for a considerable time. He judges his life, his thought and his conduct in terms of what the combat group would accept as right. In the normal case, only time is necessary for his individual superego to refunction. In the pathological case, it is necessary for a psychiatrist to hold his overseas standards of conduct up against the standards of the army in the United States and those of civilian life.

Another source of depression, less dependent on the patient's personal past, is his frequent identification with members of a strong group. By virtue of a common leader and common ideals, through experiencing danger and hardships together, a strong identification between the individual members of the group is created. A dead comrade is thus mourned as a partial loss of the soldier's self, as long as he is under the group's influence. Only when the soldier regains his own individuality after leaving the group can he lose his identification with his comrades-in-arms. This often requires considerable time for working through, and during this period various depths of depression are experienced in the process of making new identifications.

In combat, the mission of the fighter demands a stimulation of his aggressions. These he has been taught since early childhood to repress or displace, to modify for constructive purposes or to express only in sports and work. Many soldiers under the influence of a new standard of conduct, the military superego, are enabled to release their aggressions successfully in the process of killing, which is their purpose in the army. But, on returning from combat, they develop difficulties because renewal of inhibitions is not so easily effected. These men have no acceptable goal for their hostilities, no enemy to kill. They often fight among themselves for the sake of fighting, to relieve tensions, without real hostility. Others displace their hostilities to officers, civilians or the army in all sorts of rebellious expressions and behavior. Many become anxious in case they may "blow their tops" and be punished. Those superegos which in the past have been weak in dealing with aggressions refunction with difficulty, and the postcombat behavior is likely to be hostile to the point of psychopathy. It must be made clear that these patients do not belong in the category of "psychopathic personality" in our current system of psychiatric classification, although they are often erroneously so diagnosed. They become resocialized through identification with a new loved and loving father figure.

In other individuals, the excessive stimulation of aggressions required by war evokes old patterns by which the individual previously dealt with them. Our Air Forces are fortunate in that combat is impersonal and a battle of machines. But strafing of troops and bombing of factories and cities evoke serious internal repercussions. Some men, who can endure little in the way of direct expression of hostility, succumb early and become psychiatric casualties; others have a higher threshold. Stimulation of aggressive trends threatens the ego's stability. It suffers from anxiety not only by reason of forces imposed on it by the enemy, but by reason of its own unacceptable aggressions, which overburden the ego and increase the regressive processes.

Overseas the soldier has been able to deal with previous neurotic aggression and phobias based on projected hostility owing to the facts that combat rationalized them and furnished reality for the phobias and anxieties. The punishment of enduring combat also helps the aggressive individual with a sense of guilt to express his hostilities. Neurotic solutions of such conflicts become rationalized and socially acceptable to a fighting group.

Because the end result of so much aggression would be an overpowering of the ego, and the loss of hold on reality through the development of a psychosis, the danger from internal aggressions is great. The ego attempts to deal with the problem by a host of old techniques (18). None of these are entirely successful because they produce neurotic compromises but at least they preserve the ego's grasp on reality. All these methods are seen in our returnees. Some soldiers project their aggressions to external objects, creating fear of them. But although this makes for more aggression and more anxiety in the future—a vicious circle—it at least gets rid of the need for the ego to deal directly and immediately with the tremendous load of aggression, for which it is unprepared. Paranoid reactions or obsessive behavior may be used for a similar purpose. In many, guilt is produced which forces the patient to search for sources of punishment. If a well functioning superego persists, depression will result.

Aggressions in returnees are usually directed against superior officers and many tales are told of how officers have been cowardly, afraid of combat or unfair. In some cases a nucleus of reality does exist, but for the most part the soldier's reaction carries with it a high degree of emotional displacement. He is like the little child whose reaction to the cruel fate of tripping and falling over a chair is to look up and blame the first human supporting figure who failed him with, "See what you made me do!" The whole weight of hostility directed in combat toward the enemy, deriving its energy from repression of ambivalent feelings toward officers and comrades, is now released toward them directly. No longer is there a good father figure, the commanding officer, and a bad father figure, the enemy, but there is only one father figure, the superior officer, who must bear the brunt of the hostility of the regressed soldier.

The relationship to the brothers of the group was one of extreme altruism and everything was share and share alike. Hostile feelings toward individuals were so well repressed that antisemitism or antagonism to representatives of other minority groups was at a minimum overseas. The returned soldier is selfish. He thinks only of himself and has a revival of prejudices and other rationalized antagonisms.

In the process of regression, the individual reverts to a psychological stage which existed prior to the internalization of authority as an automatic check on behavior. The re-establishment of his own effective inhibitions is difficult and he responds only to external praise and punishment. If he is gratified and feels secure by virtue of receiving constant affection, all goes well, but, if deprived, he freely expresses toward figures representing authority his aggressiveness against the external world. The patient behaves like a child easily provoked to rage attacks. His internalized superego seems unable to re-establish even its past weak status, once it has been abandoned in favor of the combat group standards.

Because of this multiple source of anxiety, such therapeutic techniques as desensitization are ineffective, since they cannot lessen anxieties originating from the person's own aggression and, especially when the ego has already regressed, they make the patient worse. Simmel (56) during the First World War used straw men, officers in effigy, in an effort to release blocked aggressions with the approval of an externalized superego. In modern times, the same result is effected by narcosynthesis, during which the patient verbally expresses his displaced aggressions and at the same time gains insight into their origin. The patient may attempt to reproduce the anxiety situation in fantasy in a repetitive attempt to effect an adequate discharge. The soldier may search for stimuli in an effort to release motor expression by provocative behavior, or, avoiding collision with the outer world, he may attempt this mastery in sleep by means of dreams. But these are usually catastrophic nightmares that awaken the patient with terror. Anticipation of these experiences often causes the soldier to avoid going to sleep. These horrifying dreams are usually concerned with an airplane accident, in which the patient is about to be destroyed. In less serious dreams the patient is an onlooker at some tragic happening. These dreams do not always reproduce specific past experiences, but, whatever the pattern, they tend to be monotonously and exhaustingly repetitive.

A soldier completely cognizant of his environment and well in touch with his reality seems at night to be drawn back into the dangerous situation of battle. The process of sleep seems to reduce the ego's control over anxiety and certainly reduces its ability to discriminate reality from fantasy, because these nightmares are very vivid and real to those who experience them. The classic explanation offered for their repetitive appearance closely follows Freud's formulation, advanced in his work on the repetition compulsion. He stated that these dreams were an effort on the part of man to master or bind the anxiety situation. It is a process similar to that seen in children who play "peeka-boo" as a game by which they endlessly reproduce separation from the mother in an effort to master the anxiety arising therefrom (21).

However, these patients are not interested in mastering anxiety in the fashion that the psychiatrist thinks best. They and many nonmedical officers, to our sorrow, feel that every effort should be made to forget and dismiss from their minds the old harrowing experiences. They have to be persuaded and some-times forced to recount their experiences for the therapeutic purpose of desensitizing them. But when lying on a bed alone or when shutting their eyes, or in sleep, the present world of reality disappears and against their wills they are drawn back into battle. Fantasy, hypnogogic hallucinations or dreams carry them back involuntarily to the harrowing scenes of yesterday.

When we come to analyze the meaning of the dreams in relation to the current neurotic reaction of the patient, we find a definite personal significance in these catastrophic nightmares. They cannot be dismissed as a general technique to master anxiety. In our case reports we have indicated the special meaning of these dreams. Punishment, projected hostility, anxiety in relation to a current situation, are among a variety of meanings. A depressed patient, who castigates himself because of a huge sense of guilt, dreams of himself in a flaming ship; a passive-dependent youngster, feeling rejected, dreams of jump-ing out of a falling ship without a parachute. Anxiety in relation to his first sexual relationship is followed by dreams of explosion of a plane in midair. Innumerable examples of such personal individual interpretations of these dreams could be given. The proof of their correctness is indicated by the fact that, when the correct interpretation is given to the patient and he develops insight, often overnight, he not only gets well, but stops dreaming of catastrophes. If mastery of anxiety due to sudden overpower-ing traumatic stimuli were their cause, they should disappear only gradually with time.

Why are these nightmares of combat re-evoked in reaction to a personal problem not particularly concerned with combat?

Combat experiences overshadow any other catastrophic episode in man's life, and hence are more suitable than any other means to symbolize dire and severe punishment, whether this be in response to overly strong instinctual drives, or to discord between one's ego and superego or between the ego and the world of reality. Catastrophic battle dreams thus persist as long as punishment dreams are necessary and they recur whenever this trend is revived. We can expect that many years later new conflicts, evoking the need for punishment, will revive battle dreams. Then it will be safer to revive past trauma as punishment for current crimes than to face the contemporary possibilities of punishment.

Patients who show psychotic-like disturbances as a result of battle casualties are not infrequently seen overseas, especially among ground troops, who endure the greatest stress. The psychotic quality is imparted because a greater quantity of dissociation of the personality has occurred. The entire emotional and intellectual experience of a particular event or of a whole segment of life may be isolated from consciousness, or the feeling and cognitive aspects may be split from each other. Yet even in these amnesic, often mute, terribly fearful, severest reactions, there is no qualitative but only a quantitative difference from the more common patterns of war neuroses.

In this country, the psychotic-like syndromes are milder and consist of states of paranoia, severe weakness of the ego in its faculty of discrimination and reality testing, and certain types of severe aggressive or depressive behavior. These too represent quantitative exaggerations of normal reactions and respond fairly well to therapy. Their dynamics have been adequately illustrated in chapter 14. Like the other types of neuroses, they indicate no special biological weakness but a specific manner in which a particular personality reacts to a special stress. Like all war neuroses, they are temporary regressions, which can for the most part be undone by adequate therapy.

To summarize the dynamic trends illustrated by the war neuroses observed in returnees, we have found that they are regressive in nature. The clinical syndromes are variable, depending on the special methods by which an individual deals with his conflicts. But behind every entity are various degrees of dependence and hostility, which are uncovered by regression and then come into conflict with frustrating or repressive reality, or with opposing forces of the personality. The resulting symptoms include, in various combinations and degrees, the clinical pictures of any type of psychoneurosis and are themselves no more than the effects of the conflict. Integration into a combat unit, the stress of combat, the frustrations on return home, all expose the universal core of mankind's difficulties with the psychological representations of his biological drives. His experiences destroy whatever maturity or neurotic compromises he had made between these drives and reality and between their opposing trends. The soldier is forced to resume earlier, less adaptive, apparently more gratifying, regressive compromise solutions, but these turn out to be uneconomical, painful and subject to frustration. In the course of time most veterans re-establish their previous maturity; others need psychiatric help.

CHAPTER 16

Treatment: Psychotherapy

In MEDICAL TERMINOLOGY "psychiatric treatment" and "psychotherapy" are often confused and erroneously used interchangeably. Psychiatric treatment involves the entire medical approach to the patient suffering from a mental or emotional disorder and includes such procedures as psychotherapy, narcosynthesis, rest, sedation, activity, hydrotherapy, occupational therapy, shock treatment and continuous narcosis. When somatic disturbances are severe or have already crystallized into morphological changes, adequate medical treatment is necessary to complement the psychiatric treatment, the total constituting a psychosomatic therapeutic approach. Furthermore, it must be realized that therapy may be unsuccessful if long-continued anxiety establishes and fixes a new general physiological setting or induces irreversible changes in the neuroendocrine system.

According to Kubie (35), "psychotherapy embraces any effort to influence human thought or feeling or conduct, by precept or by example, by wit or humor, by exhortation or appeals to reason, by distraction or diversion, by rewards or punishments, by charity or social service, by education or by the contagion of another's spirit. This broadest possible use of the term would also include the temporary lift of spirit through music, art or literature.

"Simple psychotherapeutic expedients may be grouped under three main headings: (a) Practical support—consisting primarily of advice, guidance and assistance in the management of life situations and environmental difficulties through social service aids, etc.; (b) emotional support—consisting essentially

368

of sympathy, exhortation, admonition, encouragement, humor, art, recreation, companionship, etc.; (c) reorienting education —consisting primarily of efforts to alter the patient's habitual attitudes of guilt, fear, hate and depression, by educating him to tolerate his own conscious and unconscious needs and cravings, his instinctual hungers, his familial jealousies and hates, etc."

The first two are homely, nonspecific, commonplace procedures, employed by every wise teacher and parent in education. They must be tried first, especially when emotional disturbances seem precipitated by severe external stress. When these fail, the rigid repetitiveness of behavior is due to the fact that the spark of environmental stress has been adequate to touch off an explosion from unconscious internal forces. Then, simple rational methods fail and scientific psychotherapy is required.

The simpler procedures of psychotherapy require no scientific methodology and can be employed by commanding officers, friends, chaplains and the unit medical officer. They require human understanding and sympathy for people and their needs, which may include firmness but never sadism or intolerance. In the early stages of breakdowns overseas, and in the mild reactions after return home, simple procedures should be tried first but, if unsuccessful, should be given up quickly.

In discussing psychotherapy overseas we have indicated that in the early stages of the ego's struggle with anxiety the Flight Surgeon, who fills the role of the family doctor, serves to bolster the ego's defenses. This is accomplished by identification of the flier with the therapist's strength as he encourages, persuades and gently, but firmly, forces the ego to exert greater pressure on the welling-up anxiety. This is often successful in keeping the largest number of men in combat for the longest possible time; hence it has military significance. For the individual, it increases the cumulative strain on his ego and keeps him in a situation which automatically stimulates more anxiety. The breaking point is simply deferred to a later date. Those who believe that the external stresses of combat are the sole sources of neurotic reactions consider that there is no great harm in keeping a soldier under stress for the longest possible time, since at any time, when he is relieved, his anxiety will cease. When we see many men return to this country and enter hospitals for psychiatric care long after they have left the fight, when we see neuroses become overt only after return home, when we see breakdowns due to the maladaptations of altered personalities as they meet the simple problems of adjustment to life in the United States, we know that this concept is erroneous. The cost of so-called "shell-shocked" war veterans of the last war in money, crippled lives and broken homes, and the unfortunate effects on their children, are effective illustrations of the permanency of war neuroses, unless they are treated adequately and early. Although we must conform to the military needs, we should also know their consequences in future suffering.

If it is our task at home to strengthen the ego to control and bear anxiety, it is predicated that we are content to permit the springs of anxiety to continue to activate that danger signal and to continue to demand from the ego countermeasures. When we study our cases carefully, we find that the process is not stationary. Anxiety often increases with minor stimuli, such as ordinary domestic difficulties, or even spontaneously. At best an equilibrium is reached between the opposing forces in the personality. But this requires an expenditure of energy on the part of the ego to hold anxiety in check, which impoverishes its productivity and capacity to deal with other problems. The result is a crippled personality, as we see it in the obsessive-compulsive neuroses and the phobias of civilian life.

There is only one logical conclusion: in so far as possible and expedient, the unconscious sources of anxiety should be unearthed and ventilated, and the ego permitted and educated to deal with them rationally and economically.

Psychiatric therapy for combat veterans in this country likewise depends on the severity of the neurotic reactions and the degree to which personal unconscious forces are involved. Those who were unsuccessfully treated overseas and were sent home for rehabilitation obviously require treatment by scientific methods, employed by a trained psychiatrist. Among those who first develop symptoms after return home are many with mild and temporary reactions of insecurity to their repatriation and redomestication, and countless numbers with anxieties in anticipation of future difficulties at reassigned duties. Most of these mildly ill patients do well with group inspirational therapy, techniques of indoctrination and a sound convalescent program, as described in chapter 18. The greatest problem that they pose is their selection for this type of treatment, since evaluation of the degree and depth of illness is not possible by a superficial survey (cf. chapter 9). Therefore, they must be observed psychiatrically during their convalescence, so that mistakes in classification may be quickly corrected (45).

Before methods of scientific psychotherapy are discussed, its goals must be clearly understood. In the military setting the purpose, as commonly stated, is to erase from the soldier's mind the deleterious effects of his combat experiences. We should like to return the soldier to the condition in which he entered combat, so that he can readapt himself to a socially valuable life (24). To avoid perpetuation of dependence and the permanent feeling of illness which qualifies him for lifelong benefits from the government, we should like to rehabilitate the soldier in the framework of the army, so that he can be demobilized with pride, as one who finished his job. This may mean future assignment where intolerable strains are not imposed upon him again. It may mean return to civilian life in which previous adaptation was successful and where it will again be possible.

No matter how severe may have been the stimuli that precipitated the neuroses, the effect is not like the writing on a slate that can be erased, leaving the slate as it was before. Combat leaves a lasting impression on men's minds, changing them as radically as any crucial experience through which they live. Some learn and mature; others fail and regress. No matter what the effect, there can be no erasure because the experience acts profoundly on the individual's personality, causing significant alterations in the direction toward which his previous trends had prepared him.

What then are we able to change or what do we wish to change? Primarily we want to undo any process, initiated by the man's personality in dealing with psychological traumata, that has blocked his learning and directed him into regressive channels. If he has converted his anxiety into a physical symptom, if he has paralyzed a sensory system, such as sight or hearing, in an attempt to avoid perceptions that stimulate anxiety, or if he has isolated the ideational or emotional memories of combat, we want to undo these processes, because they cripple him for productive efficiency and for successful adaptation to a healthy life. If he has abandoned a mature and adult attitude and regressed to an earlier, one-time adaptive, childish position, if his stimulated aggressions create anxiety and set into action uneconomical defenses, or if his ambivalences have evoked disastrous superego punishment, he will continue to be ill unless properly treated. It is thus not possible to remove the effects of combat without encountering the soldier's conscious and unconscious complex character structure and neurotic patterns. Far from being dangerous, it is essential for successful therapy to revive some of these old conflicts in their new setting, providing this is done with skill.

In therapy we must analyze the new accretions to the old behavior patterns. Demonstrating the link between the new and the old is often followed by considerable improvement in the clinical state, as the patient becomes aware that his behavior had no essence of weakness or cowardice but was his "blueprint" of conduct. It is not possible to deal with these connections without exposing and altering the old repetition compulsions. In the words of Kubie (35): "It is not merely the recovery of an event which releases the patient, nor merely the recovery of the event plus the feelings and desires which derive from that event. It is the discovery of the totality of the purposes, the hopes, the fears, the loves and the hates which animated the individual at the moment of the event, plus what that event did to those purposes, loves and fears and hates, and how these were deviated by that event from their initial pathway onto another. This, and not less than this, is the potent discovery." The art of treatment of war neuroses consists in dealing with the new reactions without mobilizing the old to the point of stirring up emotional conflicts with which there is no subsequent time to deal. We must avoid any procedures that will harm the patient.

In the military services, brief psychotherapy is not only relatively brief in comparison with such long term procedures as psychoanalysis, but it is truly brief in intensity and extensity (25). Overseas in the rest camps or exhaustion centers, psychotherapy is minimal, consisting at best of a few words, most of which are uttered in groups. The psychotherapy consists largely in attitudes and example. In station or general hospitals in quiet areas, psychotherapy, although still brief, is composed of considerable group and some individual attention, consisting of narcosynthesis and short interviews, when necessary. For returnees with war neuroses, psychotherapy is brief because of the large number of patients and the paucity of trained personnel available for treatment. Fortunately our services have too heavy an investment in their flying officers and enlisted men to brush off war neuroses lightly as expected losses among expendables. Therefore, we have had the opportunity to work with an optimum doctor-patient ration (1 to 35), but nevertheless our allotted time is limited.

In the army in addition to the difficulties of time we have the problem of motivation. In civilian life patients go to the psychiatrist because they are ill and unhappy and they are willing to suffer the anxieties liberated by treatment for the sake of feeling better. The reward of cure for the soldier is return to battle or to duty; the reward of recalcitrance, which is a sort of superimposed malingering, is separation from the service and return home. It is clear that psychiatric therapy of members of an inducted army depends on the inherent ego-ideals of the individual patients and their motivation of the moment, which fluctuates considerably with attitudes of the public around them. This is one reason why the prognosis is so much better among flying officers than among enlisted men, who have no aspirations after military careers.

It is often helpful to indicate the steps of therapy in stages but this serves only a pedagogical purpose. Psychotherapy is scientific, yet must be accompanied, as in all branches of medicine, by art or skill derived from experience, and a certain unconscious knowledge, on the part of the therapist, that may be called intuition. Therefore the list of procedures should not be considered as representing separate maneuvers, for they all blend into each other and may go on simultaneously even at a single session. They are schematized in the following list and will be discussed separately in detail.

1. Establishment of doctor-patient relationship (transference).

2. Support, and gratification of the patient's weakened and regressed ego by means of tenderness and attentive interest, and furthering of identification with the therapist's strength.

3. Release and uncovering of isolated, repressed and suppressed emotions, memories and conflicts (abreaction).

4. Direction of attention from external rationalizations toward the patient's own inner feelings. Development of insight into the relationship between psychological reactions to combat, the past behavior patterns and their derivation, and the contemporary symptoms.

5. Decrease of severe superego reaction which has produced guilty feelings because of an actual, or a sense of, failure, or evoked punishment for repressed hostility or other ego-alien tendencies.

6. Desensitization from the memories of the anxiety-producing situations by repetitive recounting of traumatic experiences, as the therapist helps the dependent ego to discriminate between past danger and present safety, and between the world of reality and inner anxieties.

7. Re-education of the ego to more effective methods of compromising between inner desires and the obstacles of reality. Encouragement of the ego in its attempts to regain mature attitudes and adult activities, thereby giving it new confidence, and building up of self esteem on the basis of recognition of past performances.

8. Revival of support and pressure from a strong group, and competent leadership.

9. Testing emotional and intellectual insight and working through the relationship between present and past attitudes.

10. Posthospital follow-up, advice and encouragement.

We must list the dangers inherent in brief psychotherapy, especially as performed by beginners, who should be constantly under control and supervision by competent psychiatrists, and in the army situation:

1. Too much mobilization of emotion or ancient conflicts without available time for handling them adequately.

2. Acting out of mobilized trends in asocial conduct.

3. Too much gratification from a parental transference— resulting in spoiling for future army duty.

For detailed accounts of psychotherapy as applied to individual patients, the reader is referred to cases 19, 28, 29, 40, 41, 43 and 59.

The first step in therapy is to establish a *transference relationship* with the patient. He arrives in the ward with a record of a complete medical study and a brief case history including the story of his nervous difficulties. The taking of a detailed psychiatric history is not assigned to a social worker or a psychologist, because history taking is the first step in establishing a personal relationship with the patient and is the first major operation in treatment. History taking, diagnosis and therapy are not separate steps in psychiatry. It is true that a portion of our histories must be filled out according to the standard form necessary for any large institution, to insure that all the necessary data are obtained. Specific information is always contained in a certain part of the record and the whole is easily readable for future research purposes. But the actual psychiatric history is unfolded by the method of association; the patient leads the way and gives freely of himself as the material comes to his mind. The temporal relationship between these facts as they are recalled constitutes valuable clues as to their significance. The entire story unfolded in an unchronological fashion may take several sittings but this makes for a saving rather than a loss of time. The tyro in psychiatry has a tendency to break up important associations by questions based on his curiosity or on his compulsion to elicit longitudinal histories in chronological order. The young psychiatrist has an abhorrence of silences in interviews, when in reality they constitute important stimuli for the patient's progress. The trained psychiatrist is relaxed, without anxiety, with no compulsion for activity in therapy. He listens carefully in a friendly manner to every detail of the patient's account and notes every omission or blocking in his story. The psychiatrist avoids making premature interpretations or too satisfying reassurances. Unsatisfied tensions within the patient are strong forces for the patient's continued associations between his appointments with the physician (62).

The psychiatrist is the one man whose main concern is the individual soldier as a person and not as a cog in a tremendous machine. He represents to the neurotic soldier the nearest approach to that for which his whole sick being cries—in the throes of his devastating anxiety—a kindly, interested parental figure in sharp contrast with the authoritative, demanding voices of his officers. Therefore transference relationships have obviously infantile dependent characteristics, which the therapist encourages by his sympathetic interest, his assumption of complete responsibility for the patient's progress. At this stage he supports and comforts the patient, who, convinced that the whole world is hostile, accepts the support only provisionally. But the soldier's need is so great that he soon leans heavily on the psychiatrist. The transference relationship is less easily established when ego strength is less altered, in the hysterias and psychosomatic disturbances.

As a rule the transference is achieved quickly. In the American army there is little awe or inhibiting discipline in the relationship between doctor and patient, even among enlisted men. The medical officer's rank is not very important, especially in the Air Forces, where the soldiers are accustomed to regard the Flight Surgeon as a friend and advisor. Assisting in the establishment of a positive transference is the fact that our staff consists mostly of doctors who have been overseas and have experienced similar hardships and frustrations. It is thus also easier for the patients to verbalize hostility toward military men who have not yet gone overseas.

When the transference starts as a negative feeling in an irritable, sullen, withdrawn individual, we have learned that this patient usually suffers from considerable repressed hostility, is the type that early becomes fixed in an intractable state and has a less favorable prognosis for recovery. Often there is considerable resistance on the part of the patient to unburdening quickly, especially when he has come to the hospital with a negative and uncooperative attitude in order to get a discharge from the army. In such cases he does not want help and treatment is resisted. He may even try to demonstrate the seriousness of his maladjustment to the army by deliberately aggressive attitudes, violations of regulations or excessive drinking. He may include the medical officer in his negative feelings toward all persons in authority.

The medical officer's attitude toward his patient, his *counter-transference*, is of prime importance in influencing the character of the transference. The general medical officers have all had special training in the treatment of "operational fatigue" and know that they must uncover emotional difficulties and not attempt to cover them up or dismiss them with fine, high-sounding reassurances. Yet the process of identifying with the patient in his attitude toward difficulties and frustrations in the army is a great danger, often causing the physician to lose his objectivity. The patient who wants to be separated from the service may meet one of two emotional attitudes in his doctor— "Me too!" or "I have to stay in, then so will you!"—rather than the objective attitude that is proper, difficult though this may be to maintain. Our medical officers' own personal problems often create blind spots before their eyes. Chief among the difficulties which they encounter are the patient's antagonistic feelings, a negative transference, at the beginning or during the course of treatment. The physician often reacts emotionally and with retaliation to aggressiveness on the part of his patient, and does not see this material objectively for the purposes of understanding and analyzing the hostile attitudes of the patient toward authoritative and father figures. We have found it necessary to determine the special types of cases each doctor is able to treat successfully, even relieving him of the care of certain patients when transference difficulties occur. Although, as we shall explain below, transference interpretations should be avoided, negative attitudes must be interpreted early or therapy will be blocked. The patient must be made aware of the fact that his hostility to the kind physician is an irrational derivative of a feeling displaced from some other object. He should be quickly directed to the source of his hostility and to an analysis of this feeling in relation to that source.

The initial interviews are as bland and unprovocative and free from interpretations as possible. Transference interpretations are explanations of the patient's feeling for the therapist, which stimulate his insight into the nature of his feelings toward similar figures of the early family life, their subsequent imagos and most recently some person within the combat group. These, most often, are parental figures and their successors. A positive, usually dependent, relationship should not be interpreted early, if at all. It is the catalyst by which the patient is enabled to spill his suppressed emotions, gain strength within his ego and slough off the severe military superego of the combat group. Such a transference is only the subject of interpretation and analysis when regressive, dependent attitudes are overwhelming, when they must be made conscious in order to initiate self-respecting ego forces into opposition or at the termination of therapy. It is astonishing what a startling improvement is effected by gratifications within the transference relationship of the patient to the doctor. Understanding, patient attention and a modicum of tenderness often are therapeutically successful without a single interpretation. It is as if the boys had forgotten that people could be anything but hostile. A successful relationship with the doctor revives memories of the past and stimulates hope for the future, especially in those boys whose ego depletion has been profound.

Gratification of dependent needs is of course begun in the initial interviews, and is carried on during pentothal treatment and in psychotherapy afterwards. It is the basis of the transference relationship. Gratification of dependent needs is more than a trick to hasten transference feelings. As anxiety reaches consciousness, the source of anxiety becomes apparent in every incident, every story and every reaction of the patient. He demands support and comfort as he tells how he was deserted by every semblance of a protective, supporting or kindly figure. Officers, other soldiers, friends and buddies all suddenly became impotent in the face of the ever present enemy fire and activity. He was an isolated individual in the darkness and all interpersonal relations were violently torn asunder. True, we see the automatic emergency reactions to danger in reality—the defensive movements revived under pentothal—but these subside and the infantile cry still resounds. True, we see a semblance of rage as, with clenched fists pounding on the bed, the soldier screams at the Nazi bastards and what he will do to them. But these are displaced hostilities. His major anger is at his leaders, who were unable to protect him and support him when he needed them most.

We do not deny that some patients' anxieties are signals of distress because of intense activation of their unacceptable hostilities or that in many patients the emergency mechanisms stimulated by the external dangers became excessive and overpowering to the ego or failed to decrease as the danger disappeared. But in the vast majority of cases the source of anxiety was a feeling of desertion, of being left alone like a child in a dark room with the door shut and no human voices audible. It is now apparent why so much gratification and affection must be given these men. They have given far beyond their capacities and the overdraft on their psychic banks must be replenished before they are able to return from their regressed psychological positions. However, temptations to reassure the patient too greatly must be resisted if he is to cooperate in uncovering his unconscious conflicts. This requires a certain amount of tension, which activates the ego in its task of looking inward for the source of its pain. Often the patient is reluctant to talk about himself or his experiences, saying, "All I want to do is to forget." He is then reminded that for a long time he has tried unsuccessfully to forget, and that nevertheless disagreeable symptoms have developed. "Forgetting is only possible by first remembering, because you then know what you really have to forget or what problem you have to solve. You can't fight an unseen enemy."

Remembering often discloses to the patient that he is trying to fight something he did not even know existed—an unsuccessful shadow boxing. Yet the confronting of the patient with the problem in its fullest extent should not be premature.

As the patient unfolds his story freely, we hear the *release of emotional attitudes*, projected to convenient realities—the well known process of rationalization. These attitudes must be confronted by the actual reality. Unfortunately the nuclear truth to the rationalizations is often large, since in the tremendous organization of the armed forces countless mistakes must occur, and errors of omission and commission by others are often the cause of accidents that kill or maim close friends. The universality of these experiences and attitudes is explained. Comparison is made between the patient's reactions and those of others to the same realities. The patient is urged to uncover the real and personal sources of his feelings and for this purpose pentothal treatment is usually given to effect an *abreaction* (cf. chapter 17). In this procedure unconscious, suppressed, repressed and isolated material is made conscious.

Release of unconscious tensions is mainly concerned with the emotion of anxiety, the excessive quantity or the persistence of which is the nuclear problem of war neuroses. When the ego has been able to ward off successfully the overpowering subjective aspects of anxiety by the formation of conversion or phobic symptoms, resistance to conscious re-experiencing of anxiety is too great to overcome in a short time. When the personality has regressed in the face of the onslaught of anxiety, there is often too little ego remaining to establish contact with the therapist and cooperate in therapy or to endure the anxiety during the reliving of the precipitating stress. Therefore, in most of these cases, for quick results we must have recourse to the method of narcosynthesis, which will be described later. Without going into the psychophysiology, the observed effects are the reappearance of ego functions, revivification of free anxiety and loss of somatic symptoms of conversion and of excessive automatic excitation.

After the abreaction has been started and the patient has come out of his narcosis, he is forced to review the material in a conscious state. However, this is not always necessary, for insight may be reached and learning established by the unconscious ego. Conscious verbalizations are not always necessary to indicate therapeutic benefits. As he repeats his guilts, his hostilities and his desires after narcosynthesis, these are again and again tested with reality.

Recognition of the temporal and spatial present is a process which goes on rapidly up to a certain point under pentothal, but the final orientation in severe cases is slow and beset with relapses. In patients who have regressed and exposed the dependent and aggressive cores of their personalities, return to more mature attitudes, after ventilation of these trends, is tenuous and not firmly established for some time. Phobic and compulsive defenses are relinquished as long as the psychiatrist furnishes concrete evidence of his supporting presence. The patient looks through the therapist's eyes at a world here and now, which is devoid of danger, but these are only borrowed eyes. The process of learning that the world is not entirely hostile is achieved at first by an identification with the therapist, and the patient's ego span and strength are increased as he borrows the strength of the psychiatrist. This is done initially through powerful and persistent suggestion—later by rational interpretation of each and every apparent stimulus to regression. Thirdly, time is necessary for the patient, at first with the therapist's support, to test the human environment's sincerity. Here our troubles are great, for the army is not conducive to such testing. Many soldiers react to relatively mild rebuffs and rejections with such intensity that severe cases may assume the status of paranoid trends. This phase of therapy is the same as for children whose early lives have been filled with real rejections and who require patient handling and time for testing a new reality.

In *testing realities* against the patient's irrational feelings, the psychiatrist's own experiences play an important role. It is hard to understand the intimate details of a combat organization unless the psychiatrist himself knows the physical, administrative and emotional setting. Hence, for the treatment of returnees, psychiatrists and ward officers who have been overseas have a great advantage. The technique of reality testing is not forceful nor argumentative. We do not insist that the patient accept our realistic point of view; we suggest to him that his guilt, hostility or anxiety is not based on things as they really are. It may take several interviews before he grasps these facts. As he does, both the patient and the therapist realize that a question now confronts the patient: "Why then do I feel that way?".

At this point, the patient's attention is spontaneously directed *toward his own inner feelings*. This is encouraged and sometimes firmly insisted on by the therapist. Actually the soldier himself brings out the relationship between the current neurotic reaction and the past pattern of behavior. These connections are pointed out to the patient in sharply etched interpretations. This gives an initial relief because he then realizes: "I don't react this way because I'm weak, yellow and unable to take it—it's because these experiences are like what happened before and I react as I did then."

At the same time as emotional insight between past and present is beginning to be established, attention is paid to *superego attitudes* especially their severity, insincerity and anachronism. A transference relationship of tenderness with considerable gratification permits the therapist to give to the patient the liberality and reality-adaptive ideal of conduct and thinking of the nonmilitary superego through the process of identification. Without this loosening of his ego-ideal the sick person cannot continue to face his hitherto unacceptable drives, which he had rejected from consciousness. There is in this procedure an inherent danger, the release of trends which are acted-out in overt behavior. Sometimes severely aggressive attitudes, alcoholism or infantile behavior is lived out in the hospital and outside. The therapist must exert greater control on such activities in the army than in his civilian work, because release from superego pressure is not compensated for by the automatic pressure of the civilian environment.

Many patients with considerable hostility are terribly anxious for fear that they may "blow their tops." Some with guilty feelings are writhing under the strict and sadistic lashings of an irreconcilable superego. Many with dependent longings cannot permit themselves to understand their cravings because of a harsh standard of ideal adult conduct. The hostility of the superego is one of the principal forces that harass the ego and weaken it. Every patient suffers in varying degree from a sense of failure, most severe in those with strong overcompensations and those who endure anxiety for long periods of time. As long as the superego maintains its identification with the dead and living friends on the battlefield, it will remain angry and demanding. Often the ego-ideal stems from a father who carried on valiantly in the First World War, and return home in a condition of neurotic illness becomes so painful a thought that many demand to return to the battlefield as a displaced suicide attempt. As the psychiatrist hears these underlying drives expressed directly or indirectly, in conscious interviews or under pentothal, he receives them with a bland and neutral attitude or even volunteers his acceptance of them as normal or understandable. In the successful outcome the regressed personality identifies with the therapist and substitutes the latter's superego for his own. On the basis of permitting and accepting trends alien to the patient's superego and rejection of his rationalizations, the psychiatrist pushes the patient on to further work in the process of understanding. By identification with the therapist and appropriate interpretation, depressions recede and the patient sees himself as one who did the best he could and often better than might have been expected, and as one who still has a valuable function in the army.

As the process of therapy continues, the conflict is clarified. The opposing forces involved and their real meaning become clear. Ideally these should be understood in three phases: (1) the conflict as it is expressed in the combat situation, (2) the same conflict in the childhood past (rarely in the original setting) and (3) the conflict as it rages in the current situation. A fourth edition of the problem as it is played out in the transference relation is skillfully handled by psychiatrists, but rarely so by our general medical officers, no matter how well they have been indoctrinated. The following example clearly illustrates different phases of the same conflict. A regular army soldier entered the hospital because of anxiety based on hostility to members of his crew who, although recent inductees, seemed to get more praise and rewards in the form of decorations. As an orphan he had been brought up by an older sister but had left her home when her children displaced him in her affections. He reacted violently in the hospital when another patient was given a privilege denied to him. It is not necessary to clarify insight concerning the old by delving into its primary source. One does not need to uncover the earliest infantile memories in which a particular psychological pattern seemed to originate. A few screen memories from childhood are sufficient. When these and the current trend become clear, it is then that transference feelings can be understood to have the same pattern and to recapitulate the identical mechanisms. They may then be safely interpreted.

Throughout the therapy there must be a constant but gentle pressure on the patient to recapitulate his traumatic experiences in conscious verbalizations. This serves to *desensitize the ego* from its painful memories and permits it to gain complete mastery of the past. Gradually the span of its grasp on the past and its capacity to endure its recapitulation are widened. Eventually the patient is able to remember trifling and amusing incidents that happened in the combat group and the vision of his experiences in retrospect becomes an amusing adventure. At that point mastery has been achieved. But this is a late process only effective after successful abreaction, strengthening of the ego and weakening of the superego. It is impossible in the state of severe regression. Animal psychologists also recognize that, before deconditioning against traumatic incidents is possible, the animal needs much affection and support (39). Therefore, desensitization as a process in itself is not adapted to therapy of regressive neurosis. Only the reconstituted ego can be reconditioned and then needs no technique, such as records or movies of combat, nothing except repeated recounting of its own experiences.

Mobilization of unconscious trends, after the patient has substituted the physician's superego for his own and thus eased the repressive forces of his ego, is only one aspect of therapy. After unconscious conflicts have been made conscious, the ego still has to solve them. No good is accomplished by letting the boy know that he has strongly dependent regressions, unless he gains insight into their uneconomical effect, their anachronism in view of his age and the fact that regression is no longer necessary in view of the relief from external pressures of combat. The ego must be prepared to deal with these trends in a new manner. This is indeed a difficult task, hindered by secondary pain, which the ego senses at every turn. It is a process of *re-education*, through identification with the therapist, partial persuasion and an introduction of the patient to his own assets and past achievements. It is a slow process, requiring much working through and testing, so that it can only be initiated while he is still in the hospital.

By working through the soldier's rehabilitation in the framework of the army itself, dependence on family and government pension can be reduced to a minimum. In the severe anxiety states, however, dependent trends may persist with great obstinacy. This is particularly the case when the patient refuses to recognize or to accept the significance of his dependent needs. In many patients, in whom anxiety or depression, or both, continue far beyond the period when the ego should have begun to assume control, it becomes clear that the continued helplessness has a concealed purpose. Whereas initially the ego has considerable justification in regarding itself as injured and unable to cope with the environment, after prolonged exposure to a protected environment such justification no longer exists. The persistence then is due to the attempt of the ego to bribe and appease the demands of the ego-ideal. The ego says, as it were, "This is what you have done to me. I stuck it out to the limit at your behest, until I was broken and maimed; now I am weak and helpless, and in no state to return to duty. You must forgive me because it is not my fault." Thus secondary gain of illness becomes acceptable.

In many cases, especially when regressive forces have succeeded in permeating behavior, authoritative *pressure and support* may be necessary. The patient *will* go back to duty and obey regulations. Mild but definite punishments are meted out for flagrant violations of the rules (cf. case 53). The external pressure must be fair and calculated to instill confidence that good conduct is rewarded but that asocial behavior is frowned on. The punishment must be fitting for the crime, swift and equitably distributed. In no other manner than by fulfilling promises sincerely can the patient's new superego be one that fits the patient to adjust to civilized reality. We wish not only to clear up the patient's inner conflicts, his intrapsychic processes, but also to clear up his conflicts with reality. To this he must learn to adapt.

A subsequent period of *testing and working through* is allowed in the hospital, when the patient is given more freedom, and perhaps furlough or leave. He is permitted to work only in the convalescent program and to see his doctor less often. Many times we ourselves are not sure of the result and test the patient by a return to a trial of duty.

We recommend an appropriate duty status, such as full flying status or grounding, on the basis of the degree to which the ego has been able to attain mastery over internal anxieties and the capacity of adaptation to reality. The adequacy of the new job and its capacity to maintain the soldier's motivation are important in preventing his relapse. Our recommendations specify the general type of occupation, geographical location and altitude. Specific therapeutic recommendations are made to the Flight Surgeon at the next duty station and progress reports and questions are received from the doctor at regular intervals. The patient himself is asked to write periodic personal letters to the doctor at the hospital. It is surprising how well this correspondence bolsters up many men during the initial trying periods of a new assignment. This is valuable *posthospital therapy*.

Group Psychotherapy

As we discuss the procedures employed in individual psychotherapy, it becomes apparent that the time necessary for the treatment of the large number of sick soldiers requiring it and the paucity of experienced, capable medical officers available preclude their universal application. These patients need more than recreational and occupational therapy, yet there is not time enough for individual treatment of all. For this reason *group psychotherapy* has been suggested and widely employed. A negative motivation for instituting a form of treatment does not portend well for its results, since success in therapy depends not only on the physician's skill but also on his enthusiasm. Treatment of groups requires knowledge of individuals gained from long experience in dynamic psychotherapy. By personality, disposition and habit, psychiatrists who have been accustomed to dealing with patients individually do not usually feel comfortable with groups, while personalities who feel expansive and at home with groups are usually insensitive to individual feelings.

Many procedures applied to more than one individual have masqueraded under the term "group psychotherapy" (61), when in reality they constitute "group therapy". These have ranged from lectures on neurophysiology, motivation, fear and geopolitics to careful analytic work directed to common disturbances of the constituent individuals. Merrill Moore has divided methods of group therapy into two divisions. By far the greatest number are of the repressive-inspirational type. Their basic principles are to urge, persuade and force the patient to control himself, to suppress asocial or worrisome thoughts. Interest or inspiration in life work, the community, religion, art, music, etc., is encouraged. At the other extreme is the analytic method. This urges the loosening of repression and freeing of urges bound up in repression. It strives for the conscious recognition and analysis of unconscious and asocial wishes and trends. Unlike other methods, it makes no attempt whatever to direct the patient's activities toward specific goals. It maintains that, once energy is freed, the patient will himself find suitable social outlets. Many men using group psychotherapy have utilized both the above methods in combination (54, 59).

Dealing with groups has a positive value in that the group more nearly approximates the state of the human being in his natural surroundings, as a gregarious animal seeking a satisfactory niche in his social setting. His inhibitions and repressions are motivated by the mores of the group, and his difficulties in adjustment and failures to express his emotional troubles are partly the results of his ability to conform to what he thinks the group demands. Place this person in a small group that is friendly toward him, composed of fellow sufferers, and eventually he will be able to express his aggressive tendencies, his hates, his loves and his wishes without an accompanying sense of guilt. By working out his problems in a small group he should, theoretically, be able to face the larger group, that is, his world, in an easier manner.

War Department Technical Bulletin 103 states that group therapy has advantages over individual therapy in dealing with suspicious, hostile and guilty feelings, and minimizes personal feelings. Its disadvantages are that individuals may get out of hand, liberate too much hostility and acquire new symptoms through suggestion from others, which are real and important dangers. It is suggested that groups be homogeneous, patients being seen individually first and then in groups of from 7 to 25 individuals, meeting three to six times weekly for about one hour. The first few sessions should be devoted to general explanations of guilty feelings, hostilities, insecurities, etc., and subsequently individual symptoms should be discussed.

Rome indicates the advantages of group therapy in military installations as follows:

1. The similarity of symptoms relieves the therapeutic burden of any one individual.
2. Tensions based on feeling unique are dissipated.
3. Stigma is ameliorated.
4. The doctor-patient relationship is eased.
5. Emotional release is controlled.
6. A too penetrating analysis is controlled.

7. Individual sessions may be added, if indicated.

8. A twenty-four hour schedule avoids undirected lulls.

9. Monotony is avoided.

There can be no question that the patient acquires a feeling of oneness with the group and recognizes that his symptoms are not unique, hence anxiety related to his being a particularly sick or unusual person is relieved. However, the factors which are indicated in items 4, 5 and 6 are sacrifices which we have to make to group therapy, not advantages. The ideal setting is a close doctor-patient relationship (transference), resulting in an adequate emotional release and an analysis, penetrating enough to relieve the patient of the current edition of his neurosis and to relate it to his past pattern of thought and behavior.

When the group psychotherapeutic techniques used in military hospitals are reviewed, we find that they have several real advantages. They reincorporate the individual into a group similar to one in which he lived and worked and where he felt strong and secure. The whole group can be reassured and given rational explanations regarding symptoms that they learn are not their exclusive burden. Common group experiences are valuable in dealing with irrational guilty feelings. Everyone can be desensitized to dangerous stimuli of combat, to which all were originally exposed. However, extensive unburdening of personal problems or personal reactions cannot be accomplished. Wender (61), from the experience of his extensive civilian practice, states that individual psychotherapy must be carried on in private interviews during the course of group treatment. Patients are unable to accept individual interpretations directly —these must be given obliquely by hypothetical statements. We have found in our own work that, when the patient really has personal problems to expose or develops transference attitudes which stimulate anxiety, he spontaneously seeks out the therapist for an individual interview. Actually not much time is saved.

Military group psychotherapy becomes a matter of expediency, based on time and goal. With sufficient therapists, who can be obtained by a special training program for general medical officers, the goal of therapy is the only criterion. If it is desired to lift the personal load of emotional reaction to combat and free the man to the state of his precombat personality, only individual therapy is rational. The use of the same principles of therapy in small groups saves little time. If all that is desired is merely an outward appearance of unstable normality, group therapy can achieve the goal. For patients who are mildly ill, group therapy suffices, providing care be taken to separate the severely disturbed from the group as their condition becomes apparent.

· · · · · ·

We are extremely optimistic regarding the outcome of rational psychotherapy applied to the war neuroses. The responses to therapy of patients in our own hospital have been the basis of this conclusion. Yet how can these results have general applicability when trained personnel is so difficult to obtain? Even many psychiatrists are unable to carry on treatment, having spent their lives in administrative work or acting as custodians in state hospitals. Our needs must be filled by the general medical officer, the general practitioner of the army. But he must be trained to know what he is doing and not, in a fog of confusion, use irrational or unscientific methods destined to harm the patient or delay his recovery.

CHAPTER 17

Treatment: Narcosynthesis

THE INDICATIONS for the use of pentothal in the treatment of returnees are largely concerned with time. In almost all cases the same material and the same emotional release can be obtained by psychiatric interviews while the patient is fully conscious. This has been adequately proven in our work with large numbers of patients. In the brief period available for therapy in the military setting, the uncovering of anxieties and conflicts and the production of adequate abreactions require the aid of some short cut to overcome resistances. Since the military psychiatrist is short of time for individual treatment, sodium pentothal is frequently utilized for the diagnosis and treatment of our patients.

It is difficult to specify definite time relationships for the administration of pentothal. Like every other part of psychiatric procedure, timing is a skill or art based on the therapist's intuition or "feeling" for the particular problem. As a general rule pentothal should be first used only when the utmost has been obtained from the conscious patient—when the physician feels that the pathogenic material is not conscious and knows from experience that the subsequent insight will take a large amount of time. When resistances occur, pentothal may be used at that point. Probably only half of our patients require the drug.

The technique of administering the drug is the same as that employed overseas (26, 27). A 2.5 or 5.0 per cent solution is slowly injected intravenously until the appropriate stage of narcosis is reached, while the patient relaxes quietly on a couch. The quantity varies for each person. More is necessary when the patient is anxious or tense, but the usual dose varies from 0.3 to

0.5 Gm. Rapid injection frequently results in failure, for the patient may go to sleep quickly and awaken suddenly, passing rapidly through the optimum stage just between sleep and awakening. Alcoholics require excessive doses, rarely have a good response and cannot remember what transpires, so that drinking is prohibited at least twenty-four hours before the treatment. The patient is given the drug until his counting aloud ceases and he begins to take deep, stertorous breaths. A trifle more is then given. The needle should be held in the vein until it is certain that the patient has reached and maintains the proper responsiveness. If not, more may be given in the midst of the interview.

Under pentothal the various forces within the personality seem to dominate the trend of associations at different times. A patient may start talking in an overcompensatory aggressive manner, denying fear, and only later break down into a weeping longing for home and mother. He may begin by expressing superego self-punishing attitudes, followed by unconscious hostile feelings toward a comrade for whose death he blames himself.

The depth of the narcosis may determine which part of the personality is concerned in the responses, very similarly to the way in which various aspects of dreams are related to the depth of sleep. Our experience, however, indicates that the time under narcosis is a more important factor, since the deeper levels of the personality speak later in the pentothal interview after resistances are overcome, even though the narcosis is then lighter.

No patient is given pentothal treatment without adequate preliminary interviews, until a good grasp is obtained of the factual material regarding combat and past life, or until a good transference relationship has been established by the physician. The patient is given a crucial verbal stimulus to start him talking, one that deals with a traumatic experience or, if possible, a situation associated with his emotional disturbances. Sometimes a specific harrowing mission is chosen to start up his associations. Actually the beginning is not too important, for the patient will eventually talk about his important isolated memories and emotions.

The best method is to start the patient talking and let him continue uninterrupted in spite of associations leading him far from the subject of war. He should be urged to continue if he hesitates to recount severely traumatic incidents or if he blocks by repeating, like a broken record, details preceding a crucial experience. If silences last too long or if the patient seems to have gone to sleep, he may be stimulated anew. In other words, resistances occur under pentothal as well as in the conscious state and the therapist must put the patient under pressure to overcome them. Psychiatrists accustomed to the method of free association, and not disturbed by silences, have no difficulty in following this method. Younger medical officers cannot endure silences and in spite of frequent admonitions break into the patient's stream of thought with questions directed by their own curiosity and associations. This is not good technique. Especially is this true for returnees, in whom the relationship of combat experiences and past life is so important for subsequent therapy.

There are certain specific differences between the results that we obtained in this country, working with returnees, and those previously reported in the battle zone. They may be enumerated as follows:

1. The material is frequently recited in the past tense, although, when the emotion becomes intense, the patient not only speaks in the present tense, but also vividly lives out the situation with all the excitement and tenseness of that time.

2. The patient is often fully oriented and aware that there is a doctor in the room, to whom he sometimes directs his remarks. In the height of emotion this fixity to the environment is lost and he acts as if he were in his plane, the doctor becoming the copilot or another gunner.

3. The abreaction is achieved with much more hostility, when present, than we ever heard overseas, where fear dominated the material. Here, the hostile resentful attitudes toward specific individuals, especially officers, and toward the army are freely expressed.

4. The material is not restricted to combat situations or scenes, but associations from the patient's past, his childhood, his family life and the current life setting are freely intermingled. The relationship between combat stress, interpersonal problems, past difficulties and current problems clearly indicates their dynamic ties.

5. Quantitative values of interacting trends can be estimated as they are expressed in the same session. The relationship between regressive dependent needs and self-respecting ego forces and even overcompensations often becomes quite clear as the different portions of the personality are expressed in associations.

Likewise, hostilities and superego punishment because of guilty feelings may appear clearly in relation to each other.

After the pentothal has worn off, the patient is pressed to recapitulate, while conscious, the material which he abreacted or remembered while under narcosis. He frequently states that he cannot remember what he has said but with pressure most of the associations can be recalled. In many cases no urging is necessary. For other patients gaps in the material must be filled in by the therapist to the astonishment of the patient, who surprisedly asks: "Did I say that?" It is often necessary to give pentothal more than once, sometimes three and four times, when there is a great quantity of buried material. Sometimes a single treatment is completely effective. We often use pentothal to verify our impression that nothing more of importance is repressed or isolated, or to discover the effect of therapy on the underlying attitudes and emotional trends.

We have stated many times that the emotional expressions evoked under the influence of pentothal must be considered usually as an abreaction, which is rarely curative in itself but is the necessary beginning to the attainment of insight. Subsequent interviews, interpretations and "working through" are necessary in almost every case. For this purpose the patient should be able to remember, or to recall to memory by persuasion or forcing, at the same session or at later interviews, his emotional abreaction. Otherwise the episode has been only an eruption or explosion of tension, which is certain to rebuild, and it is therefore of only temporary benefit. For this reason the faculties necessary for memory or recall must be intact. Abreactions spontaneously lived through under alcohol are nontherapeutic, as we have learned from our patients who, while drunk, explode terrific hostilities in neighboring bars. For the same reason, the method of using ether to facilitate abreaction has no lasting value. Ether or alcohol narcosis may make the patient more susceptible to hypnotic suggestion, but not to insight.

It was not the property of inducing an affective abreaction that led to the use of the term "narcosynthesis" to describe the effect of pentothal. It was the fact that under the influence of the drug and during the process of abreaction, although not fully conscious, the ego, devoid of the stress of anxiety, synthesizes some and often much of the important isolated and pathogenic material into its main body. It is as if the emotions or the memories had been separated from the active ego forces as in a hysterical dissociation, because they had been too threatening to the ego's stability or productive of terrifying and unendurable anxiety. Under pentothal the ego can accept the relatively smaller doses of anxiety, decreased by the sedative effect of the drug, especially since the emotions are not primary but "relived." The ego is supported by the therapist and his strength (transference), and under the quieting effect of the sedation does not react to the emotional reliving as if it were so very dangerous. For all these reasons the ego-alien abreacted emotional experiences can be synthesized and reaccepted by the ego. It is as a result of this phenomenon that certain patients after a single session under pentothal, followed by very little or no interpretation, and apparently amnesic for their abreaction, make a complete recovery in that they lose their symptoms and feel well again. Examples of this may be seen in cases 30 and 34 of chapter 11 and case 61 to be described.

But narcosynthesis is not only the process of recapture by the ego of alienated ideas and emotions. It is also the synthesis of related feelings that have been separated by the process of dissociation. Thus, under pentothal, hostility and fear may be recombined as derivatives of a reaction to the same stress. The patient becomes aware that his anger is due to his being left unprotected in a fearful situation.

The intravenous use of barbiturates for the purpose of obtaining information from schizophrenics, especially of the catatonic type, was first described by Bleckwenn (5) in 1930 and Lindemann (38) in 1931. They used sodium amytal, which produces narcosis slowly but with long-lasting effect. After the effect of the drug wore off, the patient would relapse into his previous state and usually sleep for several hours. Gradually sodium amytal came to be used extensively for many psychiatric conditions, such as amnesic states and malingering, and in retarded persons, who found it difficult to verbalize, for the purpose of obtaining information of value to the psychiatrist. Sodium pentothal has only the advantage of faster action of shorter duration, so that the interview may be continued in the conscious state when the patient awakens. He does not have to sleep or to continue dangerously uncontrolled associations for several hours and can get back to his ward alone or continue his activities without more attention.

At the present time, aside from the method of narcosis therapy (continuous sleep), the use of intravenous barbiturates is dignified by three different terms: narcoanalysis, narcohypnosis and narcosynthesis. Each of these denotes a specific goal of the therapist using the drug. Narcoanalysis brings to verbalization, while the subject is partially asleep, repressed material which it is otherwise not possible to obtain quickly (63). In this manner of functioning it is also a diagnostic procedure (cf. cases 20 and 21). These memories may be expressions of ideas previously forgotten and isolated from associated conscious emotional feelings, or they may be emotions related to conscious ideas. The process of remembering the emotions is usually violent, or at least dramatic, and has been termed "abreaction."

The British, especially Sargent (52, 53), use intravenous pentothal to induce what they call "hypnoanalysis" or "narcoanalysis" (33). This is a chemical hypnosis in which the patient does not give vent to buried material, but in which the therapist induces strong suggestion for cure of the patient's disability without uncovering or working through the etiologic psychodynamisms. Although the method of drug administration may be identical with that in narcosynthesis, the psychiatric technique is quite different. The only resemblance between hypnoanalysis and narcosynthesis is in the use of sodium pentothal.

This subject cannot be left without a brief discussion of hypnosis and its relation to narcosynthesis. We cannot make any statements based on experience, because in our capacity as army psychiatrists we have not yet felt free to use hypnosis in view of the public's misunderstanding of the method and its association with nonmedical theatricals. We can only make comparisons with the work of others. Hadfield's (28a, 42) statements, however, require answering. Our patients are hardly ever afraid of "the needle." Contrary to his statements, pentothal properly used is more frequently successful in causing abreactions and removing amnesias than hypnosis. There have been no accidents with the use of pentothal in hundreds of cases, and, with the small dosage necessary, never any toxic effects. Hadfield unfavorably compares pentothal and subsequent free associations with hypnosis and association, stating that the drug is a "crude though sometimes necessary assault on so sensitive an organism as the mind, and, in spite of its abreactive value, often leaves the more basic moral problems unsolved." This criticism we cannot answer because we do not understand the differences between the assault of pentothal and hypnotic transference, nor do we know what the writer means by "moral problems."

On the other hand, after studying the work of Fisher (16) and Brenman and Gill (7), we believe hypnotism, when performed in the manner of inducing abreactions and effecting adequate synthesis, is of no less value in therapy than narcosynthesis. But we do not subscribe to the hypnotic technique of treating symptoms and forcing their disappearance by strong suggestion. The use of pentothal to induce a hypnotic trance and to suggest the disappearance of symptoms is equally objectionable and is not rational therapy when lasting effects are desired.

This brings us to the question of the source of the material brought forth in pentothal abreactions. Is it unconscious, preconscious or suppressed? It is all of these. We elicit material that the patient knows and struggles to keep secret from himself as well as others. Preconscious material, subject to recall but temporarily forgotten, is also brought rapidly back to conscious memory. Unconscious, isolated or repressed material comes freely to the surface. This is usually directly exposed, but is sometimes disguised, as in associations during psychoanalysis, or for that matter even in dreams. As long as there is an ego functioning during a state of wakefulness, sleep or partial narcosis, unconscious drives will be expressed with some degree of distortion. They always need interpretation in the light of their symbolism, associations, temporal connections and a host of other factors. However, so undistorted are they in narcosynthesis that the therapist is aware of their meaning and the patient also is often able to interpret them correctly without knowingly doing so. This work of the ego is part of the process of synthesis.

Under pentothal the associations of the recent traumatic experiences, the past personality and early experiences of the patient are clearly brought out. Infantile memories are not reconstructed nor are they desired. Our task is to alter quickly the undesirable effects of war. At the same time a sufficient mobilization of old patterns enables a beginning to be made toward a fundamental personality reorientation in the light of recent life experiences.

The reader is referred to examples of narcosynthesis described in detail for cases 19, 30, 33, 34, 40 and 41. The following report illustrates a narcosynthesis in which a psychological and somatic reliving took place.

CASE 61: *Narcosynthesis during which the visceral concomitants of severe reaction in combat were repeated.*

This patient suffered from subjective anxiety, insomnia and loss of appetite. The details of his history need not be recapitulated for our purposes. The psychiatrist, after inducing narcosis, said: "We are south of Rome. The enemy motorcycle is on the road. Tell me what happened."

"I came down. We split up into twos. We saw the Jerry truck on the road. We started to strafe them and then just before the rendezvous, I saw this motorcycle driven by a Jerry racing for town. I went down, strafed him and then leveled off above the trees. Then I got hit. It came in the right side of the cockpit. It made me lose my senses. I must have been out for a second or two. Then I came to. I was going to get two Jerry trucks on the road, but when I got hit I thought I was a goner. I pulled back on the stick and got up to about 6,000 feet. I was going to bail out even though I was over enemy territory. I didn't like it. I looked at my rip cord but it was shot in two. It was terrible. I felt like I was going to faint."

At this point the patient complained bitterly of pain in his abdomen, stated that he felt like vomiting and began sweating profusely; his face was a green-grey color; his pulse was nearly 150 per minute, and its volume was very poor. The therapist turned the electric fan on him and told him that the canopy of the plane was now open and that he should breathe deeply—that that would make him feel better. The patient exclaimed:

"That's better, that's much better now. I can feel the wind in my face."

Within a few minutes the sweating abated, his color returned, and his pulse improved in volume and became slower. The patient, for two or three minutes, had presented the picture of a typical peripheral circulatory collapse.

"You're much better now—you're not going to faint. What's happening now?" he was asked. The patient then replied that he was heading back to the airfield but was not sure that he could make it. He told in the past tense how badly he was bleeding from his numerous flak wounds, how cold he felt and how much pain he had. He then described how he tried to get his wheels down, but failed and had to make a crash landing. "I saw the crash truck. They put me into an ambulance. I was covered with blood and I hurt all over. They x-rayed me and sent me to the operating room and gave me ether. That made me feel good. I woke up early the next day in a hospital bed. Two days later they operated on me again."

At this point the patient was told that he was making a splendid recovery and that in a short time he would recover completely from the accident. The therapist told him that his combat experience, in which he distinguished himself so well, was now behind him and that he was in a safe place where he would be given every opportunity to recover before returning to duty. The patient said, "I want to go back to duty. I'm crazy about flying. I wish this had not happened. I used to be so much stronger than I am now. I see fellows as tall as I am who are built so much better. I used to be like that."

The patient entered the office two days later, smiling and enthusiastic. He stated that he felt very much better and expressed eagerness to fly at the earliest possible moment. He was asked to what he attributed his sudden improvement and he said, "I think that injection you gave me the other day helped me a great deal. Since then I feel very much less nervous. I've been sleeping like a log and positively eating like a pig."

This pentothal narcosynthesis was one of the most dramatic reliving phenomena that we have seen. The patient actually went into a state of "shock" with peripheral circulatory failure as he relived the experiences of being shot during combat. The material at first was expressed in the past tense, was interrupted by a "living through" and was ended in the past tense. That synthesis was accomplished without interpretation is evidenced by the striking improvement shown by the patient at his next interview two days later. The patient made a complete recovery. This history indicates that synthesis by the ego of a dissociated fear of death, sufficiently complete to effect a cure, need not be accompanied by conscious insight. It is not necessary for the patient to be able to express verbally what he has learned. Learning occurs just as surely at an unconscious level.

. . . . . .

The next case demonstrates an adequate abreaction, but recovery was effected only after subsequent psychotherapy.

CASE 62: *Pentothal interview with considerable emotional abreaction of hostility in a very brave man.*

"Tell me about your ninth mission."

"Lt. Jones got it by our own bombs. They knocked his wing off. He was a nice fellow. He was a good friend of mine. Shot down because that s— o— b— Colonel kept us over the target fifty-six minutes. He didn't know a g— d— thing about combat. There were 1250 ships in the sky. Out of our own, 12 were lost. The dirty b—d. We were flying 12,000 feet. We were riding around in circles. We lost our target and flew fifty-six minutes over the target with our bomb bay doors open. Then I saw Adam's ship. The right flag on his bomb bay doors was down. We dropped our bombs. I was anxious to get rid of them because we were hit. Jones got it then. He slept next to me in the barracks, a nice fellow. He was burning in his parachute. I knew before he got halfway down that his 'chute would be all burned up. Then we were attacked at 12 o'clock—six 109's and one 190 came in. Joe (pilot) called me up; I reassured him; I told him I had a bead on them. One after the other came in. I must have shot over fifty rounds—they missed us in the first attack but then they got our no. 2 engine. Then they started coming again, the German b—ds; they came again and I poured again. Another ship went down and then my guns jammed and I was in the nose. I tried to charge the guns. We had six ships in the element, three were already shot down, but one boy was on his first mission. Joe was just a kid, but he was a man. He was the chief of that airplane. He yelled at Al (copilot) if he got too tight. Al was only 21. My guns wouldn't work—'John, John,'—no answer. The g— d— Germans had shot out our communications. John was in a fog, with that look of fear on his face. I asked him to help me with the guns. He couldn't move; he was paralyzed. I charged the guns myself. The Germans came again. My gun wouldn't shoot. The top turret stopped firing. He couldn't take the gun off; I finally did. The Germans came in. Joe wasn't flying; Al had taken over. No. 1 and no. 2 engines were out. I kept my head against the 2 inches of glass dome. It wouldn't stop marbles. We got six attacks like that. I was amazed I wasn't killed. One b—d hit the glass; it shattered all over my face, cut me up—I thought I was dead. Al gave power to the two good engines. There was no power on either side. We turned over on our back and went into a spin. I couldn't get out of the turret. I was working our guns all the time. Then the bell rang to bail out. I needed help to open the back door. I told John to help me. He couldn't, dirty b—d. It wasn't his fault. He was in a daze. I told John, 'Get your 'chute.' He was sitting down. I couldn't get past him. I had to crawl over him and get his 'chute and put it on him, all the while we were spinning. I put my own 'chute on. John and I never got along. I told John, 'Jump.' He didn't move. Then I threw him out. Then I got ready to jump. I looked up into the nose of the ship to see if I could see the pilot or the copilot—I couldn't see them. Then I jumped. It was an ordinary feeling, my 'chute opened. I held on to my rip cord, almost broke my neck when I opened it. Then I looked up to see if the 'chute had opened and I saw our plane coming down on top of me. I struggled like a crazy man to get out of the way. The wing tip hit the top of the 'chute and collapsed the 'chute. I thought this was it, but then like a miracle the 'chute opened again. I was glad because I was braver than John. I landed and looked up and saw fellows floating out of the ships. I landed in the woods, hurt my back in the middle of a forest. I got up and called to Joe and Al, but no answer. I started to walk. About 200 yards from the plane I heard people shouting, then I saw Germans coming toward the plane. I took out my wallet and ripped up the pictures of my mother and father. I was afraid of these Nazis. I had £16 in English money. I couldn't move because they were guarding the plane. That night I went toward the plane—it was sitting like a big bird, and an ugly stench came out of it, the smell of dead people. Then I made my way down to the village. No one could see me. I sneaked up to a house. A farmer came out. He had a wizened look. He grabbed for my wings but I didn't have them on. Then I showed him my identification tag. He gave me cider and eats. Then he took me a mile from his house and stuck me in a stable. He didn't come back. The next day I waited until night. I was dirty and I was hungry and miserable and I went back to his house. I was finally picked up by the organization. They gave me a bath and a shave. I was seen by an English spy, who certified that I was an American flier. Then we were sent to Paris. I stayed with a schoolteacher. One day we were having coffee in his living room and two German M.P.'s came in. We were scared but the Frenchman used his head; he invited them in for coffee and introduced us as his friends. On the way to the border a Gestapo agent sat next to me on the train. I was in Paris for six weeks. The g— d— planes began to bomb Paris then—almost every night they bombed us."

Even the words without the expression of intonation, lost in writing, indicate the intensity of this Lieutenant's feelings under stress. He behaved bravely and efficiently even though anxious. Most of the emotional expression was one of hostility against the poor leadership and the weaker members of the crew. The patient attempted to save John at the risk of his own life, although John and he never got along well. From this abreaction the patient was able to synthesize many of his repressed fears and hates and to become conscious of both, but subsequent interpretations and working through were necessary to relieve him of depression and anxiety.

.   .   .   .   .   .

The next case reveals the relationship of a specific incident to the formation of the symptom.

CASE 63: *Pentothal treatment unearthing the relationship of a specific incident in combat to a conversion symptom.*

A 23 year old Sergeant was overseas for ten months and completed fifty missions. The second mission was very difficult; on it he lost two good friends. He developed nightmares and dreams of combat but he stifled his desire to see his Flight Surgeon. He entered our hospital depressed and restless with no interest in anything, complaining of a peculiar black spot before his eyes in the shape of a plane. The patient was worried about his future and scared of flying. He had a phobia for flying with green crews.

Under the first pentothal treatment he told about a difficult raid and then complained that his eyes were burning. He told about his brother in the marines and his buddies who were killed. A great deal of envious hostility toward the brother was loosened. Following is the second pentothal abreaction:

"I'm goin' over Bremen. We've knocked out of formation. We lost an engine going over France and one engine over the target when the fighters hit us.

"I'm no good—throw me out. I can't see. We're still over Bremen. Something happened. Something in front of my eyes.

He's going to crack. He's going to crash into us." ("Who?") "An ME 109. Get the hell out! Just get out of his way. George, you'd better come back and take over for me." ("Where are you going?") "Gettin' the hell out of here. I'm no good. I can't see a thing. I can see a little now. They're coming in again. There he goes, George. There go the pieces. Flames. There's more of them. Wish I could focus my eyes. That flak. Something just blew. The whole tunnel's apart." (The patient's eyes were troubling him from their first mention.) "They blew all the plexiglass out. My God! My eyes are leaving." ("Don't you have your goggles on?") "Yes! I'll get them on as soon as I clear my eyes. We'll never make it back today. We won't get to London after all, George. There's one coming after you, George. He just peeled off. They're coming in low—watch me, Gus. Fred, look out—there're ten of them lined up. Oh my God! My eyes are O.K. now, Doc. I can see as good as ever. I thought I was going blind. That burst was too much for me. I suppose I'm going to be grounded now, g— d—. My hands are O.K., George. Doc said I'd be grounded for three weeks. Here's your ship—it's all shot to hell but we got 'er back. Hope we don't have to go over that place again. Three times is too much.

"Whoever said a B-24 couldn't get back on two engines. I've got thirteen missions, fellow. We just got back on two engines. Tell him, George. Tell this ignorant s— o— b—, George. I'm one of the original crews. You get the air medal for five missions. I got thirteen. Now go peddle your s—t somewhere else. Don't scare these green crews. Let me hit him just once more, George. When he gets a few under his belt, he'll wise up.

"You know, George, my eyes never cleared up. I see spots and think they're fighters but when I aim at them they're gone. I don't trust them any more. I'm no damned good now. Sure, I know guns. I can't pick out fighters. What the hell good am I? I'll get on another crew. You guys are too far gone to bother with me. O.K. I'll sleep it off and we'll talk about it tomorrow. You're stickin' your necks out. You're a swell bunch of fellows or you're crazy. O.K. Good night."

The patient was asked about his blind spell in an effort to determine the cause. Although the plexiglass was blown out, it was doubtful whether it injured his eyes. The patient had a definite feeling of guilt about this, blamed himself and worried about whether or not his eye trouble would come back again.

The fact that he was tail gunner made him worry for the safety of his crew even more. He told nobody about it. "I shouldn't have done it. I was afraid to go to the Flight Surgeon after that and tell him I was scared."

The next day the blind spell was discussed. The plexiglass that blew out apparently did not touch the patient. He worried about his capacity to carry on as a tail gunner and was afraid to tell the Flight Surgeon that he was scared. The incident happened just as an ME 109 made an attack on the ship and patient was afraid it would crash into him. He said that since then he had had a "spot" before his eyes which resembled a plane. The Flight Surgeon had told him it was probably a piece of flak. When he realized that the scotoma was related to fear of the attacking enemy plane, he lost his depression and became interested in his surroundings and active in the convalescent program. He also lost his visual difficulty and was returned to flying duty.

The peculiar conversion symptom of spots before the eyes that looked like planes was found to be related to a specific threatening incident in combat. This was fixed in his mind by the unwise treatment by his Flight Surgeon. Yet the patient within himself knew of his conflict based on fear and felt depressed because of his sense of failure. Rapid recovery ensued after the relationship between the stimulus and the symptom was discovered. Subsequent psychotherapy allayed the patient's depression.

. . . . . .

The following cases demonstrate the discovery under pentothal of old etiological conflicts which were stimulated by combat.

CASE 64: *Pentothal-induced abreaction, indicating the relation of guilt to unconscious current and past hostility.*

A B-25 pilot flew forty-eight missions in combat. After the death of a friend, Lt. Graves, he anticipated disaster and became fearful of flying. He felt very guilty about Graves' death, for this pilot had taken his place in formation when he was forced to turn back because his gunner had shot out the tail. Since this fatality, the patient frequently dreamed he was going down like Graves. He developed insomnia, restlessness, tenseness and marked claustrophobia for staterooms, elevators, etc.

The patient was anxious, fidgeted and attempted to minimize his feelings, but admitted the claustrophobia, which had developed after thirty missions. He began to feel very uneasy when the seat in his plane wouldn't move back and he was afraid he couldn't get out if necessary. At the end of forty missions he went to a rest camp and got stuck in the elevator. On his return home he became panicky on the boat in his stateroom below deck, and later in automobiles and at movies, as well as in pullmans. He had to take his wife with him because of the need for her protection.

Under his first pentothal treatment, he discussed some of his harrowing experiences, during which he saw some of his friends shot up, after which he developed considerable anxiety. He cried while under the influence of pentothal but objected to the therapist pointing this out to him, saying that he never cried. He said that he even flew two missions with a severe abdominal pain, which turned out to be an acute appendicitis, for which he was operated upon. He indicated that he had to be sure that people didn't think he was a sissy. Graves' plane was shot up because he was in the patient's position. Several missions afterwards, the patient found his seat jammed, couldn't find things in their places, fumbled and seemed confused.

Under the next pentothal treatment, he described how Graves went down. He was tearful again, saying, "Those b__ds will pay for it," as though he were promising that he would avenge him. It seemed as if Graves could not get out of the plane and he frequently dreamed that Graves was struggling in his seat; he thought his own phobia was connected with this accident. When his feelings of guilt were held up to the light of reality, he began to improve and could ride on elevators and attend a movie without difficulty. It was pointed out to him that he identified himself with Graves struggling in his seat because of his strong guilt feelings and he was urged to talk about his relationships with Graves. He began to indicate certain critical feelings about Graves, who was first pilot or "big dog." The patient stated that he had to catch up with him in his missions because of the time lost having the appendectomy, therefore he flew every possible mission despite the Flight Surgeon's warning that he was overdoing it. He always compared his score with Graves; he was envious that his friend's number of missions indicated that he was going home sooner. After Graves' death he couldn't accept the position of an element leader because of his feeling of guilt related to competitive feelings. After these interpretations the patient's claustrophobia disappeared.

He then brought up considerable material about his feelings toward his father and how he had a sense of relief when his father died because then he could be independent. His competitive feelings toward his father were brought out in connection with the same feelings toward Graves. He remembered that his father always told him when he was teaching him to box or do things, 'Now, don't be a sissy." It was pointed out that he was stimulated by his father along masculine lines beyond his capacity, which brought into conflict the desire to be protected by his father. He remembered that his father used to say to him, "Always try to be a man."

This patient had developed several very restricting phobias, which were spreading rapidly. Under pentothal he abreacted freely and disclosed a conflict between his dependent trends and a strict standard of conduct imposed on him by his father. Furthermore, hostility to the pilot whom he mourned with irrational guilty feelings was found to be a derivative of earlier ambivalence toward his father. The patient was discharged back to duty.

· · · · · ·

CASE 65: *Reconstruction of amnesia by pentothal and exposure of an old unresolved conflict restimulated by combat.*

A 29 year old B-24 gunner had completed twenty-five missions, including the first Ploesti raid, his fifteenth, after which he had to force himself to fly. His chief complaint was marked tension, with excessive drinking for relief. Prior to this he had suffered minor flak wounds.

The Ploesti raid was the first that really bothered him. His formation flew in very low and many planes were knocked out. Among them were several flown by his best friends and tent-mates. Although he forced himself to fly every few weeks afterwards, tension within him reached such a point he felt like exploding or going "wacky" and he had to drink to excess. He *remembered few details of the raid;* it all seemed so vague and far away.

However, under pentothal *every detail was reconstructed* in a vivid manner: the flak and the roar of guns hidden in houses and haystacks. They flew so low they could see peasants in colorful costumes waving to them, girls bathing in the nude. He could not bring himself to strafe the civilians. Over the target he saw a man come out of a building, close the door and run across the yard. He was an old man dressed in brown and the patient was sure he was killed by fifteen second delayed action bombs. He talked about other instances of bombing and strafing towns and his horror of killing civilians. It reminded him of deer hunting; his thrill at the instant of killing and his regret afterward. The old man in brown made him think of his father and he talked of his family. When he was 8 years old, his parents separated, and he felt badly and embarrassed at not having a father. When he was 10 years of age, his parents were divorced, about the time that his father taught him to shoot on a range. He developed a "screwy" thought that father would kill him, and became fearful of him.

During his next pentothal treatment, the patient told about his childish maternal grandfather, whom he visited in a mental hospital, and his thought of how much better it would be to put insane people out of their misery. He had no recollection of grandfather's death or his funeral. He had the same feeling (disgusted) in the insane asylum as he had on the Ploesti raid.

This patient experienced a revival of old anxiety related to his inner hostilities, when he became involved in the killing of civilians. These hostilities were evidently originally concerned with his relations to his father and grandfather. Because of the speed of low-flying bombers it was not likely that the patient could have recognized the isolated figure of a man and been able to describe him so accurately as to age and clothes. The association of the civilian with his father indicated that, as aggression was mobilized, the old target of his infantile hostilities was projected to the civilian, who then appeared to resemble the father. The material that flowed from this patient, under pentothal, although stimulated by combat, indicated an old unresolved conflict toward father figures. The symptoms were evidences of guilt. After the release of this material, subsequent interpretations gave insight, and the patient recovered and returned to duty.

·   ·   ·   ·   ·   ·

In this chapter we have demonstrated by case reports the use of pentothal to facilitate abreactions as the initial phase of insight, but necessarily followed by appropriate psychotherapy. We have seen that the abreactions in returnees expose considerable unconscious hostility toward father and brother figures as contrasted with more fear abreactions in patients overseas. In this respect verbalizations are even more successful in relieving repressed aggressions with insight than Simmel's technique of permitting patients to destroy straw effigies of officers. The relationship of the pattern of the neurotic reactions to the previous personality and past experiences becomes clearly expressed and the etiological significance of habitual ambivalent attitudes toward father and brother representatives almost always becomes apparent. The capacity of the ego to synthesize the material (which is more important than the abreaction), released from its isolation, is not determined by the patient's ability to verbalize insight or to repeat the material in a conscious state. The ego often synthesizes and learns unconsciously; hence the term "narcosynthesis." Many symptoms disappear spontaneously and recovery occurs directly under pentothal. Yet even then a subsequent working through of the material is helpful in strengthening the ego's grasp on the emotional drives.

CHAPTER 18

Adjunctive Treatment—Results of Therapy

In the early days of psychiatry, symptomatic medication was all that was available for the treatment of "diseases of the mind." Palliative remedies, consisting largely of tonics and sedatives were utilized for therapy, as in other fields of medicine. As the psychogenic and emotional factors in etiology were discerned and gradually understood, rational psychotherapy replaced these drugs. But the resistant organicists never ceased to search for mechanical, operative or pharmacological remedies in the hope of cure by altering hypothetical structural abnormalities of the neurons. From these endeavors we received the mixed advantages and hazards of electric shock therapy, prefrontal lobotomy, and metrazol and insulin shock.

The urgent need in wartime for the rapid treatment of large numbers of soldiers encouraged the revival of symptomatic remedies, and techniques designed to cover up emotional reactions with the tacit assumption that invisible symptoms do not exist. We do not here refer to measures employed in exhaustion centers or rest camps for the treatment of true fatigue states by drug-induced sleep, warmth and good food. Fortunately, the standard operating procedures of these treatment and sorting centers include evacuation of soldiers, not recovered in approximately five days, toward the rear to psychiatric hospitals, so that there is no danger that psychiatric casualties are not adequately treated (42).

Electric shock treatment has been applied at rear hospitals in some theaters of operations. Psychoses developing in military personnel who have had previous attacks, or who have been precipitated into illness by military rather than combat life, often present serious problems when attempts are made to

407

evacuate them by ship to the United States. Shock therapy has quieted many of these men so that their transportation is easier. However, combat causes many psychotic-like states of dissociation of the personality, erroneously diagnosed as malignant psychoses, sometimes schizophrenia, and they too have been shocked in the name of therapy. Since the treatment had been successful in some cases, it was applied to the milder and purely neurotic reactions. Many reports will undoubtedly find their way into the literature, indicating beneficial results. It is difficult to criticize even palliative therapy, but it must be pointed out that, although these patients are quieted and symptoms are ameliorated, they cannot be returned to duty, but must be evacuated home. It is a sad commentary on medical science that a man suffering severely from a neurosis precipitated by the horrible stimuli of battle should be treated with another shock in the form of an electrically induced stimulus producing unconsciousness! In our previous work (57) we have used shock treatment cautiously and infrequently in certain intractable cases, only when no other therapy was effective. The Air Forces have interdicted shock for flying personnel overseas or in this country. Fortunately our regulations forbid men who have had a convulsion to fly.

PHARMACOTHERAPY

Narcosis or continuous sleep treatment has been used extensively in some theaters (53) and for patients in the Eighth Air Force. Hastings, Wright and Glueck (29) reported favorable results with this method and indicated a high percentage of recoveries and return to combat duty. Unfortunately, control of their results was impossible and subsequent reports from the same Air Force are less optimistic. We were unable to obtain benefit for our patients in the Mediterranean area by means of continuous sleep treatment. Nevertheless, we attempted this same treatment on returnee patients suffering from war neuroses. The one difference between these patients and those treated overseas was the greater time that had elapsed after the onset of the neurosis, although returnees were treated within a month or two after having been removed from combat. Counteracting this disadvantage was the fact that our patients were out of the dangerous combat situation and were back home.

A total of 20 cases was treated with continuous narcosis. Sodium amytal, given by mouth and intravenously, was the

drug of choice, supplemented by paraldehyde and sodium pheno-
barbital. The length of sleep varied from twenty-seven to one
hundred and ten hours. Since the details of the technique are
standardized and clearly stated in other publications, they will
not be discussed here. All our patients received simultaneous and
subsequent psychotherapy. Out of 20 patients, only three showed
some improvement, the majority being unchanged or made
worse. There is no need to recount the histories of these narcosis
patients, since they were typical samples of previously cited neuroses. Almost all of them were subsequently separated from the
service, unfit for further military duty. Improvement in a few
cases was not sufficient to warrant return even to limited service.
Some patients were made worse by the treatment, because the
sleep and individual nursing attention excessively gratified a
craving for dependence and thereby increased the regressive
trends. Sleep was a surcease for their troubles and they were loath
to awaken. Any self-respecting component of their personalities
was further weakened.

However, there is another reason why deterioration occurs
under the continuous sleep treatment. This is related to the
long period of delirium during the semiawakened state in which
the patient is fed and attends to his toilet. Unlike the brief
narcosis under pentothal, the sleep state itself is associated with
longer periods of delirium. In such a delirium, without the constant support of the therapist, the quantity of anxiety mobilized
may be extremely great and may overpower the ego, which is
at least partially asleep. Thus the prolonged and uncontrolled
sleep is fraught with danger. As a result, the patient looks back
on his treatment as days of nightmare-like horror alternating
with periods of relief. Because of our poor results, we abandoned
this type of therapy and believe that the reported excellent
results of previous observers require rechecking (36).

Since *ergotamine tartrate* has been recommended as a useful
drug in the treatment of "battle reaction," it was thought that
it might prove valuable in the treatment of "operational fatigue"
(war neuroses) in flying personnel returned to this country
from combat. This work was carried out in our hospital with
the cooperation of Russell J. Spivey (28).

Patients selected for treatment with this drug were those with
evidence of sympathetic overactivity, manifested particularly
by increased restlessness, tremor, sleeplessness, tension and

agitation. The dosage given at first was that recommended by Heath and Powdermaker (30): 3 mg. for the first dose, then 2 mg. every three hours for ten days. Because of untoward symptoms this dose was quickly modified to 2 mg. every four hours in four doses daily for ten days. All patients reported in this series were given the latter dosage except the first three, who were given the larger dose for the first twenty-four hours only. All were confined to the ward during treatment and were carefully examined each day.

A total of 16 patients received the ergotamine tartrate (gynergen, Sandoz). Of these, 13 developed toxic symptoms, notably pain in the legs and arms. Phlebitis developed in 3 patients; in 2, actual thrombi occurred. No improvement of the symptoms of sympathetic overactivity was obvious in 10 patients. Only 2 showed improvement in their tremors while taking the drug, but they reverted to their previous status when it was discontinued. There were 2 others, who showed improvement in both sleep and tremor, but one of these successes was due to abstinence from alcohol while under treatment. One stutterer showed improvement in his speech. Another slept better while under treatment, but did not show any change in restlessness or tremor. None of the benefited patients maintained improvement after the drug was discontinued.

Ergotamine tartrate was originally used because of its properties as a sympathetic inhibitor by Heath and Powdermaker, who reported success in 20 cases. Goodman and Gilman (23) state that the autonomic blocking effect of ergotamine in humans is slight and irregular. However, it damages the vascular endothelium, producing vascular stasis, thrombosis and gangrene. According to these statements, there should be little reason to consider ergotamine tartrate valuable in the treatment of sympathetic overexcitation, and toxic effects should have been anticipated. We were forced to conclude that ergotamine tartrate was not useful in treating war neuroses among returnees showing signs of sympathetic overactivity, with or without emotional conflicts, and that in tablet dosage of over 12 mg. it gave evidence of toxicity. Moreover, rational therapy of war neuroses should not be directed against the symptoms but toward the basic causes. This is as axiomatic in psychiatry as in other fields of medicine. It is for this reason that "uncovering techniques" are employed successfully.

Because of the well known effect of *hyoscine hydrobromide* on tremor and other symptoms of extrapyramidal disturbances, it was considered feasible to try it on sufferers from war neuroses. Beginning with 5 patients, 0.01 grain was given at 8:00 a. m., 2:00 p. m. and 8:00 p. m. Later this dosage was extended to include all the 50 patients on one ward. There was a very high percentage of toxic reactions, appearing early in the course of medication. These consisted mainly of vertigo, fatigue, lethargy and nausea, with gradually cumulative feelings of increased tension. There appeared to be no correlation between the severity of the patients' anxiety symptoms, or their general condition, and the reaction which they experienced, except that depressed patients were more liable to the early appearance of toxic symptoms. Hyoscine hydrobromide had no beneficial effects upon patients with objective signs of anxiety.

In consequence of some work on the relation of *hypoglycemia* to fatigue states, indicating that emotional disturbances were etiological to the mechanism of hyperinsulinism, we became interested, in association with Asher Chapman, in the blood sugars of our patients. We performed intravenous glucose tolerance tests on an unselected series of patients, without knowledge of their clinical manifestations. Those with low or flat blood sugar curves were studied in an effort to correlate the clinical symptomatology with the laboratory findings. As we have stated before, "operational fatigue," our wastebasket diagnostic term, which includes war neuroses, is not always associated with fatigue. Very few patients with low blood sugar curves gave an indication of clinical fatigue, exhaustibility and lack of endurance. On the other hand, normal controls showed equally frequent flat or low curves. However, these patients with or without fatigue were placed on a regime of frequent feedings, abstinence from free sugar and oral administration of 0.01 grain of atropine after each meal. After ten days, another blood sugar tolerance test was performed. No striking clinical improvement was observed, and, after atropinization, the blood sugar curve although slightly elevated did not return to normal. Chapman found that some of the low blood sugar curves showed no rise after adrenalin was injected intramuscularly, although other sympathetic excitatory effects were present. It is apparent that metabolic disturbances in our war-weary patients are frequent but extremely complicated. Not one syndrome but many types of disturbances exist, none of which have as yet been accurately and finally determined (43).

These are psychosomatic problems of an extremely complicated nature and the inter-relationships between the emotional, endocrine and metabolic factors are highly complex. All gradations and complicating disturbances of function may exist, and they require much investigation. It is certain that prolonged emotional disturbances are etiological to many of these physical changes, but equally true is the fact that the physical hardships and the physical results of neurotic reactions reverberate and affect the emotional state of the same individual. Complicated circular effects result, requiring investigative attack by psychiatrists and internists, approaching the problem with different techniques but maintaining a psychosomatic point of view (32).

Many of the veterans of combat have lived for long periods of time overseas on far distant air bases where supplies were deficient. Even when there was no shortage, the food was monotonously uninspiring. This, combined with excessive heat and continuous anxiety, frequently caused severe loss of weight. Among those with "operational fatigue," sleeplessness and anorexia assisted in producing an excessive loss of weight. Many soldiers returned home extremely thin, looking old beyond their years, some bald or with greying hair and with numerous carious teeth. It has therefore been our policy to furnish the mess with large quantities of *food with high caloric value* and give opportunities for frequent feedings. Snack bars are open until late at night and bottles of milk are in every ice box. The quantity of food ingested is tremendous and gain in weight is usually rapid and adequate. Partly contributing to the excessive appetite is the neurotic tendency to use food and drink as a source of gratification for dependent trends. However, many patients have a poor appetite, although this is not related to any clinical syndrome.

It often becomes necessary to supplement the natural food intake by *vitamin* administration. Thiamine chloride and multiple vitamin mixtures are given in large quantities. Some patients are benefited in gaining appetite and becoming more active by the ingestion of 3 grains of thyroid extract daily. We have no controlled observations of the effect of these drugs on body weight and general physical health, but we can say with certainty that vitamin administration does not contribute to the relief or cure of war neuroses. It is not an avitaminosis that causes these nervous disorders; they produce avitaminosis by affecting the appetite.

Small doses of *insulin* are sometimes administered before meals to patients who have lost much weight and have little appetite. Beneficial weight gains have been observed but we have witnessed no profound effect on the neurotic reaction itself from this drug, such as has been reported by some observers.

Sedatives have always been invaluable therapeutic aids in psychiatry for symptomatic relief of sleeplessness (51). Even when uncovering techniques are utilized, during the early phases of therapy it is essential to ensure rest for soldiers whose anxieties create intense insomnia. Either our patients have difficulty in going to sleep because of hypnogogic hallucinations repetitive of battle experiences, or they are awakened from sleep by severe catastrophic nightmares. They resort to self medication in the form of alcohol, which has its harmful by-effects, for it causes loss of appetite and increased tension when liquor is not obtainable, prevents the full effects of psychotherapy being felt and increases resistance to the desired effect of pentothal. Furthermore, it permits release of asocial hostilities which evoke punishment from the civilian and military police. Yet alcohol is effective in temporarily decreasing tension and the accompanying somatic symptom of tremor, which suggests that this action of the drug is on the central nervous system.

For the purposes of quieting down severely anxious patients and ensuring sleep, sedatives are frequently prescribed, especially in the first few days of hospitalization before definitive therapy has achieved effective results. Night-time sedation should consist of a combination of a rapid-acting drug, such as seconal, to ensure speedy induction of sleep and a slowly acting sedative with a prolonged effect, such as barbital, nembutal or amytal, to guarantee sleep for the entire night. Thus lengthy initial light sleep and waves of semiawakening are prevented, for it is during light sleep that dreams appear and frighten the patient. There is never any reason to use morphine to induce sleep. Kubie suggests that the severely ill patient should be awakened artificially and rapidly in order to avoid gradual return to consciousness, thus dispensing with the period of light sleep early in the morning before awakening when the nightmares occur (36). In our experience many patients awakened by this method are confused and aggressive, feeling that they are still dreaming and acting as if the nurses and attendants were figures in their dreams.

We soon found that, in spite of otherwise rapid relief of symptoms and marked improvement, many patients continued to complain of sleeplessness and they lined up at the nurse's desk each night for their sleeping medicine. This inconsistency was astonishing, until we found that cleverly disguised *placebos* produced the same beneficial effect and were as eagerly accepted by the patients. It became apparent that the night-time capsule or tablet administered by a nurse or ordered by a doctor became a symbol of interest and attention, simply gratifying a dependent need of the insecure patient. This is an important finding, because addiction to barbiturates, with their known toxic deleterious effects when ingested over long periods of time, must be avoided. Realization that the need for the medicine is not for its pharmacological but for its psychological effect indicates the necessity of considering craving for sedation as a subject for further psychotherapy.

From this chapter, it may seem as if we were therapeutic nihilists, abandoning all hope of successful pharmacotherapy. Actually we have done much research in attempting to find therapeutic medicinal aids. We fully realize the necessity for adequately treating all physical symptoms, such as dyspepsia, diarrhea, anorexia, cachexia, insomnia and tremor. But the appropriate treatments cannot, we think, be considered as more than symptomatic remedies and they are certainly not panaceas. They must be accompanied by rational therapy for the emotional etiological disturbances which are reflected in the physical symptoms (8).

CONVALESCENT THERAPY

The actual time the patient spends in any form of psychiatric treatment is relatively small, no matter what technique is used, leaving many waking hours to be filled with activities. Patients can only eat and drink so much and enjoy entertainment up to a point without being surfeited and bored. This extra time is obviously a valuable period for adjunctive therapy which supplements the more definitive treatment. Furthermore, after strenuous months of strain on physical endurance and severe tension in combat, many individuals have a desire to rest, sleep and lie around in an effortless existence. Our patients carry this to an exaggerated degree, since their neuroses are regressive in nature. They try to make life in the hospital a complete gratification of these infantile trends. They want only to eat and sleep, and object to the slightest restriction of their liberty, which they caricature to the point of license. If permitted, they would not get up until noon, and some have actually requested to have breakfast served in bed. They resent having to make their beds and would rather throw their cigarettes on the floor than move two feet to an ash tray. It therefore becomes obvious that steps must be taken to assist the psychiatrist in combating the regressive tendencies of these youngsters. It is of little avail for him to attempt ego-strengthening processes and measures calculated to adapt the patient to reality, if that reality is more like that of an infant than of a grown man.

As we have indicated several times, the transition from the cohesive group life to independent individualism is too sudden and becomes disconcerting, so that the soldier is like a lost and bewildered child. We should like to see a gradual decompression from the strong and tight groups of combat life to the looser organizations in the Continental army and civilian life. Therefore an inspirational program, designed to reinstill a group spirit with a gradual transition to the setting of the American scene, is highly desirable. This group spirit is best instilled in a *convalescent program* concerned with physical rehabilitation. Our patients need much physical rehabilitation, since they show various degrees of physical deterioration resulting from the hardships of their prolonged and repeated combat experiences, poor living conditions and the infrequency of rest periods.

The Army Air Forces have recognized the importance of physical fitness for coordination and endurance. Competitive team games of skill have been used extensively to sharpen the eye, to improve muscle coordination, timing and endurance and to instill a group spirit. The psychology of fitness and well-being was well explained to convalescent patients by S/Sgt. Max Baer on a recent visit. Baer told of shamming illness and going to bed for a few days before a big fight. He had intended to fool and impress his opponent, but confessed that after a day or two of this inactivity he really began to *feel* sick and to be convinced himself of the folly of his plan.

The principles of the adjunctive treatment of "operational fatigue" consist of healthy and purposeful mental diversions, which are carefully coordinated with a graded and popular physical and recreational program. The key to success is the attractiveness of the activities to the patient, since the individual's pleasure is paramount in gaining his interest and co-operation. To facilitate integration into a group, each man is assigned to a numbered or lettered group corresponding to his room, wing or floor. This closely follows the Air Forces' organization into tactical units. These men then play and work together, again forming close relationships on teams and recreational units. There develops considerable competition between these groups, which produces a spirit of group morale.

The patient's day is scheduled according to specific times for compulsory arising, policing, classroom studies and physical activities. This is equivalent to the "total push" method of psychiatry. During each day there is time for development of personal hobbies in appropriate workshops, or the patient may use this period for privacy since many men need time for solitude. They also have considerable free time in the evening, since we are liberal with passes. Experiences in nearby towns help and test the capacities for resocialization. The classroom and shop work are partly military and partly educative. Orientation lectures, news analysis, geopolitics and current events are among the popular classes from which men receive accretions to their knowledge. The patient is urged to enroll in extension courses as well.

Because of the unique opportunity to observe the behavior of the individual as a member of a group, and to modify his behavior, the "Convalescent Services Division" is in a position to render valuable service to the general therapeutic mission of the hospital. That this is an "adjunctive service" does not mean that it confines its aim to entertaining the patient, taking his mind off himself or getting him interested in something. Though these are respectable therapeutic goals, the Convalescent Services Division provides more valuable service by setting up for itself two definite goals, one diagnostic, the other therapeutic, which elevates the whole purpose of the organization and ties it in firmly with the general therapeutic aim. These are:

(1) To provide the professional and psychiatric services with additional diagnostic and follow-up data regarding the

behavior of the patient in a group. The psychiatrists observe the patient only in the particular transference situation: the doctor-patient relationship. Unlike the Flight Surgeon overseas, who can easily observe for himself the behavior of his patients in the group, and can compare this with information obtained from the interview situation, the psychiatrist in the hospital has a unilateral view of his patient. No matter how intuitive, sensitive and skilled, he may be led astray, especially with reference to the patient's ability to compensate for his dependent needs. The transference situation brings out the dependence but provides no real way of testing the weak ego's power of synthesizing and working out its difficulties. For this we often have to fall back on the uncertain "trial of duty." Certainly the behavior of the individual in the convalescent program is the nearest approach we have to a test situation. Psychiatrists are frequently amazed to find a patient vigorous and active in the program, who in personal interviews is silent, resentful, negativistic or full of anxiety and psychosomatic complaints. We observed one of our patients playing a brilliant game of basketball. In interviews he complains constantly and bitterly of backache, pain in the chest, hemorrhoids and inferiority feelings. If his symptoms were taken at face value, it would be all he could do to get out of bed and face the world. By keeping the psychiatrist informed of the progress and behavior of the difficult patients with a poor prognosis, the Convalescent Services Division provides yeoman service.

(2) To modify unrealistic, regressed, dependent attitudes by group pressure and renewed group identification. The ego is encouraged in its experimental attempts to regain mature attitudes and to attempt mature activities, thereby gaining new confidence. This is a therapeutic aim and very tricky. To a large extent it depends upon the character or composition of the group, especially in discussion groups. In order that the instructor may not have too large a proportion of antagonistic individuals stacked against him, it is necessary to stage-manage some of the groups, artificially influencing their composition. For this purpose it is necessary to import some suitable returned fliers with strong egos and good superego attitudes, whose continued hospitalization is dictated less by the degree of their operational fatigue than by their value to the groups. With the aid of such individuals, the instructor more easily exposes and neutralizes

the dependent attitudes of a segment of the group. This purpose is adopted not only for the official discussion groups but also by all other sections, no matter how individual or remote the activity. The expressed attitudes of the instructors always have important psychotherapeutic implications.

All that has been described is conducted in a regime in the Convalescent Services Division under the direction of Raymond G. Vinal and Ottis E. Hanes. It has been found to be a valuable adjunctive to psychiatric rehabilitation. It has the following functions:

1. Instillation of group spirit.
2. Physical rehabilitation.
3. Intellectual stimulation.
4. Theoretical review of military specialty.
5. Recreation and amusement.

Results

We have now had sufficient time and experience to evaluate our results. Since February 1944, our hospital population has varied from an initial minimum of 14 patients to a maximum of 780. We have treated and discharged from the hospital a total of 888 officers and 2316 enlisted men suffering from "operational fatigue." The senior author personally scrutinizes almost every patient and his record before permitting him to return to duty in order to prevent errors in that direction by his personal physician or psychiatrist. To make sure that separation from the service is actually indicated, not only has the patient-candidate to be passed on by a special board of medical officers, but, in addition, one medical officer for a time has done nothing but interview these patients before passing them on to the board. In many cases patients recommended for duty or for separation from the service are sent back to the wards for re-evaluation or for further therapy.

One of the chief concerns of the psychiatrist at this point lies in knowing whether or not his patient has sufficiently re-covered to enable him to cope with the life situation into which he is being discharged. How do we know that a patient, who, for example, seems to be making an excellent adjustment in the hospital, is actually ready to meet the infinitely greater demands and stresses which will beset him in a return either to duty or to civilian life? May not a particular transference situation between patient and physician actually prevent the physician from seeing, and the patient from displaying, some evidence of latent disturbance as long as the conditions are optimal for his achieving stability?

In the hope of obtaining an objective measure of the degree of an individual's recovery, a recent attempt has been made to develop a standardized test along these lines. The "stress tolerance test," devised by Molly Harrower-Erickson, subjects the patient to certain psychological "stresses" in the form of colored lantern slides of dramatic combat scenes. These pictures, projected in a darkened room, to a greater or less degree reactivate old traumata, causing the patient to show various forms of disturbed behavior, either overtly or in the responses which he is called upon to write after looking at the pictures.

The stress tolerance test combines, and uses in its evaluation of the individual's performance, principles and concepts from both the Rorschach technique and Murray's "apperception test." It uses both inkblot stimuli and pictures portraying persons and action. In a somewhat similar manner to the group Rorschach the instructions call for the individual to write down what the inkblot pictures remind him of, and also what first comes to his mind in regard to the pictures of combat action. It differs from the above-mentioned techniques in that its criteria for evaluation are infinitely simpler, since it has been demonstrated without question that the patients who are clinically still considerably disturbed express this disturbance in ways which need no subtle nor intricate scoring system.

The test is so constructed that the ten combat pictures (the stress situation) are preceded by one series of five inkblot pictures, and followed by another. Five of the Rorschach original inkblots and five parallel and equated inkblots from an alternate series are used. If an individual has been profoundly disturbed by the intervening stress situation, it has been found that he is less able to cope with or reply to the second inkblot series. Even if only the most objective criteria are taken into account, it will be found that the number of times that an individual "blocks" or fails to answer will be increased. Thus one way of estimating the patient's disturbance lies in the discrepancy between his first and second performances on the inkblots.

But there is a vast amount of material which can be determined from his answers to the combat pictures, and both phases of the test are used as a basis of judgment. The acutely disturbed patient may actually leave the room during the series because of the unbearable reality of the pictures for him. He may fail to write any answer to them at all, blocking sometimes on the whole series, sometimes on particular pictures which seem to be the most disturbing to the group of patients as a whole. Again, he may show by his personalized answers that situation after situation is sufficiently similar to his own experience to make him see the picture only through his own eyes, warping it or disregarding its more obvious features (my copilot crashing, etc.). There are also other manifestations of disturbance, such as a forced facetiousness or cynicism, or evasion of the real issue of the picture by attention to some irrelevant detail.

Using only the criteria of failure to reply, of personalization in the war pictures and of an increased number of failures in the second inkblot series, reliable statistics have been obtained which show that there is a marked difference between cases of "operational fatigue" and "normal" controls. This difference holds whether the control groups are drawn from precombat personnel without psychological disturbances or from returnees without "operational fatigue." There is also a significant difference between severe and mild cases of "operational fatigue."

Such a test demonstrates, even in its initial stage, that it is possible to obtain some kind of objective yardstick as an index of the extent to which traumatic experiences still hold the individual in their grip.

.   .   .   .   .   .

Our therapeutic achievements or failures should be evaluated from several points of view, as follows:

1. Results prior to discharge from the hospital.

2. Efficiency in maintaining stability on return to military duty in this country, including full flying duty.

3. Ability of flying officers and enlisted men to return to combat.

4. Fate in civilian life of those too ill to remain in the service.

On discharge from the hospital to duty, prognostic estimates concerning the subsequent course of the patient are made. Among those with poor prognoses are soldiers returned for a trial of duty as the final test of fitness to remain in the military service.

TABLE 1

RELATION OF OCCUPATION TO DISPOSITION OF 820 RETURNEE FLYING OFFICERS DISCHARGED FROM THE DON CESAR CONVALESCENT HOSPITAL

Occupation	Full Flying		Grounding				Transferred		Retired		Total	
			Temporary		Permanent							
	No.	%	No.	%	No.	%	No.	%	No.	%	No.	%
Pilot............	337	74.9	35	7.7	62	13.9	6	1.3	8	1.8	448	54.6
Navigator.......	105	65.5	7	4.2	46	27.9	1	0.6	3	1.8	162	19.8
Bombardier......	101	50.5	18	9.0	72	36.0	1	0.5	8	4.0	200	24.4
Other..........	6	75.0	0	0.0	2	25.0	0	0.0	0	0.0	8	0.9
Not given.......	0	0.0	1	50.0	0	0.0	1	50.0	0	0.0	2	0.3
Total..........	549	66.9	61	7.4	182	22.3	9	1.1	19	2.3	820	100.0

TABLE 2

RELATION OF OCCUPATION TO DISPOSITION OF 1960 RETURNEE FLYING ENLISTED MEN DISCHARGED FROM THE DON CESAR CONVALESCENT HOSPITAL

Occupation	Full Flying		Grounding				Transferred		Separated from Service		Total	
			Temporary		Permanent							
	No.	%	No.	%	No.	%	No.	%	No.	%	No.	%
Bombardier......	4	23.5	2	11.7	4	23.5	0	0.0	7	41.3	17	0.9
Engineer........	90	27.9	43	13.3	112	35.0	13	4.0	64	19.8	322	16.4
Radio-operator...	109	28.3	52	13.6	141	36.6	6	1.6	77	19.9	385	19.6
Gunner.........	251	21.6	140	12.0	481	41.3	31	2.7	261	22.4	1164	59.5
Other..........	9	19.6	7	15.2	10	21.7	3	6.5	17	37.0	46	2.3
Not given.......	4	15.4	0	0.0	5	19.1	13	50.1	4	15.4	26	1.3
Total..........	467	23.8	244	12.5	753	38.4	66	3.4	430	21.9	1960	100.0

The accompanying tables indicate the disposition of flying officers and enlisted men. It may be observed, in summary, that

97.7 per cent of officers and 79.1 per cent of enlisted men return to some form of military duty.

No significant difference in these figures was related, in either enlisted men or officers, to position in the airplanes, except for pilots who returned to full flying duty in 74.9 per cent as contrasted with the figures of 65.5 per cent for navigators and 50.5 per cent for bombardiers. The percentage of grounding was somewhat higher for A-20 flying personnel than for that of other ships. On the other hand, more B-26 crew members returned to full flying duty. The evadees returned to flying duty in a lower percentage and were separated from the service in about the same proportion. The percentage of men from the China-Burma-India and the Southwest Pacific Theaters who were temporarily grounded was slightly higher than that of personnel from other sources. The few officers who required retirement on psychiatric grounds fought in those combat theaters from which rotation home is slow and often delayed.

When we contrast the figures for officers with those for enlisted men, who were separated from the service, the ratio is approximately 1 to 10. Even on casual observation it may be seen that the enlisted men are far sicker than the officers. There are a number of reasons for this phenomenon:

1. The enlisted men did not pass through psychological and psychiatric screening before being accepted for flying status. As a matter of fact, many enlisted men were "washed-out" cadets. Others had been picked from ground echelons overseas, because of the great need for gunners, and given only a minimum of training. Many combat crew members had no desire for flying and were ordered into this particular job. On the other hand, the officers were fairly well chosen from many points of view including educational background. Their selection was based not only on an original examination but also on their capacity to endure a rigorous training program. Thus the caliber of the officers was higher from the standpoint of ability to endure stress.

2. Officers, having a greater sense of responsibility, were more likely to consult Flight Surgeons and take prophylactic rest periods when they felt unfit. Enlisted men were more determined to finish their duty as quickly as possible and continued flying in spite of anxiety and fatigue in order to get home. They were not as well informed as to the need of preventive care.

3. Flight Surgeons paid more attention to officers and grounded them earlier. They were more likely to give officers personal attention, to attempt earlier therapy with them and to refer them earlier for specialist's advice and care.

4. The officers had more motivation to continue in the Air Forces and hoped to continue noncombat flying. They frequently wished to continue this occupation in the peacetime army or in civilian aeronautics after the war. The enlisted men had no future interest in flying and felt that, having done their share in the war, there was nothing of importance to keep them in the service. They thought of their future in nonflying civilian jobs. Furthermore, as subordinate enlisted men, they had more rationalized grievances against the army.

Results according to type of case are very interesting and are impressionistic rather than statistical. The most successful therapy is accomplished in soldiers who have a sense of guilt and depression. The regressed-dependent youngsters are, as a rule, benefited and relieved of their troubles, and for their own good many are returned for a trial of duty. The patients with psychotic-like reactions also have fairly good prognoses but are definitely unfit for further combat duty. Those with hostile-aggressive and psychopathic-like reactions have the poorest prognoses.

At the onset of selective service there was a controversy among psychiatrists concerning the wisdom of drafting youngsters of 18 to 20 years of age. One group advocated the induction of older men, who would be more stable and less likely to develop war neuroses. Although stability is a property of an individual and cannot be averaged, events have proved that the older men stand up under the stress of poor living conditions, separation from home and the horrors of war much less successfully than the youngsters. After they become ill, recovery is slower and less complete. The rapid recovery of the younger men shows again the resiliency of the youthful ego, which can re-establish itself with rest and after removal from the holocaust of battle, or after the relief of unconscious tensions. Especially those who have had a good life in the past bound back with optimism for their future.

The second problem is the stability of men on return to duty. Each patient is asked to write us a personal letter once a month and recently Flight Surgeons at his new duty station have been asked to report the patient's status to us after one, three, six and twelve months. These letters have made it clear to us that, for enlisted men especially, the fate of our patient's stability is partially dependent on the type of work to which he will be reassigned and the attitudes of the personnel in the group, base and command in which he will perform his new duties. The using agencies to which our patients are discharged have a serious responsibility in aftercare. For this reason we inform everyone concerned as to our post-hospital recommendations. Just as in our work overseas, weeks of careful psychotherapy can be undone quickly by poor handling or malassignment. The ramifications of this matter cannot be gone into here but they are serious. A large percentage of men whom we are now forced to discharge from the army for medical reasons with a psychiatric diagnosis, thus making them eligible for veterans' pensions, recover promptly on discharge. For these soldiers an administrative discharge for reasons of nonadaptability would be far more advantageous for the men and the service.

We have not yet been able to test the efficiency of our treatment in enabling a flier to return to combat. This will eventually be possible when and if a second tour of combat duty becomes an established policy. We have no large number of reports concerning veterans separated from the service, all of whom are given vocational guidance and counseling before discharge. A few have written after making good adjustments in jobs. The sickest we have referred to veterans' facilities or to state or urban psychiatric agencies, but these are not yet adequately prepared for their task of treating the discharged veteran, although progress is being made in a few large cities by enlightened volunteer civilian organizations.

PART V

Civilian Applications

CHAPTER 19

Applications from Military to Civilian Psychiatry

Even the greatest scourges of mankind, epidemics and war, produce beneficial side effects. Not in the Machiavellian sense of our enemies, but from the constructive by-products derived from mobilization of our scientific, inventive and productive capacities, do these results accrue. During the emergency of war, governments encourage and subsidize research concerned not only with the successful prosecution of war but also with the health and treatment of the soldiers. War has almost always been accompanied by great advances in the medical sciences. It is obvious that large numbers of sick and wounded demand from the ingenuity of doctors better methods of diagnosis and treatment. A host of new discoveries develop concurrently as necessity demands, and old fetishes, maintained by inertia and conservatism, are relinquished. The essential new factor to which everyone in military service is sensitized is speed. New and shorter therapeutic techniques are the goals of all military medical officers.

Our experiences as military psychiatrists serving combat soldiers and fliers for the last two and a half years have taught us a great deal about human beings under stress. These experiences are of value not alone for their applicability to an understanding of the problems and treatment of the psychiatric casualties of war; they are equally valuable for the understanding of the psychology and psychopathology of people under the stresses of ordinary civilian life. These may not be as continuous or as catastrophic, or their effects as sudden or dramatic, yet in essence they bring into action the same forces within the individual as do the terrifying stimuli of battle. Like any advance in medicine stimulated by war, our work should be applicable to civilian psychiatry.

It is not possible to recapitulate in terms of civilian life the many details of the psychology and psychopathology of men under stress, which we have discussed throughout this book. Nevertheless, we shall attempt to summarize certain high points, from which general applications can be made to our knowledge regarding human personality, especially in regard to therapy and ego psychology. Intellectual and emotional blind spots and closeness to the problem have probably caused us to overlook many conclusions of importance. Therefore, we have documented this book with detailed case reports as freely as space permits, in order that others may use our material for their own researches and for their own conclusions.

In the First World War, the brilliant work of Harvey Cushing and his associates placed neurological surgery on a firm basis as a separate division among the medical specialties, although surgery of the nervous system was by no means new (40). From this global war, it is psychiatry that will consolidate its position in medicine, for several reasons: (1) Millions of civilians and soldiers under catastrophic conditions of stress have created far reaching recognition of the need for psychiatric help. (2) Psychiatric knowledge and experience have reached a stage of practical application which has enabled psychiatrists to accomplish their missions satisfactorily whenever permitted. (3) Countless numbers of soldiers have received the benefits of psychiatric care and thousands of general medical officers have been assisted in the treatment of their patients by psychiatrists, who have given them practical and valuable instruction.

Only the third reason needs amplification. The public's interest in psychiatry has always exceeded that of medical men, who were often disinterested or even antagonistic to the field. But the young medical officer working directly with soldiers finds that the greatest number of his difficult problems in diagnosis and therapy relate to the influence of emotional disturbances on bodily functions. In combat areas he is confronted with war neuroses and their manifold somatic manifestations. The medical officer is usually convinced of the etiological importance of disturbed emotions when he is confronted with this frequent psychosomatic problem: a combat soldier without conscious anxiety has gastrointestinal disturbances, with no evidence of organic disease, and is not improved by the usual medication. His doctor quickly senses the need for a psychosomatic approach, and is eager to learn what are the basic emotional difficulties and how to treat them. This is the beginning of insight for the general medical officer and often leads to real interest and a sincere quest for knowledge, not for the purpose of becoming a psychiatrist, but in order to become a better doctor no matter what his chosen specialty may be.

As the public and medical men become increasingly aware of the need for psychiatric help and the goals of rational psychotherapy, the paucity of well trained psychiatrists becomes increasingly apparent. It is estimated that for future needs of peacetime America, 10,000 to 17,000 additional psychiatrists will be necessary. Because of the length of time necessary for training, the relatively few teaching institutions and the limited number of aspirants, it is obvious that decades will elapse before psychiatric services to the people of the United States will even approach their needs, which will steadily increase in the interim.

Again our military experience offers a solution. We must train, in medical schools, in hospitals during internships and residencies, and by means of postgraduate courses, general practitioners to utilize the simpler techniques of psychiatry. The small town doctor, as a result of an adequate medical education, is capable of performing standardized surgical operations and treatment. Only for unusual complications does he require specialized help. Can this be made true for psychiatry? We believe it can, on the basis of our personal experiences in teaching general medical officers, providing we develop a large number of competent teachers.

We have trained many general medical men, worldly wise and in their early thirties, who have had experience overseas with men in combat and who were impressed with the frequency of emotional factors in the etiology of somatic symptoms. Most of them planned to return to their own specialites or to their general practices after the war. But they will not return as they left; they will have a new understanding of the total personalities of patients whose diseases alone they had been accustomed to treat. One young surgeon stated that he learned how often he had operated on patients unnecessarily. Another realized how important it was for him to understand his patients' emotions during their postoperative care. All of these men will be foci of educational stimuli as they disperse throughout the country.

These physicians are taught the simple dynamics of the human personality in nontechnical language. We try as much as possible to erase scientific jargon from our vocabularies, recognizing that this usually disguises unclear thinking, especially among psychiatrists. We are able to teach these medical officers the simpler procedures of psychiatric therapy as applied to relatively normal men who have succumbed to severe external stress. They are able to work with the method of free association and to use narcoanalysis and narcosynthesis. They are able to deal with problems of regression, to work effectively and constructively with ego forces, and to relieve superego pressures. They develop understanding of unconscious trends. Techniques fairly well standardized for typical problems are easily grasped and practiced. These skills are acquired in spite of some fairly intense initial resistance to our working concepts.

How much easier would this education be for the future general practitioner if this teaching were begun in the second year of medical school, before students become indoctrinated with the inevitable concepts of cellular pathology and the organicist's therapeutic nihilism! Instead of being taught psychiatry in the back wards of a state mental hospital or in the chaotic halls of a detention psychopathic hospital, demonstrating the rarest type of mental disturbance that the future doctor will see—the psychotic—he should be exposed to the optimistic, everyday problems of the psychoneuroses and the psychosomatic disturbances. These problems he will meet daily, for they will comprise over half his practice. With this material he should have an intimate acquaintance, made possible by extensive contact in therapeutic situations. His psychiatric training should be greatly expanded not only in scope but also in time, extending through his entire medical curriculum. We have tried this type of teaching in the Army Air Forces and it works!

.   .   .   .   .   .

For a consideration of the applicability to civilian practice of treatment as utilized in the military services, we naturally turn first to the so-called traumatic neuroses. Patients classified under this heading have suffered some bodily injury or have narrowly escaped a catastrophic physical accident. However, this classification is too sharply limited, because it excludes the most frequent traumata, which are psychological and not necessarily catastrophic; actually all neuroses are "traumatic." As we have indicated, neuroses cannot be differentiated according to the nature or intensity of their precipitating causes.

Certain general factors increase a person's tendency to react uneconomically to external stress. These are concerned with fatigue and exhaustion in their most severe form. The capacity of the ego to deal with fear-evoking external stimuli, and to cope with internal anxieties increased by external events, is dependent on its defensive capacities or span of energy. In combat, men are continuously on the alert and expectant of danger, they must constantly mobilize all their automatic reactions and be prepared for new emergency maneuvers. Even when this preparatory state becomes automatic after long-continued practice, the progressive effects of lack of sleep, improper nutrition and extremes of weather eventually decrease the ego's capacity to deal with anxiety-producing stimuli from within or without, and affect its abilities to hold emergency reaction down to an economical quantity.

In the army an individual thus depleted is prophylactically rehabilitated after a few days of complete rest and adequate sleep. The unit surgeons are able to recognize the signs of incipient fatigue by evidences of insomnia, irritability and other personality changes. The same safeguards should be maintained in industry, particularly when a man or woman is engaged in the control of a dangerous machine. The sheer monotony of such work as, for example, driving a truck, added to lack of sleep and of proper food, may prepare these workers for accidents with serious sequelae if an emergency situation arises. Considerable attention has already been paid in industry to the accident rate in relation to fatigue states and even in relation to various times of the day when workers are most tired. Improvements in working conditions, the removal of monotony and even the use of music are some of the measures adopted. These do not suffice, nor does a temporary lay-off, if the exhausted individual is not by prescription forced into actual rest with adequate sleep. However, natural sleep may be impossible even under optimal conditions, because of the increasing excitation within the central nervous system. We have learned from wartime psychia-

try, practiced in exhaustion centers and rest camps, that sedation is necessary but that it must be adequate. The dosages of
the various drugs given in the pharmacopeia are actually
minimal. If any good is to come from relief of monotonous work
and rest, it must be accomplished by large doses of sedatives to
ensure adequately continuous and deep sleep.

Once an accident has actually occurred, early treatment is
extremely important in order to prevent chronic neurotic disabilities, which inevitably necessitate compensation for a lifetime
of illness. Industry and insurance companies are lavish in their
procurement of medical attention for individuals who have
suffered near accidents or who have actually been injured, only
after it has become clear that the worker's disability will eventuate in a claim for compensation. We once made an unsuccessful
attempt to convince certain large companies that they were
overlooking the main prophylactic procedures against chronic
disability. If the patient is seen immediately after the accident
by someone who knows the possible psychological effects and
proper early treatment, the number of chronic traumatic
neuroses will be cut down considerably. It is just as important
that early supportive treatment be given to individuals suffering
from reactions after psychological blows in the form of frustrations, disruptions of interpersonal relations and lack of gratifications. It is important that steps be taken as soon as possible to
avoid a spreading of the neurotic reaction and to prevent a
geometrical increase of the disturbances by retreat of the ego to
old and latent infantile trends. The longer the time that elapses
before active therapy, the more opportunity is there for regression, secondary conflicts and secondary gain to become
established.

The first thing to be done is to deal with any physical difficulty immediately and adequately. After an accident, if at all
possible, the patient's ability to move his body and extremities
should be demonstrated by passive and active maneuvers. He
should be permitted and encouraged to ventilate his initial
feelings about the situation and abreact as much as the immediate situation permits. Since under the impact of an unexpected
accident the ego's synthetic powers break down, and its span
contracts, the energies of the personality are indiscriminately
diffused without goal. A confident and calm, yet tender person,
who need not be a psychiatrist, can substitute during this crucial

initial catastrophic state for the victim's ego, making decisions, giving explanations and assuming responsibilities. Too often the whole human environment of the accident becomes a helpless, shattered group, disintegrated for lack of leadership. The disturbed and excited friends and relatives should be dismissed from the patient's vicinity. After this, he should be given sufficient sedatives to ensure prolonged sleep, and should be isolated from all those individuals, including lawyers, who would suggest that the injury was catastrophic. Just as in the exhaustion centers, the patient should be given the feeling that he is well taken care of and that he will be able to go back to work. The nature of his initial anxiety reactions should be explained to him and he should be assured that they will disappear. His need to recover because of his responsibility to his family and his job should be brought to his attention, just as we indicate to the soldier that he still has a responsibility to his comrades in the combat unit. If all this is done with a therapeutic enthusiasm, there is no doubt that many crippling disorders will be prevented. For those patients suffering from psychological traumata who consult the physician early, the same supportive therapy should be instituted. It must be stressed at this point that this supporting, persuasive, ego-strengthening rational therapy is not of value in the later stages of neurosis. Then scientific uncovering methods must be used.

It is not sufficient to accept the fact that an individual seems to be unaffected at the moment of physical or psychological impact. We have learned from military situations, and we know from occurrences in civilian life, that there will be a considerable latent period before the stunned ego reacts in retrospect to the dangers it has escaped or the frustrations it has experienced. This is especially true in regard to psychological blows. For this reason many judgments that have been passed down by insurance companies and courts, regarding traumatic neuroses, are unfair. Witnesses are produced to show that the individual had little emotional reaction after the trauma. When it develops that these reactions appeared some hours or even days later, it is assumed that they have been acquired as a kind of malingering. Actually they are often bona fide reactions that have been slow in developing. Therefore, the fact that a person is apparently psychologically unchanged immediately after the trauma should not deter one from employing the same vigorous psychotherapy.

The catastrophic effects of purely psychological traumata, such as loss of relatives or friends, violent disturbances in interpersonal relations, and economic and social disturbances, may not become obvious until after a long latent period, often after the precipitating stimulus has been forgotten. We can see, therefore, that the early treatment developed for the military casualties, diagnosed temporarily as cases of "exhaustion," are rarely applicable to civilians except those who have had a physical injury or a narrow escape. Therefore, civilian patients consulting physicians, after initial latent periods have long since passed, must be treated by uncovering methods vigorously, at once, to prevent spreading of the neurotic pattern from the immediate problem to all behavior and to prevent permanent secondary physical changes.

· · · · · ·

Just as in the other medical specialties, speed is an essential in psychiatry to enable few men to treat many patients. But psychiatrists are not accustomed to working quickly. So-called *brief psychotherapy*, developed from civilian practice, is in reality not brief. Each session takes at least an hour and, although not frequent, consultations are spread over many weeks or months. In the armed services, brief is truly brief and means short, infrequent interviews concentrated into the span of only a few weeks. The military psychiatrist cannot spend months or years psychoanalyzing his patients, nor can he continuously act in a parental role to effect superficial amelioration of symptoms through constant support. Brief psychotherapy has been used primarily because of necessity, but it has been continued and developed in the military setting because it has proven successful. It can be applied to certain types of neuroses of civilian life under specific circumstances. The ever present load of civilian neuroses will be multiplied greatly after the war, when millions of soldiers come home and find difficulties in adapting their postcombat personalities to the minor frustrations of civilian life. Should a severe economic upheaval occur, these problems will become enormous. It is therefore necessary for us to be prepared with adequate brief methods of psychotherapy. Even with these shorter methods, there are not enough psychiatrists to do the job, but some of these techniques can be entrusted to adequately trained medical men for the treatment of the simpler and more typical reactions to external stress.

When a patient consults the psychiatrist and gives a long history of a lifetime of neurosis, or has a severely crippled character and has lived out his neurotic trends, brief psychotherapy is hardly possible. Good candidates for brief psychotherapy are patients who, even though unstable, have been able to maintain a reasonably efficient existence but are thrown off balance by some environmental disturbance, such as loss of a member of the family, loss of job or money, or some acute environmental change. The fact that the neurotic background becomes immediately apparent is no contraindication against a good prognosis for the relief of the newly acquired symptoms. Unfortunately, it has been the goal of most psychiatrists to treat such patients, not for the purpose of returning them to their previous adaptation, but with a view to a reorientation of the total personality. They forget how well the individual functioned previously, neurotic or not, and have an idealistic concept that these people should be "made over" (2).

Uncovering all infantile conflicts which are basic to the current neurosis is a theoretically sound philosophy of therapy. If one can bring to consciousness the earliest roots of the neurotic pattern and if the ego has the capacity to learn more economical methods of dealing with these earlier trends, a beneficial reorientation of the personality is possible. We know that this is not always possible. Not only is the concept of rebirth through therapy a neurotic manifestation and an infantile magical concept of the patient, but it is also a wish for a magical state of omnipotence by the psychiatrist. After long years of behaving repetitively in the same pattern, the ego's repetition compulsions can only be moderately modified. The time involved often seems endless and the dependent relationship of the patient to his doctor often persists for years. Nevertheless, in treating the war neuroses with brief psychotherapy, we have found that the past personality patterns, as they have been responsible for the neurotic reaction, come to the surface with little resistance when the individual is away from the combat situation. It is remarkable how dealing with the current edition of the neurotic pattern frequently causes a sufficient reorientation of the total personality to result in considerable psychological change. This is particularly true in young individuals, who are in the process of psychological development, and whose egos are less crystallized and still resilient.

There seems to be a paradox in what we have just stated. Yet it is in no way contrary to psychiatric experience of civilian life. Many patients on recovering from a psychosis show an astounding improvement. It is as if the temporary retreat from reality had permitted the unconscious drives to attain a much needed gratification and the ego to gain in strength through its rest. Likewise war neuroses with only partial loss of contact with reality stimulate the whole personality into a period of rapid and concentrated learning. If such learning is goal-directed into constructive channels by a psychiatrist who understands such dynamic processes, the catastrophe of a war neurosis often turns out to be a disguised benefit.

Among the methods of brief psychotherapy are techniques such as support, persuasion, gratification and authoritative forcing. They may be utilized as temporary crutches during stress or as palliative methods of expediency. The brief psychotherapy, as we know it, is based on an understanding of the psychodynamic structure of the total personality. The interrelationships between the forces of the dynamic unconscious, the ego and the superego, their interplay to form the personality and its reactions to reality must be known. Brief dynamic psychotherapy is an uncovering technique by which the isolated, repressed or dissociated aspects of the unconscious mind are made conscious, and the patient acquires insight into them and synthesizes them into his total ego.

There is no need for us to recapitulate the technique of brief psychotherapy as applicable to civilian neuroses. The details of the methods as discussed in chapters 16 and 17 are sufficient to indicate their psychodynamics and practice. A short cut to overcome resistances by the use of sodium pentothal should be attempted in brief psychotherapy for a variety of civilian neuroses, especially those of recent origin.

As we have pointed out previously, the use of pentothal has three purposes: (1) as a means of inducing chemical hypnosis, (2) to evoke abreactions and (3) to effect a narcosynthesis. We do not advise its use for a hypnotic effect. However, in our attempts to strengthen the ego to endure the liberated anxiety of the dosed abreacted material, we assist the sedative effect of the drug on the ego by reassuring the patient after he abreacts that he is now safe and out of danger. Again it must be stressed that abreaction is not curative. It is only like making a slight opening for temporary drainage in a carbuncle that needs a crucial incision. Abreaction is the beginning of insight and must be followed by learning. Narcosynthesis, on the other hand, when achieved, effects a beneficial learning, which may or may not reach the level of consciousness (cf. chapter 17).

In military as well as in civilian psychiatric practice, patients often get well without insight through the effects of the transference situation alone. People who have been psychologically hurt and narcissistically wounded need considerable tenderness. In their regressed states they need and demand love, which also seems to heal over the ego's lacerations. The therapist must give this affection and become a representation to the patient that there are kind and considerate people in the world. Bruised from hostile attitudes, it is as if the psychiatrist reassures the patient through the experience of a single good relationship that there are other safe and protective persons in the world— in his own environment and his own life. As psychiatrists we have tended too much to be objective, bland screens on which our patients may project their emotions. We seem afraid to indulge in countertransference feelings, as if we could endanger our patient's subsequent independence. On the contrary, this procedure, if natural and sincere, first gratifies and then hastens maturity, for the ego can only give out in an altruistic, mature fashion if it has a surplus. It can only spill over and give to others if it has itself received sufficient gratification. After indulging in this gratification temporarily, the patient may develop some secret unconscious insight into the nature of his attachment to the therapist, rebel against his dependence and regain his previous overcompensations to sally forth into the world again as he was before—neurotic but functioning. Or still better, his ego may rebuild a reserve strength from passive gratification, have its depleted energy restored and be able once more to seek for object relationships outside itself.

The danger is that in some cases the dependent gratification from the transference may increase regression to the old and well tried infantile pleasures, which the patient will be reluctant to abandon. The psychiatrist has a difficult task to gratify needs and give affection, as at the same time he attempts to stimulate efforts toward maturity and augmentation of self esteem. Each case presents an individual problem and only experience enables the physician to know when he is neither too gratifying nor too demanding. Intuition guides him in knowing when to stop being a haven of refuge, and when he must become a stimulator of activity.

This brings us to an important consideration of the role of re-education. In civilian practice psychiatrists have depended to a large extent on the working-through process, by which the ego, after repetitively experiencing particular emotional patterns, spontaneously begins to learn how to deal with them. We find that it is necessary to give up a good deal of the passivity that is so characteristic of the dynamic psychiatrist and take an active role in directing the ego toward mature attitudes in dealing with external pressures and the internal infantile wishes. It cannot be overstressed that active ego re-education, far from making the individual dependent on the therapist, is a technique which, if properly developed, will rapidly broaden the ego span and sharpen the aim of the goal-directed behavior. This sort of re-education is not a general instruction about emotions or attitudes but it is a specific and dynamic pedagogy directed to the individual and his personal problems. In a sense, the performance of an adult behavior pattern at the behest of the therapist and with full understanding of its meaning is actually what is done by children in their own personal development. It is simply repeated in adult life, and, although it first requires a conscious volition, it later becomes an automatic pattern.

When to stop the therapy is difficult for anyone to judge. Complete and conscious insight is not necessary for therapeutic success. Often the unconscious ego has been able to synthesize conflicting tendencies which have been isolated, and yet is unable to verbalize the work accomplished. A bare suggestion of insight may be followed by pronounced success in future learning through the processes of living. Too deep probing and mobilization of buried ego-alien tendencies may not only destroy the current success but may make the patient worse.

It will not always be possible to return the patient to his original occupation or environment, just as soldiers must often be reclassified for limited service and are not always returned to combat. But the soldier does not receive a reduction in his pay because he works at a safer job. He has no immediate desire for compensation, although under the stress of economic difficulties in later life he may apply for a government pension. In industry the state industrial laws place a premium on compensation, hence the secondary gain from prolonged neurosis is of great importance to the patient and tends to prolong his illness. It has become quite clear to us that, if any disability benefits are to be given, they must be in the form of a single settlement rather than a continuous pension. Few men will recover as long as there is a financial benefit for them in staying ill.

The problem of the return to constructive, efficient life after illness has many facets. Among them motivation looms large in the military setting. In civilian life it is only disguised and not so easily visualized. The motivation of which we speak is not related to the conflict between the man's desires for prolonged dependence on a parental figure and his desires to be mature and independent. Rather is it concerned with man's capacity to be motivated by his social units, his groups' goals and attitudes (47). Serving along with them he may function well although he may be ill or weak himself (cf. chapter 3). In civilian life, motivation should have been instilled in early years at home and in school. Since this is not yet sufficiently understood by our educators, it often becomes the psychiatrist's responsibility to stimulate his patients' motivations, set his goals and direct his sublimations. This too demands an activity on his part which he has been reluctant to use but which he should accept in the future as part of his therapeutic procedure.

. . . . . .

Careful reading of our case histories will convince the reader that war neuroses are important for the advancement of our knowledge of ego psychology. It is this force of the personality that receives the impact and must deal with the stresses originating from the external environment, the internal pressures of the individual's psychological drives and the tensions created by the internalized superego and the external group ideals. The subjective feeling-tone of anxiety, with its appropriate objective physiological concomitants, is the signal that the ego feels in danger, no matter what may be the source of the stress.

Sometimes expressed openly, sometimes tacitly, is the assumption that unconscious affect-laden memories which cause the feeling of anxiety are encapsulated in some mysterious crevice beneath the surface of the ego and only occasionally erupt some volcanic discharge. Or it is assumed that the buried material lies encapsulated, evoking only a steady counterpressure on its ego overcovering. It would only be necessary to make a crucial incision to let the evil purulence out in the form of an abreaction. But war neuroses clearly demonstrate that anxiety flows from psychophysical springs and constantly exerts a dynamic pressure on the whole personality. Not only is it recreated but it augments itself; it is common knowledge that "anxiety feeds on itself."

Anxiety is a signal of a normal biological reaction to danger, becoming pathological only when experienced in excessive quantity, or for too long after an appropriate stimulus, or when persisting without adequate external provocation. It is the subjective feeling-tone that accompanies the physiological reactions, which occur predominantly in the sympathetic nervous system and its innervated smooth muscles and glands, in preparation for or during external emergencies. Because the ego projects all tensions from within to the outside, and treats them as if they were evoked by external agents, anxiety is also a signal of internal dangerous tension. Anxiety may arise from a state of tension between the ego and the incorporated attitudes and ideals of parents, teachers, priests and leaders, acting now within the person as his ego-ideal. The disapproving punishing attitude of the superego to actual or threatened unacceptable thoughts or behavior stimulates subjective anxiety and objective physiological responses as if danger threatened from without. Likewise, the powerful pressure of instinctual drives threatens to overwhelm the ego, which then sets into action the same phenomena of emergency reactions. The poor ego is beset by the forces of inner drives, its superego and the hostile external world and is made aware of these dangers by the signal of anxiety (20).

In war the internal response to the holocaust raging around the individual is hostility. In civilian life, desertion by supporting figures, losses of all sorts, frustrations, etc., also evoke reactions of rage. It is the quantity of this evoked hostility that is the essential difference in war neuroses. Some stimuli evoke rage spontaneously as a primitive biological emergency reflex. Especially is this true of real external danger. Other stimuli cause similar responses only because they have dangerous meanings to the ego, and after such interpretations they are treated as threatening noxious agents. Once rage is activated, it is translated into action and its energy must be expended in some form of action, since it evokes profound and rapid mobilization of emergency physiological forces. Small quantities incite physiological preparedness and a state of apprehension, which alert the organism and sharpen the projicient senses. Large quantities are not self-contained and need an effector apparatus and a goal. In the absence of these, disturbances within the internal organs develop and may become irreversible (12).

The stimulus may be so catastrophic that the person has no time for response, and in fact may become unconscious before action can occur. There may be no weapon or means at hand with which to liberate aggression. The man may be so pinned down literally in war or figuratively in civilian life that aggression becomes destructive to himself. The initiated physiological reaction may exert such a powerful effect on the ego that, as after the initial stimulation of consciousness in an epileptic fit, it blacks out to a state of helpless unconsciousness (49). The civilian superego may deter the ego from expression of hostility. Thus, because of prohibitions from the past, the counteracting pressure of reality or an overwhelming strength of rage, the ego may not be able to express its energy adequately. This blocking may occur whether that energy is stimulated by a single catastrophe or built up by a series of repeated smaller frustrating events.

The ego is then faced with the threat and actuality of external dangers, with intense hostilities engendered from within so powerful that they threaten its very existence, with its personal superego which disapproves of the quantity of mobilized aggression and with its group superego which abhors the ever present thought of flight to escape the danger. The ego must deal with all these forces and maintain its cool objective discrimination in order to preserve its existence. Alone it would fail; as part of a group, its span is often large enough.

In our discussion of the aggressive responses stimulated within the individual by catastrophic external events, we also mentioned the ego's interpretation of certain situations as being significantly dangerous to it. This personalized meaning is the crystallization of all the person's past experience and his reaction is his stereotyped pattern. In this sense, as well as in his re-creation of his social or combat group in the light of his family constellation, he demonstrates a repetition compulsion. But even more important as a repetition compulsion is the reaction to anxiety, once it overwhelms the ego. Anxiety then seems to be interpreted by the ego as a signal that old unresolved conflicts are again active. It is as if, once the ego's discriminatory powers are lost, anxiety rather than being projected to the contemporary threatening external events is often attached to the safer conflicts of the distant past. It is internalized rather than projected. This is the same mechanism that permits a man to have battle dreams of past combat in distant lands rather than nightmares portraying his real fears of the present time.

.   .   .   .   .   .

The relationship between the individual and his group is like a pulsation that varies in amplitude under different conditions. There seem to be optimum degrees of independent individualization and dependence on a group for each person. An excessive amount of either, depending on the culture and the times, is pathological. Independence of all human contacts or shunning of group activities and complete dependence on the group are quantitative polar opposites. In the former category have been some of our greatest inventive geniuses and scientists as well as the schizoid and the product of a background of deprivation causing mistrust of all social units; in the authoritarian nations the latter attitude represents a successful social adaptation. In times of danger the pulsation extends further out to the group; in times of peace it remains closer to the individual. The psychiatric casualty loses his capacity for extensive integration into a group. Thus in varying conditions of stress, of culture and of time, independence and dependence vary in their acceptable and economical quantities. There are no fixed quantities of each. In the realm of psychopathology it is now clear that an individual may become so habituated to an optimum quantity of group compliance that he becomes maladapted to the individual life inherent in our democracy. He then must struggle anew to effect a successful adaptation and in his temporary failures develops added neurotic symptoms. This brings us to a discussion of the social implications of the war veteran in his struggles for readaptation to society.

CHAPTER 20

General Social Implications

In the preceding chapters we have been concerned with the effects of combat stress on the soldier in the active combat zone and after his return to army life in this country. The emphasis has been on the individual and his reaction to his environment, abroad and at home. The story, however, would not be complete without an epilogue re-evaluating what we have learned about the individual in terms of the society of the future. To lift the veil of the future in this way is an uncertain procedure, but it is neither presumptuous nor premature. We know what has happened to many individuals as a result of their combat experiences. We have learned how and why they have changed. We have seen how our patients have been broken by their experiences and how, to various degrees, they can be helped back to strength and mastery. For some, knowledge of their human weaknesses has developed in them humility and tolerance, making more civilized men of them. For many the return from regression and helplessness to strength and assurance will not have been complete by the time of their discharge to civilian life. At the present time such men are entering civilian society in a small but steady trickle. They form too small a segment of the general population as yet to create an observable effect. There is still time to anticipate this effect before the trickle swells to a flood tide at the war's end.

Too high a priority cannot be given to this problem at the present time. In the future, when appreciably large numbers of men with regressed attitudes and damaged confidence enter civilian life, it may be too late to correct or control the immediate

443

emotional reaction which will be aroused by their impact upon civilians who have had no experience or knowledge of the war. In no previous war have so many soldiers been in service for so long a time, so that our problems will be both intensive and extensive. In the absence of an intimate knowledge of the feelings and problems of the combat veteran, it is easy to see how over-solicitous or overharsh attitudes in the nonmilitary public could lead to a vast confusion. If the public mind should become clouded by strong emotion based on excessive sympathy, guilt or envy—and this has been the past history of civilian reactions to soldiers returning from other wars—then it will be extremely difficult to institute reasonable policies and a rational program. Furthermore, the returned soldiers, although a part of the general public, will be in a position to influence or perhaps dominate policies by virtue of their numbers and capacity for organization. Thus it is possible to anticipate a deep cleavage in the social structure, with former soldiers and their sympa-thizers lined up on one side and their nonmilitary opponents on the other. It might then easily become a question of how far the veterans, who will comprise one third of the voters, could force or persuade the public to gratify their needs through legislation.

If such a conflict, with the emotional blind spots and extreme attitudes which inevitably follow in its wake, is to be avoided, if the returned soldier, especially the psychologically changed soldier, is to be successfully reintegrated into civilian society, and if that society is to be headed for social progress rather than regression, then much depends upon everyone's understanding of the basic forces which have molded the returned combat veteran and have brought him to his present condition.

In order to recapitulate the reactions of the individual American soldier to combat stress in terms of our contemporary society, let us delineate a hypothetical American. Naturally, no thumbnail sketch can encompass the many variables based on differences of class, economic background, race or section. It is intended rather to picture the most salient features of the American as a social being. It is intended, furthermore, that this portrait should be idealized, representing what is generally wished to be the best in our national culture as a symbol of the product of a democratic society. If such a symbol should prove on closer examination to be inaccurate and unrealistic, especially for certain minority groups, this would merely serve to point up sharply some of the culturally determined fissures in the psychological armor with which the soldier faces strains of combat.

The typical American is a lover of liberty and independence. He has a strong conviction and confidence that he can maintain his economic independence by aggressive activity, by hard work, without having to sacrifice his freedom of action. Similarly he can maintain his freedom of belief without endangering his economic independence. If he does not like his job, he can quit and find another without reference to his politics. His independence extends to the realm of political action, where he is free to choose men who will govern him in the way he wants to be governed, and to indulge in activity designed to modify existing customs, procedures or laws in the direction he considers most beneficial to himself. What he does not like he can criticize through any of the existing means of communication, through humor, art, the press, radio or, most common of all, through direct verbal attack. His independence is inclusive of social activity, pursued according to his taste in matters of dress, amusement, recreation and choice of friends, if not without censure, at least without prohibition. He can obtain as much education as he needs or wants, treat his wife and children much as he pleases, and go whither and when he wills.

The only limitation placed upon this magnificent independence and mastery of his personal destiny is that imposed by his conscience, by the personal rights of others and by the law. Thus the social group impinges on this symbolic American and modifies his independence. Whether the rights of others exert their pressure internally, as the force of conscience, or externally, as the law, the effect is the same, and personal liberty must be thereby curbed. Yet the limitation thus imposed is relatively slight, requiring only that the independence and personal integrity of others be not violently abused. The symbolic American is voluntarily responsive to an ethical control based upon the principle that the freedom of action of one individual or group shall not forcibly nullify that of another or of the larger social group, and that any differences of opinion regarding this matter are to be settled by arbitration and majority opinion rather than by force. The aversion to the use of violence, ruthless strength and arbitrary authority as a means of reaching decisions and settling disputes between individuals or groups marks the essence of his democratic political and social practice. Out of such an ethical concept, he places the maximum value on the preservation of his own and every man's life, dignity and well-being, and recoils from destruction and waste of property. Although he tries to be realistic in regard to his own imperfections and those of his world, he is essentially optimistic, believing that with time, patient work, intelligence and imagination everything will get better for everybody. At the heart of this optimism lies the conviction that in his social order it is possible to be aggressive, independent, to look out for his own interest, in short, to be a man, without exploiting, enslaving or doing violence to another man or group of men.

The limitation of his complete independence which the American accepts as his ethical obligation to the community imposes a certain dependence on the community. Since, no matter how strong or able, he is not permitted to satisfy all his needs and desires by his own aggressive activity, he must then rely on others for their satisfaction, paying for this through his service to the community or group. The dependence is not limited to economic or material support from the group, but also includes emotional support. Although it is true that a man cannot live on love alone, neither can he live without it, and the American thrives on the respect and regard in which he is held in the community. In many other ways the community demonstrates its love for and interest in him: by protecting him from human harm; by safeguarding him against the violence of nature whether manifested by flood, fires, famine or epidemic disease; by guaranteeing in essence that, no matter what happens to him, no matter to what helpless state he may fall, he will be taken care of, provided he has not grievously sinned against the community. As a result, the idealized American's dependence upon the community or group is in a nice balance with his independence. This balance, which can be taken as the sign of his social maturity, is in harmony both with his pride and self respect as a man, and with his conscience and ideals as a citizen. Accordingly, he is a satisfied, productive person, well adjusted to his peaceful way of life.

To what extent the above description is a true picture of the actual state of affairs will be considered at a later point. At the present time, our chief concern is this: can such an individual, so well adjusted to a peaceful and democratic society, successfully adjust to the stress of war? And if so, how? The author of "Mein Kampf" was so dubious of this possibility, so scornful of the product of a democratic way of life, that he did not hesitate to provoke a war against nations whose material resources and available manpower could far outnumber his own. The American's self satisfaction was taken as complacency. His emphasis on a high material standard of life was called luxury-loving. To the fascist mind, his love of independence and freedom appeared as a lack of discipline entirely inconsistent with the rugged self sacrifice demanded of soldiers. That a nation composed of such fundamentally "weak, selfish, immature and politically naive people" could rouse itself sufficiently to make war and to wage it effectively was merely a bad joke to the Nazi mentality.

But it was no joke to the American, once attacked; and in the Nazi analysis there was at least some truth: it was not easy. To wage war successfully required a strenuous reorganization of the American character, effected only through a long "training" period. This change reached its fullest elaboration in the development of the "combat personality," previously described, but took place in some degree in soldiers and civilians throughout the nation. It required a varying sacrifice of all that was most precious, reaching its most poignant expression in combat troops. For whatever independence and freedom had been their lot, they had to substitute acceptance of ever present authority and restriction of activity. In place of personal strength and individual control of security, they had to rely on the strength of the group as protection against situations of undreamed of insecurity and threat. Their characteristic self interest had to be transformed into a devotion to the group which could transcend personal interest. Their aggressive energies, which in a lifetime of training they had learned to direct into creative and socially fruitful channels, had now to be exploded into hostile and destructive activity (9). In payment for this ignoble activity they reaped only continued hardship, anxiety and suffering. The only immediate or honorable release from this payment was through injury, illness or death.

Yet all this was accomplished successfully, and with tolerance and humor. The independent American became submissive to authority and dependent upon the group. He found a way to sacrifice his personal interest and to tolerate the enormous anxiety and suffering. He was roused to war, not because of the strength of his political convictions regarding the necessity of the conflict, but because of his feeling that his country and his people were in trouble and needed his help. He was able to endure combat, not through any romantic attachment to war or the glory of a soldier's life, but because of the strength of the emotional ties that developed between himself, his comrades and his leaders. Guilt toward them would be too great a punishment to permit his desertion of his responsibilities. What the fascists had not counted on was that the American's love for his fellow American was sufficiently strong to warrant any sacrifice. Furthermore, they had not reckoned with the American's ability to throw himself into large organizations or teams on a voluntary basis, rather than by force, which was the only basis the fascist could comprehend. The American regarded his submission to the combat leader and his dependence upon the combat team as a necessity of the moment, rather than as a blueprint for an ideal society, and never ceased to long for the time when he might be free again as a civilian.

However, after he has been in combat for a long time, something may begin to happen to the American soldier; a change may occur within him which must raise a serious and tragic doubt whether he can easily or ever again completely regain his former independence and freedom. When this change is due primarily to a physical injury, the disability is easily apprehended and understood, though the way to help him back to independence may be difficult to find. But, when the damage is psychological, the disability is more subtle, and the way back harder to discern. The psychological injury comes from his prolonged exposure to stress and threat in a position of dependence upon a group and complete submissiveness to authority. The combat soldier can seldom take care of or protect himself. Almost always his security, his life, depend upon the effectiveness and strength of the group of men to which he belongs, and upon the way they are led. Even if they are strong, he will feel some anxiety and insecurity if the enemy has any combat effectiveness. If the enemy's ability to retaliate becomes intense, or the group's ability to fight off the enemy and thus protect him becomes weak, then he feels increasingly helpless, unprotected and weak. The terrific psychological force of anxiety arises to combine with physical fatigue in further increasing his helplessness. Crippled from within by anxiety and fatigue, deserted from without and abandoned more and more to the punishing force of the enemy, he can hardly avoid losing confidence in himself and losing faith in everyone else. There is no object upon which he can release his gathering rage at being so abandoned and being rendered so helpless. Even if he should be able to hold himself together so that he never becomes a psychiatric casualty, some degree of psychological injury takes place. If he cracks, then he has the added psychological burden of guilt for having deserted his comrades still in combat, or for some specific error of omission or commission which resulted in the loss of a buddy.

The above forces play with varying intensity on the varying backgrounds of the American soldier, so that, while there are many on whom they have only a transient effect, there are also many like the patients described in this book on whom the effect is more permanent, outlasting removal from the combat scene. These men have had their birthright of independence exchanged for psychological and physical symptoms, inferiority feelings or socially unadapted behavior. At the bottom of their actual symptoms and behavior lie the shattered confidence and continued helplessness which have been the product of their combat experiences, and which have enforced a regression to and perpetuation of dependent and immature attitudes. Yet, just as in combat their dependent position payed off principally in anxiety and helplessness rather than in security, so now there is no real satisfaction in it. The returned soldier comes back not a strong hero, but physically and psychologically depleted. For what he has given out, he must receive back from others, now, at home; yet how can he collect it? If the injury has not been too deep, he soon replenishes himself and regains his confidence. If the injury has been extensive, then repair is difficult, because the dependent need for love, sympathy and support from others is so insatiable, confidence in the ability to get satisfaction and through satisfaction renewed strength is so weak, and the reaction of the pride to being so helpless and dependent is so painful. Who can satisfy the man who needs the amount of love usually afforded the child? Nowhere can the environment satisfy him, except possibly through caring for him as an invalid, which is the closest possible approximation to the child's role. Because of the inevitable frustration and difficulty in getting satisfaction for such an unquenchable need for love and support, the man becomes angry and hostile. He feels cheated. He feels angry on a further score, because his pride is so hurt and humiliated as a result of his weakened condition and dependent needs. This humiliation is frequently manifested in his inability to tolerate the slightest authority, bursting into rage at the first show of strength on the part of another. Again, just as in combat, it is a question of what he can do about feeling so angry. Not only his recent combat experiences, but every day lessons with society teach him that to become hostile and destructive, to "blow his top," leads only to further punishment, anxiety and weakness. His accumulated anger thus becomes an added source of anxiety and weakness, and, as a result, he is thrown back into more regression and dependence. Truly he is caught in a vicious circle.

The possible implications to society of the future in returning large numbers of such angry, regressed, anxiety-ridden, dependent men to civilian life can now more easily be seen. A far cry from the self-reliant American, previously described, he offers little hope that his resocialization will be easy. To anticipate that in the normal process of events he will fit himself into his old routines, and not bother the nation with a new veteran problem, is indulging in naive and wistful optimism. Because he is so unhappy, so full of intense longings, so inadequate to satisfy himself through his own activity, he will be driven to seek a solution somewhere. Where will he find it?

In the absence of a comprehensive, national plan for adequate individual psychotherapy and social aid of whatever type is necessary, some of the possible solutions can be anticipated. Some of the men will seek the type of support they need from their families, clinging to them because of despair of ever regaining maturity and strength, and because the gratification, once established, may be too difficult to give up. Others will seek the same type of gratification and economic support from the government, demanding veterans' pensions and all sorts of bonuses on the theory that because of their sacrifice the government now owes them a living. Still others will continue to seek gratification through their physical symptoms, spinning out their lives as invalids in a veterans' hospital, or, if they have funds, in a private establishment.

There are other ways in which such men may attempt to solve their problems. Many feel the urge to get completely away from other people. This is due to their disillusionment with the possibility of establishing normal human relations with others, and this is a true evaluation of the difficulty, inasmuch as they have no capacity to enter into any other than a very passive or a very hostile relationship. Their solution of this difficulty will be a desire to go back to the farm, where they need seek nothing from other men but can have a very close relationship with mother earth. The opportunity to "be your own boss" and thus gain the outward form of independence is extremely appealing to such men. Far from being a healthy sign, it indicates the continuance of their lack of adjustment to society. Such spurious "independence" may also be manifested in nomadism, in frequent changes of employment because of sensitivity to being "pushed around" by bosses, or in more frankly asocial or criminal behavior (48). In this connection, however, it is important to remember that destructive, antisocial behavior is not dictated by the habit of savagery learned in combat so much as by the violent anger arising in the individual as a result of his weakness and dependence. Violence and hostile retaliation is often a delusory solution for weakness both in individuals and in nations. Only as strength and maturity are achieved can temperance and control replace violent reactions or abject submission.

Probably the most common solution for these difficulties will be the search of the veterans for a group with strong leadership to which to bind themselves regardless of its ideology. Such a group would afford them the care, interest and dependent gratification which they have so missed in civilian life. Unlike the army group, to which they had become partially habituated, but in a damaging way, the new group must have the virtue of fighting for their own interest, or at least be able to convince the men that such is the intent. This is important because dependence within the army group required the individual to pay the high price of constantly risking his life. On this account, it is often felt that the army, even the government, is owed nothing but resentment, antagonism or hatred. Whether or not the new group is actually for the interest of the veteran would not be nearly so important as its ability to convince him that it is, by aggressive activity in fighting for matters of importance to the veteran. In this the veteran may not be seeking personal independence or real strength and maturity, so much as a security based again on the strength of a group. Again, through identifying himself with the strong group, in a repetition of the technique which was so necessary in combat, he may himself feel strong. Similarly by finding an external enemy on which to blame the weakness and unhappiness of the veteran, the group may find an acceptable object for his pent-up hostilities and aggressions, actually arising from internal sources. The volume of hatred and aggression thus released could easily assume a dynamic force not easy to stop or control.

What form such a group would take, whether it would be a political party, purely a veterans' organization, a labor union, or some as yet unpredictable organization, is not of great significance. At the present time, one can merely note the possibilities of the trend. What is apparent is that the tendency toward the development of dependent relationships in groups, which was learned in the army and fixed by the regression incident to the trauma of combat, has a way of perpetuating itself, and of seeking new forms of expression. It is as if independence and maturity, once given up, are difficult to regain, especially in the face of ever new difficulties. Strong groups then present attractive possibilities, and are probably necessary to the individual, until such time as he can again feel strong enough to take more responsibility for himself.

This fact raises the extremely important question of the character of the group with which an individual identifies himself—its psychology, purpose within the social structure and intent with regard to the individual. This question, so fundamental to political and social psychology, can be stated briefly, though with considerable oversimplification, by contrasting two theoretical groups. The first is intended to fix the individual in a dependent position, requiring of him absolute submission to authority, tolerance of deprivation and personal frustration, with the aim of creating an excessively strong and effective group, a modern counterpart of which is the fascist dictatorship. The second is dedicated to furthering the independence and strength of the individual by supporting him and fighting for his individual needs, at the same time permitting him free choice of gratifying his needs from any other group which would be to his interest. This second group is represented today by the political parties and special pressure groups within a democratic state.

In the first group the individual may or may not voluntarily identify himself with the group, but at any rate he has little choice in the matter. If he refuses to join or submit to the group, he is eliminated by being economically neutralized so that he cannot live, or by being socially isolated. This identification by force offers the individual the reward of being loved and taken care of by the group as long as he submits without question to its authority and does not protest the discomfort and sacrifice involved. Although the individual is thus deprived of his independence and freedom of action, any humiliation suffered by his pride in this connection is rendered painless in two ways. First, the strict hierarchical stratification of social organization imposed by such a group places the individual in a position where, although he must submit to authority from above, he can impose the same sort of authority on some one below him. Secondly, although this makes it most difficult for those at the bottom of the social scale, even the lowliest are strengthened through their identification with the glory and strength of the group itself. Lastly, any resentment or shame left over from such a frustration of masculine independence and authority is absorbed by the group's exceedingly hostile and destructive activity toward its external enemies. Thus rage and aggressions coming from many personal frustrations are displaced against the external enemy, which minimizes friction within the group. The projection of hostility to the "cruel enemy" not only increases the individuals' need for and loyalty to each other but also removes any guilt over the hostile, destructive activity initiated by the group. Never having developed complete confidence in this technique for removing guilt, the modern fascist state has attempted to supplement it by destroying the ethical basis for guilt over destruction, inherent in Western civilization, by substituting the dogma of the superman and master race not bound by such an ethical code. It is not necessary, however, to resort to this trick in order to liberate hostile, destructive activity toward a supposed enemy, inasmuch as Western civilization has long been able to tolerate a certain amount of guilt in this matter without too much difficulty, by relying on the technique of projection and displacement to the "guilty" enemy, and concluding every conflict with the argument over who started it.

It is not difficult to see how the individual, once he has become habituated to the psychological mechanisms implicit in such a group, can become well adjusted to his dependent position, feel secure, and function effectively and without severe intrapsychic conflict—as long as the group remains strong. And how could a group such as this, composed of such well coordinated, well disciplined, aggressive individuals, not continue to be strong? Only through the failure of the leadership of the group, or through the too effective retaliation of the enemy. Should the strength of the group collapse in defeat or dissolution, then each individual is thrown into a state of complete helplessness, and suffers the severe anxiety and hostility born of being abandoned in a dependent and helpless position to the cruel and punishing enemy.

These are the mechanisms which enable the individuals belonging to fascist groups to function so effectively in peace or war, and which make them, after their defeat, such a severe problem to societies oriented toward more democratic policies. It comes with something of a shock to realize that these are also the mechanisms which apply to the American combat soldier, both in psychological health and in the illness which overtakes him. In order to become an effective soldier, he must learn to adapt himself to a completely undemocratic group, which requires of him submission and fixation in a dependent position. The fascist enemy, which is in essence a military group, cannot be dominated or held in check by a democratic society unless that society to some extent regresses to the level of the former. The first step in that regression is the formation of a large and effective military group. Whether or not this is also the last step in the regression, whether or not, after a victory, the remainder of the democratic world can proceed along its accustomed path and retain the personal dignity of the individual, cannot easily be foreseen at the present time, inasmuch as it depends upon the temper, skill and understanding of the men who make the peace. A question more germane to the present discussion is whether or not an American soldier, once conditioned to this regressed and dependent position, can be helped back to independence and good health, or whether he must remain continually unadjusted, physically or psychologically ill, or forever in search of a strong group to give him the illusion of the strength he lost as a member of the military group.

It has already been stated that many recover quite spontaneously. Many others are helped by skillful psychotherapy, as outlined in previous chapters in which the individual is permitted to abreact his severe anxieties and hostilities, learning from this experience how to recover his confidence and how to re-establish his faith in mature human relations. But there are still many men who will not have the advantage of such help and some will fail to be greatly improved after the somewhat brief psychiatric help which is all that can be provided in the army setting. What of these?

Examination of those men who fail to readapt to life in our democratic social structure shows, with considerable consistency, that they were predisposed in a characteristic way to the irreversible change which overtook them under the stress of combat. By predisposition is meant not a pre-existing neurotic illness nor a familial trait, but a weak spot within the personality, a concealed Achilles' heel, which rendered the individual particularly sensitive to the forces which act upon him in combat. This sensitivity is characterized by the existence of strong emotional dependence or of strong overcompensatory trends against dependence. As we have repeatedly stated, dependent trends exist within everyone. The question in regard to predisposition to illness is that of degree: how much, what type, and what are the strengths of the opposing personality forces? In the cases under consideration, study has revealed that these trends have existed in quantities more intense than is consistent with the biological maturity of the individual, even though many of them are still in the postadolescent years, yet not sufficiently intense to have become manifest as neurotic illness prior to the stress of combat. The discovery of these trends among so large a portion of American youth as represented in the army, and the examination of their social and psychological background, bring into sharp focus the inaccuracy of the portrait of the symbolic self-reliant American, described at the beginning of this chapter. Beyond the truism that we are not a homogeneous nation, and therefore can never be represented by so simple a symbol, lies the fact that large numbers of us have never been free from the internal inertia and forces dragging us back toward the childish state of dependent gratifications. We have set up a straw man not merely to burn it down, but to underline the distinction between what we are and what we would like to be, between the psychological and social fact, and the ideal we have set for ourselves. Because the difference between the ideal and the fact is sometimes so great, a severe intrapsychic tension is established which, with an increase in the degree of external stress, often leads to psychological illness.

For each individual, psychological growth results only after a painful process of gradual maturation from the prolonged immaturity and dependence characteristic of the human animal. Biologically man is less able than any other animal to exist without prolonged and effective support from parental figures. Certain factors within our American culture, however, seem calculated to prolong this dependence beyond its usual biological duration. Among these factors the most important are overprotection and spoiling, and their opposites, deprivation and frustration.

In many ways both American parents and American society as a whole encourage and even force an individual to maintain an emotional dependence for long years after he has become biologically self-sufficient. Compulsory education is imposed upon him through adolescence. The law prevents him from working independently in most states until he reaches the age of 16. He is prevented from marrying without the consent of his parents, or from voting, until the age of 21. In our country, thousands of boys are expected to continue their education in colleges and universities until their middle or late twenties. In fact, a college education is almost a social necessity for those who wish to advance rapidly in white collar jobs. Thus society increasingly demonstrates its intention of depriving boys of the responsibility which forges maturity until they have reached a late age compared with the time of biological maturity. Parents have contributed even more effectively than society as a whole to the delay in emotional maturation. We have been struck, while dealing with our patients, by the different ways, some subtle, some forthright, in which parents, especially mothers, attempt to bind the boys to the family bosom. Sometimes the call is economic and the boys are continually reminded of their obligation to support mother, father, grandmother or sister, preferably by remaining at home. This casts the individual in the role of the mature provider but is frequently a rationalization to cover the fact that the boy is wanted at home by his parents. Chisholm (9) has pointed out how, in this age of emphasis on "safety first," parents frequently urge their children to take no chances, and this is confirmed by our experience with patients whose parents constantly bombard them with admonitions and warnings concerning their personal safety which are completely inappropriate to the activities engaged in by the sons. In view of the ordinary inertia which makes it difficult to give up the gratifications of a dependent childhood, it is small wonder that the children of such individuals have difficulty with the process of emotional maturation.

Just as deleterious to the achievement of real emotional independence as spoiling and overprotection are frustration and deprivation. We have become acutely aware of the extent of psychological starvation and its crippling effect in observing the average American youth in the army. Deprivation is a common experience of children coming from the homes of low wage earners. This is due not so much to the lack of the ordinary necessities of life as to the frequency of broken homes and rejecting parents. Parenthood is often forced on these people by ignorance or lack of contraceptives. There can be no more effective argument for planned parenthood through the use of contraceptives than the disastrous later life of the unwanted child. The frequency of broken homes due to parental alcoholism or severely neurotic behavior is astounding. Separation, divorce or the substitution of cruel stepfathers is a recurrent item in the histories of our patients, many of whom had a fairly good, if tenuous, adjustment prior to the stress of combat. Such individuals feel intensely cheated of the dependent gratification which should be every child's lot, and enter into each human relationship with a strong need to receive such gratification, and an equally strong despair of achieving it. As a result they may remain distant, cold or remotely hostile, but carry on in their work until an increase in external stress deprives them even of the ability to be independent of others. Then, having no emotional gratification of any sort, they are thrown into a severe illness.

All these factors, plus the fact that economic security through independent aggressive activity is by no means guaranteed in our civilization, tend to increase a desire for strong emotional support in our youngsters. Our civilization has developed attitudes that prevent or delay normal maturation in its children, among which are increasing nurture of the growing child and the increasing feminine dominance of family life. Yet these attitudes are tacit and are concealed not only from the people affected but from those who are responsible for promulgating them. Actually, our society still maintains as its theoretical ideal the free, independent individualistic man of its frontier days. Thus the strong dependent needs of the boy are in serious conflict with the forces pushing toward aggressive, independent, masculine and competitive existence. This is the normal conflict of adolescence in any age, but at the present time we are responsible for increasing the intensity of the conflict. We demand independence, yet block it at every turn. In so doing we create a confusion in ideals, which finds its repercussions not only in the difficulties of the individual, but also in the uncertainty of the nation in foreign and domestic policy. Rugged individualism with social security, freedom with complacency, internationalism without sacrifice of sovereign rights, are all part of the same confusion. This confusion of ideals leads increasingly to corrupt individual ego-ideals and cynicism, in which the ideal is considered with suspicion (1).

The cynical mask only feebly conceals the underlying tragedy, resulting from the wide differences between frustrating reality and the beloved ideal. Such attitudes, fortunately, have only a partial acceptance among the public. It is true that during hard times, when reality becomes particularly difficult, we begin to hear voices raised for the total scrapping of the ideal. Then more authoritarian political systems are eyed by a few with envy, and we begin to hear of the need for stronger and more determined leadership as a substitute for government reacting to the will of the people. In general, however, optimism regarding the possibilities of fulfillment of the American ideal of freedom and independence coexists with disillusionment and is the stronger of the two. But there is good reason to fear that this may not be the case with the returned soldiers who have been psychologically and physically wounded. For so many of them, their conflicts had never been successfully resolved, either because of their youth or because of blocking of previous efforts toward independence. Then, having been seriously wounded in the spirit or in the body, and having lost confidence in their ability ever again to achieve effectiveness and independence in the future, they must either remain angry and depressed or give up the ideal of independence. If the latter should occur, they may seek out any group whose strength will lend them support, without any consideration of the ideal or ethics of such a group. They may perhaps even be attracted by a group whose announced or tacit policies are undemocratic or in opposition to the American ideal of liberalism and freedom, happy again in the feeling of comradeship, unity, warm affection and support afforded by strong men who are interested in them.

In order to forestall this danger, and in order to rehabilitate and restore the returned combat soldier to a maximum social adjustment, a national program based upon a thorough understanding of the problem by every segment of the population is needed. This understanding must embrace the following considerations. Although many of the physical complaints, the anxieties and the resentments of the veteran are based upon perfectly legitimate grounds, many will be derived by displacement and projection from unconscious sources and thus will be irrational and not susceptible to reasonable argument. The critical force, initiated by combat stress, behind these difficulties is regressive, resulting in immature attitudes characterized by strong dependent needs for affection and care and permissiveness from the man's environment. These needs and the symptoms they evoke cannot be influenced by persuasion or condemnation, but only by wise understanding, which temporarily permits the regression, and supports the need for care and affection as long as is reasonable and necessary for the replenishment of the depleted reservoir of passive gratification. When the dependent needs have had some fulfillment and active and independent trends become increasingly evident, then the environment must facilitate these efforts socially and economically by furnishing satisfying outlets, lest a new frustration cause a return of the regression. Then as he becomes more and more active and self-confident, his irrational complaints and behavior will tend to disappear and the veteran will be able to fit himself into his normal social groove.

It has been sometimes stated that the veteran does not want people to pay attention to him, that he wants to be let alone and ignored. This does not coincide with our experience. Actually the veteran does not want to be ignored; he wants to be understood and helped. It is only because of his inability to understand himself, and of his lack of faith in the capacity of others to understand or help him, that he prefers to be alone with his difficulties or in the company of other combat veterans. He is usually as quickly responsive to those who actually understand his problems and know how to help him, as he is cold to oversolicitous, insincere or thoughtless approaches. The understanding which means help should begin in the bosom of his family, the first line of civilian therapy. It must, however, be supplemented by public attitudes which avoid the twin evils of oversolicitousness and indifference, while providing adequate medical care and social and economic outlets for activity. The nation or the community should be prepared with a comprehensive plan for ambulatory medical and psychiatric care, for hospitalization, for job analysis and placement, and for social aid of all types including family counseling. If this is done, the veteran should have the feeling that, because of his sacrifice, his country is truly doing everything possible to restore to him as much feedom and independence and good health as will be possible in the world which follows the war.

As psychiatrists we are able to indicate the psychological trends of individuals and groups as they develop under stress and afterwards. We can treat the individual patient with his powerfully regressive tendencies, but we can have no effect upon the regressive trends within society. The principles of this social therapy, however, are the same and are based on an understanding of dynamic social psychology. Gratification of needed dependence, direction of aggressions into constructive channels, each in its essential proportions, are essentially processes of good democracy. The details of the treatment, which in the social sense we call education, are a task for a host of specialists who are expert in social, economic and political techniques. There are difficult times ahead for all of us, and a decent solution of our many future problems requires the cooperation of everyone of good will and intelligence among the general public and in the government. The groundwork for these activities requires information of what goes on, possible only through frank and open dissemination of current knowledge. For that reason we have felt it necessary to write what we have learned about *men under stress*.

References

1. ALEXANDER, F.: Our Age of Unreason, Philadelphia, J. B. Lippincott Company, 1942.
2. ALEXANDER, F.: The indications for psychoanalytic therapy, Bull. New York Acad. Med., 20:320, 1944.
3. ALEXANDER, F., et al.: The influence of psychological factors upon gastro-intestinal disturbances: a symposium, Psychoanalyt. Quart., 3:501, 1934.
4. BARRETT, W. G.: Psychological armoring for the Air Forces, War Med., 5:142, 1944.
5. BLECKWENN, W. J.: Narcosis as therapy in neuropsychiatric conditions, J. A. M. A., 15:1168, 1930. The use of sodium amytal in catatonia, Proc. A. Research Nerv. & Ment. Dis., 10:224, 1931.
6. BRACELAND, F. J., and ROME, H. P.: Anxiety and fatigue, Connecticut State Med. J., 7:827, 1943.
7. BRENMAN, M., and GILL, M. M.: Hypnotherapy, Josiah Macy, Jr., Foundation, Review Series, vol. 2, no. 3.
8. CANNON, W. B.: The Wisdom of the Body, New York, W. W. Norton & Co., Inc., 1932.
9. CHISHOLM, J. B.: Some factors in the high rate of neuropsychiatric casualties, Bull. Menninger Clinic, 8:36, 1944.
10. COBB, S.: Review of neuropsychiatry for 1944: neuroses and the war, Arch. Int. Med., 75:65, 1945.
11. DOLLARD, J., et al.: Frustration and Aggression, New Haven, Yale University Press, 1939.
12. DUNBAR, H. F.: Emotions and Bodily Changes, ed. 2, New York, Columbia University Press, 1939.
13. DUNBAR, H. F.: Psychosomatic Diagnosis, New York, P. B. Hoeber, Inc., 1943.
14. DUNBAR, F., and ARLOW, J.: Criteria for therapy in psychosomatic disorders, Psychosomatic Med., 6:283, 1944.
15. DUNN, W. H.: The psychopath in the armed forces, Psychiatry, 4:251, 1941.
16. FISHER, C.: Hypnosis in treatment of neuroses due to war and to other causes, War Med., 4:565, 1943.
17. FREEDMAN, H. L.: The unique structure and function of the mental hygiene unit in the army, Ment. Hyg., 27:1, 1943.
18. FREUD, A.: The Ego and the Mechanisms of Defense, London, Hogarth Press, 1937.
19. FREUD, S.: Group Psychology and the Analysis of the Ego, London, Hogarth Press, 1922.
20. FREUD, S.: The Ego and the Id, London, Hogarth Press, 1927.

21. FREUD, S., FERENCZI, S., ABRAHAM, K., SIMMEL, E., and JONES, E.: Psychoanalysis and the War Neuroses, London and New York, International Psychoanalytical Press, 1921.

22. GOLDSTEIN, K.: On so-called war neuroses, Psychosomatic Med., 5:376, 1943.

23. GOODMAN, L. and GILMAN, A.: The Pharmacological Basis of Therapeutics, New York, MacMillan Company, 1941.

24. GRANT, D. N. W.: The medical direction of human drives in war and peace, J. A. M. A., 126:607, 1944.

25. GRINKER, R. R.: Rehabilitation of fliers with operational fatigue, Air Surgeon's Bull., 2:18, 1945.

26. GRINKER, R. R. and SPIEGEL, J. P.: War Neuroses in North Africa: the Tunisian Campaign (January–May, 1943), New York, Josiah Macy, Jr., Foundation, 1943.

27. GRINKER, R. R., and SPIEGEL, J. P.: The management of neuropsychiatric casualties in the zone of combat, Manual of Military Neuropsychiatry, Philadelphia, W. B. Saunders Company, 1944.

28. GRINKER, R. R., and SPIVEY, R. J.: Ergotamine tartrate in the treatment of war neuroses, J. A. M. A., 127: 158, 1945.

28a. HADFIELD, J. A.: War neurosis: a year in a neuropathic hospital, Brit. M. J., 1: 281, 320, 1942.

29. HASTINGS, D. W., WRIGHT, D. G., and GLUECK, B. C.: Psychiatric Experiences of the Eighth Air Force, First Year of Combat (July 4, 1942–July 4, 1943), New York, Josiah Macy, Jr., Foundation, 1944. Sodium amytal narcosis in treatment of operational fatigue in combat air crews, War Med., 5:368, 1944.

30. HEATH, R. G., and POWDERMAKER, F.: The use of ergotamine tartrate as a remedy for "battle reaction," J. A. M. A., 125:111, 1944.

31. HENDERSON, J. L., and MOORE, M.: The psychoneuroses of war, New England J. Med., 230:273, 1944.

32. HOCH, P. H.: Some psychosomatic and therapeutic aspects of war neuroses, Bull. New York Acad. Med., 20:333, 1944.

33. HORSLEY, J. S.: Narco-analysis, London, Oxford Medical Publications, 1943.

34. KARDINER, A.: The Traumatic Neuroses of War, New York, P. B. Hoeber, Inc., 1941.

35. KUBIE, L. S.: The nature of psychotherapy, Bull. New York Acad. Med., 19:183, 1943.

36. KUBIE, L. S.: Manual of emergency treatment for acute war neuroses, War Med., 4:582, 1943.

37. LEIGHTON, A. H.: A working concept of morale for Flight Surgeons, Military Surgeon, 92:601, 1943.

38. LINDEMANN, E.: Psychopathological effect of sodium amytal, Proc. Soc. Exper. Biol. & Med., 28:864, 1931.

39. MASSERMAN, J. H.: Behavior and Neurosis, Chicago, University of Chicago Press, 1943.

40. Medical Department of the United States Army in the World War, vol. 10: Neuropsychiatry, Washington, D. C., Government Printing Office, 1929.

41. MELTON, A. W.: The selection of pilots by means of psychomotor tests, J. Aviation Med., 15:116, 1944.

42. MILLER, E., and others: The Neuroses in War, edited by E. Miller, New York, MacMillan Company, 1940.

43. MILLER, H. R.: Central Autonomic Regulations in Health and Disease, New York, Grune & Stratton, Inc., 1942.

44. MURRAY, J. M.: Psychiatric aspects of aviation medicine, Psychiatry, 7:1, 1944.

45. MURRAY, J. M.: Some special aspects of psychotherapy in the Army Air Forces, Psychosomatic Med., **6**:119, 1944.
46. NEWELL, T. E.: Neuropsychiatry in the Japanese Army, J. A. M. A., **126**:373, 1944.
47. OGBURN, W. F., and NIMKOFF, M. F.: Sociology, New York, Houghton Mifflin Company, 1940.
48. RADCLIFFE, R. A. C.: Service men in industry, Industrial Welfare and Personnel Management, **25**:289, 1943.
49. RADO, S.. Pathodynamics and treatment of traumatic war neuroses (traumataphobia), Psychosomatic Med., **4**:4, 1942.
50. RAINES, G. N., and KOLB, L. C.: Combat fatigue and war neurosis, U. S. Nav. M. Bull., **41**:923, 1943.
51. ROME, H. P.: The role of sedation in military medicine, U. S. Nav. M. Bull., **62**:525, 1944.
52. SARGENT, W.: Physical treatment of acute war neuroses, Brit. M. J., **2**:574, 1942.
53. SARGENT, W., and SLATER, E.: Acute war neuroses, Lancet, **2**:1, 1940.
54. SCHWARTZ, L. A.: Group psychotherapy in the war neuroses, Am. J. Psychiat., **101**:498, 1945.
55. SCOTT, R. L.: God Is My Co-Pilot, New York, Charles Scribner's Sons, 1943.
56. SIMMEL, E.: Psychoanalysis and the War Neuroses, London, International Psychoanalytic Press, 1921. Self-preservation and the death instinct, Psychoanalyt. Quart., **13**:160, 1944.
57. SOLOMON, H. C., and YAKOVLEV, P. I.: Manual of Military Neuropsychiatry, Philadelphia, W. B. Saunders Company, 1944.
58. SPIEGEL, H. X.: Psychiatric observations in the Tunisian Campaign, Am. J. Orthopsychiat., **14**:381, 1944.
59. THOMAS, G. W.: Group psychotherapy—a review of the recent literature, Psychosomatic Med., **5**:166, 1943.
60. WEISS, E., and ENGLISH, O. S.: Psychosomatic Medicine, Philadelphia, W. B. Saunders Company, 1943.
61. WENDER, L.: Group psychotherapy—a study of its application, Psychiatric Quart., **14**:708, 1940.
62. WHITEHORN, J. C.: Guide to interviewing and clinical personality study, Arch. Neurol. & Psychiat., **52**:197, 1944.
63. WILDE, J. F.: Narco-analysis in the treatment of war neuroses, Brit. M. J., **2**:4, 1942.

Index

A

Abandonment of comrades, guilt of, 114
Ability to identify with group, 40
Abnormal personalities as fliers, 12
Abreaction, 170, 172, 173, 175, 379
   under alcohol, 392
   under ether, 392
   under pentothal, 395
Accidents, civilian, 349, 431
   malingering after, 433
   proneness to, 13
   industrial, monotony causing, 431
   safeguards against, 431
   possibility of, as source of anxiety to crew, 34
Adaptation, failure of, discharge for, 424
   psychopathic, 79
Adjunctive treatment, 407
Adjustment, lack of, postwar, 451
Aerial versus ground force combat, 136
Aero-otitis media, from power dives, 31
Aerosinusitis, from power dives, 31
Age, as factor in operational fatigue, 214
   as factor in stability, 423
Aggression, 89
   hostile, causes of, 325
     prognosis for cases showing, 423
     (*see also* Hostile-aggressive attitude)
   inhibition against, renewal of, after return from combat, 362
   neurotic compromise in, 363
   paranoid reactions in, 363

Aggression, paranoid, with homosexual conflict, 331
   reactions in, 307
   (*see also* Killing)
Air sickness, psychogenic, 13
Alcohol, 131, 413
   abreactions under, 392
   to induce sleep, 156
   to reduce anxiety, 69
Alcoholism, 248, 306, 359, 381, 457
   gratifying passive needs, 250
Altitudes, high, affecting combat crews, 31
Americans, civilization of, 123
   idealized picture of, as social beings, 444
     contrasted with neurotic trends in many soldiers, 450, 455
   Nazi appraisal of, 447
   as soldiers, accepting necessity for killing, 43
     contrasted with allies and enemies, 38, 49, 125
     employability of, after war, 451
     loyalty of, to combat group, 448
   training of, killing foreign to, 43
   typical, 445
Amytal, in continuous narcosis, 408
   effect of, compared with pentothal, 170, 393
   in psychiatry, 393
   used in interview, 170
   as sedative, 156, 413

K

Killing, as foreign to American training, 43
  guilt of, identification with group preventing, 132
  necessity for, accepted by American soldier, 43
  renewal of inhibitions against, on return home, 362
  without guilt, through identification with group, 132
  (*see also* Aggression)

L

Leader, qualities needed in, 46
  affecting morale, 46, 126
  responsibilities of bomber pilot as, 23
Libido, as causative factor in war neuroses, 354, 355
Lobotomy, prefrontal, in psychiatry, 407
Loss, of friends, in combat, as source of emotional stress, 35
  of judgment, in free anxiety states, 84
  of weight, in combat zones, 32
Lost crews, survivors of, suffering disabling anxiety, 94
  person, returnee resembling, 358
Love, somatic expression of need for, through craving for milk, 140, 276

M

Maladjustment, postwar, 451
Malingering, accusations of, in early neurotic reaction to combat, 57
  after accidents, in civilian life, 433
  and anxiety, 141, 346
  and fear of flying, 77
  not involved in patients recovered from anxiety states, 191, 346
  and phobic mechanisms, 191
Marriage, flights into, by returnees, expressing regression, 359
  readjustment to, by returnees, 187

Mechanisms, emergency sympathetic, numbing of, in prolonged stress, 222
  neurological and psychological, in anxiety, 144
  phobic, and malingering, 191
Medical men, overseas experiences of, affecting postwar practice, 429
Metabolism, possible involvement of, in operational fatigue, 220, 222
Metrazol shock therapy, 407
Milk, craving for, as somatic expression of need for love, 140, 276
Misclassification for combat duties, case of, 76
Misinterpretation of passive-dependent trends in war neuroses, 225
Missions, frequency of, relating to fatigue, 30
  last few, emotional reactions of flier during, 183
Monotony, of industrial work, causing accidents, 431
Moral fiber, lack of, reacting to combat, 69, 77, 135
Morale, 37, 48
  and capacity for identification, 39
  deterioration of, effect of, 69
  factors in, 37
  and faith in common purpose, 38
  and faith in leadership, 46
  geography affecting, 27
  grounding affecting, 278
  of "hard luck" units, 26
  and hostile paranoid personalities, 78
  of "hot" units, 26
  identification with group as aid to, 40
  interpersonal ties as aid to, 279
  leadership as factor in, 46, 48, 126
  and military tradition, 41
  and news from home, 48
  and patriotism, 40
  and punishment of activity harmful to group, 48
  relating to emotional illness, 69
  and self sacrifice, 45
  of "snafud" units, 26
Morphine, as sedative, 413